General Science

THIRD EDITION

J. Albert Mould
Saul L. Geffner
Milton S. Lesser

When ordering this book, please specify:
either **N 413 P** or GENERAL SCIENCE

AMSCO SCHOOL PUBLICATIONS, INC.
315 Hudson Street/New York, N.Y. 10013

Please visit our Web site at:

www.amscopub.com

ISBN 0-87720-017-3

Copyright © 1991, 1974, 1959 by Amsco School Publications, Inc.

PRINTED IN THE UNITED STATES OF AMERICA

Preface

The role of science in our lives has increased dramatically. Computers have already revolutionized our daily existence. The pollution of our air, water, and soil is a matter of imminent concern. Conquest of disease, especially AIDS, poses a tremendous challenge. Programs to combat the use of drugs require the highest priority.

Increased scientific literacy can contribute much to the solution of the many problems that confront us. To provide for greater scientific literacy, the content of science programs requires frequent upgrading. Although the emphasis must be on usefulness and application, the understanding of fundamental principles cannot be compromised.

The third edition of *General Science* has been designed with these broad aims in mind. The scope of this book is sufficiently diversified to permit it to be used in many learning situations. The language employed recognizes the different vocabulary levels of young students.

The outstanding features of this book are as follows:

1. Presentation: The content has been organized into four major units—biology, chemistry, physics, earth science—containing the necessary topics to serve as a foundation for high school science. Each of the units is divided into a series of chapters to make the content more easily understood. Wherever possible, concepts and generalizations based upon experimentation have been developed.

2. Visualization: To make the presentation of content more meaningful, numerous diagrams, expertly drawn, appear throughout the book. In most instances, a legend, designed to further the student's understanding, accompanies the diagram.

3. Recent Developments: Appropriate content related to environmental preservation, ecology, mental health, drug abuse, space science, and nuclear energy appears in this book. Many of these current topics, as well as other subjects of common interest to students, have been selected for individual treatment in brief essays. Displayed in boxes on separate pages, the essays, as you will notice, strike the reader's attention and provide him or her with tidbits of light reading on themes pertinent to the text.

4. Questions for Practice, Review, and Testing: To insure mastery of subject matter, each topic in a chapter of a given unit is followed by adequate testing material in the form of a variety of reasoning questions and objective-type questions. These are generally arranged in such a way as to parallel the presentation of content in the text. Thus, upon completion, the student has a topical outline of the essentials of each unit. To provide additional review, each unit is terminated with numerous essay questions. For practice in preparing for term examinations, a series of final review questions is also included.

This book will prove invaluable to those students who want to learn science, rather than to learn about science. In this way, they can adjust and hopefully solve some of the many problems that face them.

THE AUTHORS

Contents

V

Unit I.
Life Science: Become Familiar With Living Things and Their Environment

Chapter 1. Characteristics of Living Things

1. WHAT IS A LIVING THING?

Living things perform certain activities, called the *life functions*, that distinguish them from non-living things.

  a. Living things take in food and use it to obtain energy, to grow, and to repair injured or worn-out body parts.
  b. Living things take in and use oxygen.
  c. Living things get rid of wastes that their body produces.
  d. Living things are able to move. Plants, however, cannot move from place to place because they are firmly anchored in the soil by their roots.
  e. Living things reproduce, that is, produce more of their own kind.
  f. Living things respond to changes in their surroundings. For example, they react to light, heat, strange odors, and chemicals. They respond by moving or turning toward or away from the changing condition.

All living things are made up of one or more tiny units of matter called *cells*. Just as a building is composed of bricks, a body is made up of cells!

2. HOW DO LIVING THINGS DIFFER?

Many different kinds of organisms (living things) inhabit the earth. Yet all can be classified into three main groups, or *kingdoms*. Every living thing is either a plant, an animal, or a protist. A *protist* is a simple organism that is considered to be neither plant nor animal.

Living things differ, chiefly, as follows:

1

a. Plant Kingdom. Plants cannot move from place to place because they are firmly fixed in the soil by their roots. Plants contain a fairly stiff, woodlike substance, *cellulose*, that forms a *cell wall* around each plant cell and prevents movement. The green parts of plants contain *chlorophyll*, a substance that enables plants to make their own food.

b. Animal Kingdom. Animals can move around from place to place. Animal cells do not have cell walls. Animals cannot make their own food; they depend on the food produced by green plants. While some animals eat plants directly, others live on animals that feed on plants.

c. Protist Kingdom. Some protists are like animals in being able to move from one place to another. Some are like plants in having chlorophyll and cell walls. Still others have characteristics of both animals and plants. It is possible that in the distant past some animallike protists gave rise to animals, and that some plantlike protists gave rise to plants.

3. KINDS OF ANIMALS

More than a million different kinds of animals are known, varying in size from the enormous whale to the tiniest microscopic form.

All animals, as well as all other living things, are identified according to their similarities in structure and development. For example, all animals having a backbone are classified by scientists as *vertebrates*, and those animals that lack a backbone are classified as *invertebrates*. There are many more invertebrates on the earth than there are vertebrates.

As shown in Table 1, "Types of Vertebrates," animals with backbones include *mammals*, *birds*, *reptiles*, and others. Mammals have hair on their body; birds have wings for flight; and reptiles have two pairs of legs for locomotion.

On the next several pages, you will be engaged in the study of animals, plants, and protists according to the scientific system of classification.

Table 1-1. Types of Vertebrates (animals that have a backbone)

Type	Characteristics	Examples
Mammals (the most highly developed animals)	1. Have hair or fur on their body. 2. Are warm-blooded. (Body temperature remains the same even though the temperature of the surroundings may change.) 3. Breathe by means of lungs. 4. Have special glands which produce milk for feeding the young.	Human Horse Whale Bat Elephant Squirrel
Birds	1. Feathers aid in flight and also insulate the body to prevent the loss of heat. 2. Are warm-blooded. 3. Breathe by means of lungs. 4. Most birds have wings for flight.	Robin Oriole Crow Hawk Chicken
Reptiles	1. Body covered with tilelike scales. 2. Are cold-blooded. (Body temperature varies with the temperature of the surroundings.) 3. Breathe by means of lungs. Water-living reptiles come to the surface to breathe air. 4. With the exception of the snake, all reptiles have two pairs of legs for locomotion.	Snake Turtle Lizard Alligator Crocodile
Amphibians	1. Body covered with a thin skin which may be either smooth, warty, or slimy. 2. Are cold-blooded. 3. Breathe by means of gills in the early water-living stage; adults breathe by means of lungs. 4. Most amphibians start life in water; as adults, they live both in water and on land.	Frog Toad Salamander
Fish	1. Body usually covered with overlapping scales. 2. Are cold-blooded. 3. Breathe by means of gills. Water containing dissolved oxygen enters the mouth and passes over the gills, which absorb the oxygen. 4. Most have an air bladder which allows fish to swim at any level.	Bass Perch Trout Flounder Carp

Table 1-2. Types of Invertebrates (animals that lack a backbone)

Type	*Characteristics*	*Examples*
Insects (the group having the greatest number of species)	1. Have an external skeleton composed of a flexible, tough material. 2. Have three pairs of jointed walking legs. 3. Most insects have two pairs of wings. 4. Breathe through tiny openings in their body, called *spiracles*. (Many insects destroy crops, fruits, and trees, and spread disease.) (Other insects make useful products for humans, and a few destroy harmful insects.)	Destructive: Grasshopper and corn borer Tent caterpillar and peach-tree borer Gypsy moth Fly and mosquito Useful: Honeybee Silkworm Praying mantis
Spiders	1. Have an external skeleton. 2. Have four pairs of jointed walking legs. 3. Are chiefly land dwellers. (Spiders benefit humans by eating harmful insects.)	Black widow spider Garden spider Trap-door spider Tarantula
Shellfish (Crustaceans)	1. Chiefly water dwellers. 2. External skeleton contains lime. 3. Have 10 pairs of jointed walking legs.	Lobster Crab Shrimp
Hard-shelled Animals (Mollusks)	1. Some live in water, some on land. 2. External skeleton of one or two hard shells. (In some, the shell is small and covered with soft flesh.)	Octopus Squid Slug Snail Clam
Spiny Animals (Echinoderms)	1. Live in salt water. 2. Body resembles a five-pointed star. 3. Sharp projections are present on body of most.	Starfish Sea Urchin Sand Dollar
Segmented Worms (Annelids)	1. Have a soft body without an external skeleton. 2. Body is divided into a series of compartments, or *segments*. 3. Live in water or moist places. Some are parasites. (*Parasites* live on or inside other organisms from which they obtain their food.)	Earthworm Sandworm Leech (The earthworm is valuable because it helps keep the soil loose and aerated.)

Table 1-2. (*Continued*)

Type	Characteristics	Examples
Jellyfish and Relatives	1. Water-dwellers. 2. Soft jelly-like body. 3. Have tentacles (grasping organs) with stinging cells.	Hydra Coral Portuguese man-of-war

4. KINDS OF PLANTS

About 300,000 different kinds of plants abound the earth. Except for a few that are parasites, plants are green and make their own food. Plants are found almost everywhere on the surface of the earth, and in streams, lakes, and oceans. They vary in size from the tiny mosses to the giant redwoods of California, which may grow to a height of about three hundred feet.

Table 1-3. Types of Plants

Type	Characteristics	Examples
Mosses	1. Live in moist places. 2. Have tiny leaves and hairlike, rootlike branches, but lack stems and roots.	Sphagnum moss Peat moss Pigeon-wheat moss
Ferns	1. Live in shady places. 2. Have leaves above ground, and stems and roots underground.	Christmas fern Horsetail Tropical tree fern
Flowering Plants	1. Most live on land as herbs, shrubs, or trees. 2. Have broad leaves and stems above ground, and roots underground. 3. Have flowers that produce seeds inside their fruits. 4. Shed leaves or die during the winter.	Oaks Roses Lilies
Cone-bearing Plants (Conifers)	1. Trees or shrubs. 2. Have needlelike leaves that remain green all year. 3. Produce seeds inside their cones.	Pines Spruce Hemlock

5. KINDS OF PROTISTS

About 125,000 different kinds of protists are known. Many can be seen only with a microscope; others are large enough to be seen with the unaided eye.

Table 1-4. Types of Protists

Type	Characteristics	Examples
Bacteria	1. Live only in moist places. 2. Microscopic, one-celled. 3. Lack chlorophyll.	*Useful types:* Soil bacteria Cheese bacteria *Harmful types:* Cause diseases such as pneumonia.
Fungi	1. Plantlike. 2. Single-celled or multicelled. 3. Lack chlorophyll.	Yeast Mold Mushroom
Algae	1. Plantlike. 2. Single-celled or multicelled. 3. Live in moist places. 4. Contain chlorophyll.	Pond scum Seaweeds Giant kelp
Protozoans	1. Animallike. 2. Live in moist places. 3. One-celled. 4. Most lack chlorophyll.	Ameba Paramecium Euglena

As you take more science courses, you may find other systems of classification. One such system divides living things into five kingdoms by splitting the protists into three separate kingdoms. In this book, however, we will be using the three-kingdom system described in section 2, pages 1-2.

6. TREES

A tree is a large, woody plant that grows erect and has a single stem, or *trunk*. Very similar to trees are shrubs. Shrubs have several separate stems growing from the root. They do not grow as tall as trees.

There are over a thousand different kinds of trees in North America alone. Trees differ in many ways: size, appearance of the bark, appearance of the branches or twigs, types of buds, and types of flowers and fruits. One of the outstanding differences in trees is the size and shape of their leaves. This difference provides us with the easiest way of identifying trees.

The following drawings will help you recognize some common trees.

a. Trees with Needlelike or Scaly Leaves. Most of the trees in this group produce seeds in cones (conifers).

Pine

There are over twenty different kinds of pines in North America. In almost all, the needles are arranged in clusters of from two to five needles in each.

1. *White pine*—soft, blue-green, pleasant smelling needles from 3 to 5 inches long, arranged in five to a cluster. Long, narrow cones.
2. *Longleaf pine*—long (8 to 18 inches), flexible needles, arranged three in a cluster. Needles are a shiny dark-green. Cones have sharp points.
3. *Pitch pine*—found in sandy, barren regions. Short (3 to 5 inches), stiff needles in clusters of three. Cones are oval in shape and have sharp points.

Spruce

1. Spruces have short, slightly curved, four-sided needles.
2. Needles are arranged in spirals around the twigs.
3. Cones always hang down.

TREES: LOVE THEM, AND LET THEM GROW!

Trees, like all other plants, make their own food—mainly in their leaves—as they take carbon dioxide from the air and give off oxygen. The oxygen released by plants is taken in by humans and other organisms for their life activities. The carbon dioxide that plants take from the air also helps humans and other organisms because carbon dioxide—colorless and odorless—is, nevertheless, a dangerous gas, as it contributes to the warming of the planet Earth.

Trees, you see, are of prime importance to us for their gas exchange of carbon dioxide and oxygen. But there is more. Trees beautify and shade our environment; some provide food, fuel, and lumber; and all bind the soil with their roots, thus preventing the removal of valuable topsoil by heavy rains and winds.

Hemlock

1. Needles are short and flat, dark-green on upper side and have two white lines on lower surface.
2. Needles are arranged in two flattened rows on the branch.
3. Cones are small and hang from the ends of the branchlets throughout the year.
4. Tip of tree droops.

Juniper

1. Short, blunt, scaly leaves and short needles.
2. Fruits are bluish berries—really cones. They are usually called "juniper berries."

b. Trees with Broad Leaves (Flower Bearers). The leaves of these trees vary in breadth but are broad compared to the needlelike leaves. Each kind of broad leaf has its own distinctive vein pattern. In addition, the leaf may be simple or compound. A *simple leaf* consists of one piece, even though it may be indented. A *compound leaf* is divided into a number of smaller parts, each part called a *leaflet*. The broad-leafed trees are not evergreens; that is, they shed their leaves before winter.

Willow

There are over 100 different kinds of willows in North America.
1. Long, narrow, lance-shaped leaves.
2. Usually found growing in moist soil and along rivers.

Elm

1. Edges of elm leaves have sharp teeth.
2. One side of the base of the leaf is lower than the other.
3. In winter, branches of the American elm give the tree the appearance of a Y.

Birch

1. Leaves have fringelike notches on edges.
2. Most birches can be identified by the appearance and color of their bark.
3. Branches of all birches droop.

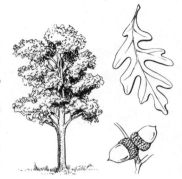

Oak

Oaks produce acorns, and can be divided into two general groups:

1. *White oaks*—acorns ripen in one year. The leaves have deep indentations and rounded projections. The bark is usually pale in color.
2. *Black oaks*—acorns ripen in two years. The leaves have deep indentations and sharp-pointed projections. The bark is generally dark.

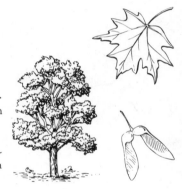

Maple

Many kinds of maple are found in North America.

1. All have palm-shaped, indented leaves that grow in pairs—one leaf opposite the other on the twigs.
2. All have paired, winged fruits.

Some kinds of maple are: Norway maple, sugar maple, red maple, silver maple, the box elder (also known as the ash-leaved maple).

Ash

1. Leaves are compound, composed of from 5 to 9 leaflets.
2. Leaves grow in pairs on opposite sides of the twigs.
3. Fruits are made up of a single wing. The winged seeds hang in clusters.

Poison Sumac

Poison sumac grows as a small tree or shrub to a height of about 25 feet. Grows mainly in swamps or very wet ground.

1. Compound leaves are made up of from 7 to 13 leaflets.
2. Leaflets are shiny green on top surface and have a red vein.
3. Edges of leaflets turn red in the fall.
4. Have yellowish berries in winter.

   Do not touch the leaflets. They are more poisonous and irritating than poison ivy.

Poison Ivy

Poison ivy grows as a shrub or climbing vine. It is found almost everywhere in the temperate regions of the United States.

1. Leaves have long stalks.
2. Leaves are compound, consisting of three leaflets. Leaflets are from 1 to 4 inches long and may have smooth edges or blunt teeth.
3. Dull gray berries are formed in compact clusters.

   Poison ivy may produce severe skin irritation. Do not touch or go near this plant.

7. LEAVES CHANGE COLOR IN THE AUTUMN

In the fall, the green leaves of broad-leafed trees change color. This happens because, at that time of year, chlorophyll is destroyed by certain chemical changes. Then the leaves become yellow, gold, orange, and crimson.

While a leaf is turning to its autumn color, a corklike layer is forming between the leaf and the branch to which it is attached. In time, due to the thickening of the layer, the leaf falls off the branch. The region on the branch where the leaf had been attached is called the *leaf scar*. Within each scar can be seen many small dots. These dots are the sealed ends of the tubes that had carried liquids to and from the leaves during the summer.

As a tree loses its leaves, it cannot make food. It can use only the food it has stored during the previous growing season. At the same time, the tree becomes less active and finally passes into the resting stage of winter.

A GREAT AMERICAN HOBBY: BIRD-WATCHING

John Kieran, a one-time sports reporter for *The New York Times*, found himself with lots of time during his work. He would spend his mornings, especially when no sporting events were being held, observing the behavior of birds. He claimed he had lots of fun while becoming an outstanding naturalist.

You, too, can develop an interest in this enjoyable activity. You can go out on your own or team up with a group. All you need is an inexpensive set of binoculars, a notebook, and a guide, such as Roger Peterson's A FIELD GUIDE TO THE BIRDS. With this simple equipment, you can identify different birds, their songs, calls, and nests.

You will progress slowly at first, recognizing a few birds at a time. Take notes and make sketches so that when you see a bird the second or third time, you will recognize it.

The pages that follow list the characteristics of a variety of birds, accompanied by a sketch of each. Follow up your observations with a little study. If you become a bird-watcher, you will be rewarded with many pleasurable hours of leisure as well as with knowledge of some of nature's most fascinating creatures!

---

8. BIRDS

Birds are found almost everywhere on the earth—from the frozen polar regions to the steaming jungles. Many kinds of birds are important to people. Some destroy harmful insects, some eat great quantities of weed seeds, some feed on field mice and other pests, and some aid in the reproduction of plants.

You may recognize a bird by the shape of its body, its wings, and its tail. Look for special markings such as color, tail pattern, wing pattern, and wing bars. Other clues that help to distinguish a particular bird can be found in its behavior. For example, does it climb trees? Does it swim or wade?

The following drawings will help you identify some interesting birds.

English Sparrow

1. Widespread city bird.
2. Male has a large black bib and brown and black wing stripes. Female is less attractive with a plain, dingy breast.
3. Feeds on or near the ground on insects and seeds.
4. Serious pest—drives away other useful birds.
5. Nests vary—in angles of buildings, birdhouses, or trees.
6. Beak is short and stout.

Chickadee

1. Black-capped; body feathers have white edges; lower throat has white-tipped feathers.
2. A woodland bird, but frequents orchards and shade trees.
3. Feeds chiefly on insects, but also eats berries and seeds. Frequently feeds upside down.
4. Bird named after its characteristic high-pitched call: chick-a-dee.
5. Nests in cavities in trees.
6. Can be attracted to a feeding station containing seeds or suet.
7. Beak is short and straight.

Mourning Dove

1. Resembles a pigeon, but is slimmer and has a long, pointed tail. Tail has white spots.
2. Feeds on seeds and fruits.
3. Has a melancholy call which gives the bird its name.
4. Beak is slender and swollen at its base.

House Wren

1. A small, brownish bird without any distinctive markings.
2. Carries its tail almost vertically, and has a slightly curved bill.
3. Feeds on small insects.
4. Sometimes punctures bird eggs or kills the young in the nest of other birds.
5. Utters deep, grating sounds.
6. Nests in tree hollows, but will also nest in a birdhouse.

Crow

1. Large, stocky, and black.
2. Deep, steady wingbeat.
3. Feeds on insects and grain but may eat mice, eggs, and young of birds.
4. Nests in trees.
5. Beak is stout and pointed.

Hummingbird

1. The smallest and swiftest bird, and the only one able to fly backward.
2. Feathers of changeable colors.
3. Hovers almost motionlessly about flowers from which it extracts nectar with its long, needle-shaped bill; also feeds on small insects and spiders.
4. Builds nest of plant material above ground on limbs of trees.

Blue Jay

1. Colorful—blue, white, and black markings.
2. Noisy—whistles shrilly, screams, and sometimes sings softly.
3. Usually inhabits open fields or wooded areas.
4. Nests in trees.
5. Larger than a robin.
6. Beak is stout and pointed.

Robin

1. Most common songbird of eastern United States.
2. Dark gray back and brick-red breast.
3. Found in wooded areas as well as in residential sections.
4. Feeds on fruits, earthworms, and insects.
5. Makes a variety of noises—from loud, piercing calls to cheerful songs.
6. Nests on the ground or in trees.
7. Beak is yellow.

Sea Gull

1. Long-winged swimming bird.
2. Abundant along the Atlantic and Pacific coasts and parts of the interior along lakes and rivers.
3. Has webbed feet.
4. Feeds on fish, clams, and garbage.
5. Flies with its beak straight forward.

Great Horned Owl

1. Large, powerful bird. Usually has a white throat; appears not to have a neck.
2. Has ear tufts held flat against head when in flight.
3. Feeds on all types of animal life—rats and other rodents, snakes, and various birds.
4. Varying noises—but the most common is a deep, hooting sound repeated from five to seven times.
5. Rarely builds own nest but takes over the nest of some other large bird. Also nests in caves and hollow trees.
6. Beak is hooked.

Be cautious when approaching an occupied nest. The owl may strike a visitor on the head or back.

Bluebird

1. Is bright-blue in wings and tail, with a chestnut-brown breast.
2. Early spring visitor.
3. Prefers open country with scattered trees.
4. Feeds on ground insects and berries.
5. Battles the starling for nest sites.
6. Nests in tree cavities and old woodpecker holes.
7. Can be attracted by proper birdhouses and seed cakes.

Kingfisher

1. Is blue-gray in color, but the female is more colorful than the male, having brown sides and breast. Has a large head and a ragged crest. Is about the size of a blue jay.
2. Found wherever there is water—lakes, rivers, seacoast.
3. Feeds chiefly on fish which it catches by diving into the water. Also eats insects and fruits.
4. Harsh, rattling notes.
5. Builds nest in chambers burrowed into steep banks.
6. Beak is strong, pointed, and longer than its head.

Woodpecker

1. Climbs up and down tree trunks.
2. Braces itself against the tree by its stiff tail feathers.
3. Taps and bores into tree bark with its strong bill in order to reach insects, which it removes with its long tongue.
4. Woodpeckers nest in a cavity in a tree.

Meadow Lark

1. Has white outer-tail feathers and a yellow breast with a black V.
2. As it walks, tail opens with a nervous flick.
3. Prefers open meadows and grain fields.
4. Feeds on insects and weed seeds.
5. Loud, clear, whistled notes.
6. Nests in hollows on ground where there is a cover of weeds or grass.
7. Beak is fairly long.

Starling

1. A clumsy, short-tailed bird with long, pointed wings and a long, pointed beak.
2. Noisy—sings and imitates other birds.
3. Feeds on insects on ground and on fruits and seeds.
4. Nests in woodpecker holes in tree, or any opening in buildings or cliffs.

Swallow

1. Long, pointed wings and forked tail.
2. Makes long, graceful flights, usually gliding.
3. Many kinds of swallows are found near water.
4. Beak is short and flat.

KEEPING LIVING THINGS IN THE CLASSROOM

9. HOW WE BENEFIT BY KEEPING LIVING THINGS

Interesting plants and animals may be raised successfully in the classroom or at home under suitable conditions. Raising living things provides us with:

a. An opportunity to study plants and animals and their activities at close hand.

b. An understanding of the environmental needs of organisms.

c. A valuable and interesting hobby.

d. A respect for life.

10. SETTING UP AND KEEPING A FRESH-WATER AQUARIUM

A varied assortment of water plants and animals can be maintained in an aquarium. An aquarium may be set up as follows:

a. Obtain a rectangular tank holding five or six gallons of water.

b. Clean the tank and cover the bottom to a depth of one or two inches with aquarium gravel that has been thoroughly washed.

c. Place the tank in medium light; strong light may cause an excessive growth of algae that will cloud the water. Add clear pond water or conditioned water from another tank to a level of from two to three inches above the bottom of the tank. If tap water is used, it should be allowed to stand for about two days to allow gases, such as chlorine, to evaporate from the water.

d. Place both rooted and floating plants in the aquarium. These plants (1) provide oxygen needed by the fish, (2) use the carbon dioxide given off by the fish, and (3) provide a place for fish to lay their eggs and protect their young.

e. Allow the aquarium to stand a few days until the water has cleared. Add fish to the aquarium. For each fish one-inch long, a gallon of water is required; a four-inch fish should have four gallons of water, for example. Add six to ten snails to act as scavengers.

f. Feed the fish sparingly. Remove excess food; the excess may decay and foul the tank.

g. As the plants grow, occasionally remove some plant life; an excess may die and decay, fouling the tank.

11. COLLECTING AND RAISING INSECTS

Many kinds of insects are plentiful in the fall. Among those that may be picked or caught are grasshoppers, beetles, ants, termites, moth cocoons, and walking sticks. The following equipment is needed: collecting bottles, tweezers, small pill-box, and nets.

Raising insects in the classroom allows you to observe them for a long period of time. Because jars with curved sides distort the appearance of the size and shape of the insects, they are best raised for observation in straight-sided aquariums or jars. Under proper conditions, you will be able to raise water-living insects, moths, butterflies, and many others.

Multiple-Choice Questions

Write the number preceding the correct answer.

1. One difference between plants and animals is that only plants contain (1) carbon (2) oxygen (3) cellulose (4) living matter.

2. A living creature that keeps a fairly constant blood temperature is the (1) frog (2) garter snake (3) human (4) turtle.

3. An animal whose body is covered with scales is the (1) bat (2) fishworm (3) porcupine (4) snake.

4. An animal that breathes with lungs is the (1) codfish (2) haddock (3) whale (4) tuna.

5. An animal that obtains oxygen from the water during part of its life and from the air during the rest of its life is the (1) minnow (2) frog (3) cricket (4) sea gull.

6. Mammals differ from birds in that mammals (1) have a backbone (2) have a brain (3) have blood (4) produce milk for their young.
7. Feathers are most useful to birds because they (1) are good heat insulators (2) have bright colors (3) lessen the weight of the bird (4) protect the bird from gunshots and large mammals.
8. All living things are made up of (1) muscles (2) cells (3) cellulose (4) chlorophyll.
9. Of the following living things, the group that has the greatest number of species is the (1) dog (2) human being (3) insect (4) whale.
10. Insects are different from other animals in that they (1) are small (2) live on plant life (3) have three pairs of legs (4) lay eggs.
11. An animal with eight legs is the (1) ant (2) housefly (3) mosquito (4) spider.
12. An insect takes in oxygen by means of its (1) gills (2) lungs (3) moist skin (4) spiracles.
13. Earthworms are desirable animals because they (1) destroy harmful insects (2) help keep the soil loose (3) kill weeds by eating the roots (4) produce nitrates from nitrogen in the air.
14. An example of an animallike protist is the (1) pond scum (2) ameba (3) seaweed (4) gypsy moth.
15. A cold-blooded vertebrate that has overlapping scales is the (1) lobster (2) crow (3) snail (4) trout.
16. Which of the following is an evergreen tree? (1) maple (2) oak (3) willow (4) spruce.
17. The needles of a pine tree are its (1) leaves (2) twigs (3) flowers (4) seeds.
18. A tree that does not shed all of its leaves in the fall is the (1) American elm (2) horse chestnut (3) sugar maple (4) Norway spruce.
19. Some protists are useful because they (1) are eaten by plants (2) cause disease (3) are used in making cheese (4) use oxygen from the air.
20. Plantlike organisms that do not have leaves are (1) pine trees (2) potato plants (3) grasses (4) mushrooms.
21. All fungus plants (1) are gray or brown in color (2) are poisonous (3) are unable to manufacture food (4) grow on trees.
22. Seaweeds are examples of (1) flowering plants (2) protists (3) cone-bearers (4) mosses.
23. A shrub differs from a tree in that a shrub may have (1) more than one trunk (2) chlorophyll (3) no wood (4) flowers.
24. A maple leaf changes color in the fall because of (1) a chemical change (2) dry weather (3) frost (4) wet weather.
25. Which bird is the smallest and swiftest? (1) sparrow (2) swallow (3) hummingbird (4) wren.
26. Which one of these birds has such aggressive manners that it often drives away the more desirable birds? (1) bluebird (2) robin (3) sparrow (4) wren
27. A bird with a shrill call is the (1) bluebird (2) blue jay (3) chickadee (4) mourning dove.

28. A bird that may build its nest in a birdhouse is the (1) bluebird (2) crow (3) kingfisher (4) bobolink.
29. A robin's nest is most likely to be found (1) hanging from a tree branch (2) high among the rafters of a barn (3) in a hole in a mud bank (4) in a tree.
30. A substance placed in feeding trays to attract chickadees in winter is (1) shredded paper (2) suet (3) straw (4) string.

Completion Questions

Write the word or expression that correctly completes the statement.

1. Animals that have a backbone are classed as _____ .
2. An animal whose body is generally covered with scales and that breathes by means of lungs is classed as a (an) _____ .
3. An animal that has gills one part of its life and lungs during the other part is classed as a (an) _____ .
4. An insect that is destructive to trees is the tent _____ .
5. The housefly and some mosquitoes are undesirable because they may transmit organisms causing human _____ .
6. The praying mantis is valuable in the garden because it _____ .
7. All fungi lack _____ , which is necessary for food making.
8. A tree which has the appearance of a Y in the winter is the _____ .
9. A poisonous shrub having compound leaves is the _____ .
10. To attract hummingbirds, a feeding station should contain _____ .

Thought Questions

1. Although birds and bats can fly, they are not classified in the same group of vertebrates. Give two reasons why.
2. Upon returning from the moon some years ago, the astronauts brought back some soil. Scientists here examined the soil and concluded that life did not exist on the moon. What led the scientists to that conclusion?

Chapter 2. Living Things Depend on One Another

1. HOW LIVING THINGS DEPEND ON OTHER LIVING THINGS

No living thing is able to live completely independent of others. For the essentials of life, all organisms depend on other living things for food, oxygen, and water. The relationships among living things and their environment is the study called *ecology*.

2. ANIMALS AND PLANTS DEPEND ON EACH OTHER

Green plants are the basic source of food for all animals. In addition to food, green plants provide animals with oxygen, as green plants remove carbon dioxide from the air and release oxygen. Animals also depend on plants for shelter and places to live. The squirrel and raccoon, for example, use hollow trees for homes. Birds not only obtain insects and berries in forests for food, but also use plant materials to build their nests. For example, the goldfinch lines its nest with the silky material it obtains from ripened thistles.

Green plants need carbon dioxide and certain nitrogen compounds to make their food. Much of the carbon dioxide is provided by animals, as they take oxygen from the air and give off carbon dioxide. Much of the nitrogen compounds that plants need comes from decayed *organic* matter (wastes and other matter derived from living things).

3. SOME ANIMALS DEPEND ON ANIMALS OF THEIR OWN KIND

In some species of animals, the members live and work together for the benefit of each other. (A *species* is a natural population of similar organisms that reproduce only among themselves.)

Animals that live in communities and work together are called *social animals*. Two outstanding examples are beavers and bees.

a. Beavers. Working as a colony, beavers use their sharp teeth to cut down trees. Using mud, twigs, stones, and the fallen trees, beavers construct a dam across a shallow stream to form a pond. Each family then builds its home. The home consists of a large hollow mound above the surface of the water. The home can be entered only through an opening below the surface of the water. Here a beaver family lives and raises its young.

b. Bees. Thousands of bees live together in a large colony. Each bee works for the welfare of the entire colony. The members are divided into three groups: *workers, drones,* and *queens.* The workers visit flowers to gather the raw materials from which they make honey and other food; they produce the wax from which the honeycombs are built; they clean the beehive and nurse the young; and, finally, they guard the beehive against enemies. The only job performed by the drones is to mate with the queen to produce new bees. After mating, the drone dies. The queen bee spends her time laying eggs which develop into new bees.

4. SOME ANIMALS DEPEND ON OTHER SPECIES OF ANIMALS

Some animals live in partnership with other species of animals, one species helping the other to obtain the necessities of life. For example:

a. The Termite. This animal feeds on wood, generally in forests and buildings. The termite chews the wood into small pieces and swallows them, but cannot digest the particles. In the digestive tract of the termite reside certain microscopic protozoans that perform the process of digestion, changing the wood particles into materials that the termite can use for food.

In return for this service, the termite provides the microscopic organisms not only with food, which is wood, but also a place to live.

b. The Aphid and the Ant. The aphid is a plant louse that sucks juices from plants. When its back is stroked by the antennae of a worker ant, the aphid releases a sweet fluid much desired by the ant.

The aphid supplies the ant with food; the ant protects the aphid against its enemies and also cares for the aphid's eggs by storing them in ant nests during the winter.

Some animals depend on other animal species for their life needs, but give nothing in return. For example:

c. The Rabbit and the Woodchuck. The woodchuck digs a very deep burrow in which it *hibernates* (spends the winter). The upper tunnels of the burrow become the winter home of certain species of rabbits that do not hibernate and whose body parts are not suited to digging burrows.

Although the woodchuck gives the rabbit protection against cold weather and enemies, the rabbit gives the woodchuck nothing in return.

d. The Lion and the Zebra. The lion is a flesheater. It catches and feeds upon other live animals such as zebras. The lion is an example of a *predator*: an animal that feeds on other animals. The zebra is its *prey*: the animal that falls victim to the predator. The teeth and other body parts of predators are suited to capturing, holding, and tearing flesh.

5. OTHER BENEFICIAL PARTNERSHIPS

Just as there are beneficial partnerships in the animal world, there are similar relationships in the plant and protist worlds. For example:

a. Legumes and Nitrogen-fixing Bacteria. *Legumes* are plants such as peas, clover, alfalfa, soybeans, and peanuts. Found on the roots of a legume are tiny swellings called *nodules*. These serve as the home for millions of microscopic protists, called *nitrogen-fixing bacteria*. The bacteria help the legume by converting nitrogen from the air into nitrogen compounds, which the legume uses to build more of its own living material. (See Fig. 37-3 on page 363.)

b. The Lichen. This organism commonly grows on the bark of trees, rocks, and sometimes on the ground. Although it resembles a plant, a lichen is not a plant. It consists of two protists living together—an *alga* and a *fungus*. Since the alga is green, it manufactures food and releases oxygen. The fungus cannot make its own food, but uses the food made by the alga, and the oxygen released by it. At the same time, the fungus absorbs moisture that the alga uses.

6. SOME PROTISTS LIVE ON DEAD ORGANISMS

a. Bacteria. Since bacteria are not green, they are dependent upon other organisms for their food. Some bacteria, called *bacteria of decay*, live on dead organisms or the waste products of living animals. Bacteria of decay convert the dead or waste materials into substances that can then be used by other living things.

b. Fungi. The bracket fungus is frequently found growing on decaying tree trunks. Mushrooms, like decay bacteria, live on dead organisms and animal wastes.

7. PLANTS AND ANIMALS THAT ARE PARASITES

Some organisms obtain their food at the expense of some other living organism by living in its body or by being attached to its surface. A living thing that obtains its food in this manner is called a *parasite*. The organism that supplies the food for the parasite is called the *host*. Study the following table for other parasitic relationships.

Parasites and Their Hosts

Animal parasite	Animal host
Flea	Dog or cat
Tapeworm	Human, other animals
Tick	Human, dog, cat, cattle, other mammals
Mosquito (female only)	Human, other mammals

Animal parasite	Plant host
Aphid	Rose bush
Sawfly	Wheat
Corn borer moth	Corn

Protist parasite	Animal host
Fungus of athlete's foot	Human
Tuberculosis bacillus	Human, cattle

Protist parasite	Plant host
Bracket fungus	Birch tree
Rusts and smuts	Corn, oats, wheat

8. FOOD CHAINS AND FOOD WEBS

Many relationships exist among organisms only because of the need for food. Often the relationship develops into a *food chain*. This is a one-sided relationship in which, usually, a large organism feeds on a smaller organism. Regardless of the number of links in a food chain, the chain always begins with a green organism, either a green protist or a green plant. Thus, it is clear that green organisms are the original source of food for all living things.

A typical food chain exists in lakes and oceans. Living in the water are millions of microscopic green algae. Feeding on the algae are small animals called water fleas. These water fleas are in turn eaten by small fish. Feeding on the small fish are larger fish, such as pickerel, which in turn may be eaten by even larger fish or by humans. Thus, in a food chain the organisms at the start of the chain are usually smaller and more numerous than the organisms at the end of the chain.

Food chains often meet and cross one another. For example, an animal that is part of one food chain may eat an animal that is part of another food chain. The crisscrossing of many food chains is called a *food web*.

Multiple-Choice Questions

Write the number preceding the correct answer.

1. All living things require food, oxygen, and (1) carbon dioxide (2) darkness (3) water (4) high temperatures.
2. An animal that works in groups to cut down trees is the (1) beaver (2) muskrat (3) squirrel (4) woodchuck.
3. An animal that lives and works in large colonies is the (1) woodchuck (2) honeybee (3) kingfisher (4) garter snake.
4. The queen bee mates with the (1) aphid (2) worker (3) drone (4) larva.
5. When bees visit flowers they (1) get food (2) lay eggs (3) make a home (4) sting the flowers.
6. A relationship beneficial to both animals exists between the (1) cat and mouse (2) termite and the microscopic animals in its digestive tract (3) rabbit and woodchuck (4) tent caterpillar and ant.
7. Ants have established a beneficial relationship with animals called (1) termites (2) bees (3) corn borers (4) aphids.
8. An animal that uses the burrow of a woodchuck but does not benefit the woodchuck is the (1) woodpecker (2) beaver (3) otter (4) rabbit.
9. An animal that uses thistle plant material to line its nest is the (1) oriole (2) tern (3) hawk (4) goldfinch.
10. One means by which plants obtain nitrogen is through the action of nitrogen-fixing bacteria. One type of these bacteria lives on the roots of (1) clover (2) oats (3) rye (4) wheat.
11. A beneficial relationship between two different plants exists in (1) roses (2) oats (3) lichens (4) wheat.
12. The bracket fungus (1) is cultivated by farmers (2) is able to make its own food (3) obtains its food from dead trees (4) has flowers.
13. The organism on which a parasite lives is called the (1) host (2) prey (3) parasitic partner (4) flowering plant.
14. An example of a parasite is a (1) bird in a tree (2) flea on a dog (3) frog in the water (4) rabbit in a hole.
15. An insect that feeds on the blood of animals is the (1) aphid (2) cockroach (3) mosquito (4) wasp.
16. Grasshoppers are often eaten by frogs, crows, and sea gulls. This is an example of part of a (1) parasite (2) partnership (3) host (4) food web.
17. The relationship between the lion and the zebra is one of (1) benefit to both (2) predator and prey (3) benefit to the zebra only (4) parasite and host.

Completion Questions

Write the word or expression that correctly completes the statement.

1. The basic source of food on which all animals depend is the _____.
2. Plants give off _____ to the air, a gas that all animals need.
3. Animals that work together as a group are known as _____ animals.
4. An animal whose home can be entered only through an opening below the surface of the water is the _____.
5. The _____ bee's only job is to lay eggs.
6. The diet of a termite consists chiefly of _____.
7. Aphids provide ants with a (an) _____.
8. Certain bacteria living in the nodules of legumes convert _____ into materials that plants can use.
9. In a lichen, food is manufactured by the _____.
10. Mushrooms live on _____.
11. All food chains end with animals and begin with _____ plants.

Thought Questions

1. Certain bacteria obtain their food by decaying meat that has not been refrigerated. We consider such bacteria to be harmful. Yet, under natural conditions, the same bacteria decay the bodies of dead organisms. In this case, we consider the bacteria to be helpful. Why?
2. Explain the following statement: In the planting season after alfalfa had been harvested, the field produced a larger corn crop than before the alfalfa had been planted there.

Chapter 3. Organisms Are Fitted to Live in Various Environments

1. LIFE IS WIDESPREAD

The natural home, or environment, of any living thing is called its *habitat*. The habitats of living things vary—from the frozen wastelands of the Arctic and Antarctic to the hot equatorial region. Living things are abundant in regions of moderate heat and moisture, as in the temperate zones.

The conditions in an area that make it a favorable habitat for one species but unfavorable for another are the following: *(a)* temperature, *(b)* amount of water, *(c)* amount of sunlight, *(d)* type of soil, and *(e)* elevation.

2. LIVING THINGS DWELL IN DIFFERENT HABITATS

Field mice live in regions having a heavy growth of weeds. Some species of ants build their homes (ant hills) in sandy areas. Animals such as the sowbug and millipede live under rocks or other objects that have been lying on the ground for some time. Various kinds of insects may be found feeding on the leaves of certain types of trees and bushes. The types of plants growing in fertile soil are usually different from those growing in poor soil.

The special body structures such as wings that an organism possesses and the way the organism lives—whether alone or in colonies or in flocks—help an organism fit its habitat and survive. These structures and ways of life are called *adaptations*.

3. ANIMALS WHOSE HABITAT IS THE SOIL

The soil is the habitat of a great variety of animals. Some examples of animals that have adaptations for living in the soil are:

a. Insects. Many species of insects, such as the mole cricket, spend most of their lives in the soil. They have strong front feet adapted to digging underground.

b. Worms. The earthworm is adapted to dig, or burrow, into moist soil that contains its food (dead plant matter). The earthworm swallows the soil, and as the soil passes through the worm's body, the plant matter is digested. Upon leaving the body, the soil and the worm's body wastes are deposited onto the surface of the soil. The earthworm is important because its body wastes enrich the soil, and its burrows help air and water to enter the soil.

c. Mammals. The soil serves as the habitat for mammals such as the mole, the shrew, and the woodchuck. These animals have strong front feet adapted to burrowing underground. Although the mole may be considered a nuisance as it tunnels under a lawn, the mole is really useful. It consumes large quantities of young insects that destroy plants.

4. ANIMALS WHOSE HABITAT IS THE LAND

The animals with which you are most familiar are those whose habitat is the land. Such animals are adapted to breathe in oxygen by means of lungs, as mammals do, or by means of air tubes, as insects do.

a. Animals That Run or Hop. Animals such as the deer, rabbit, horse, and even the grasshopper have strong legs that help them escape their enemies and that aid in searching for food.

b. Animals That Store Food. In many regions, the food supply for certain animals may be available only part of a year. During warm months, the squirrel, chipmunk, and mouse store up a food supply for winter use. Certain insects, such as bees and ants, which live in colonies, also store food for winter use.

c. Animals That Eat Meat. The mink, owl, weasel, fox, and wolf are examples of *carnivorous* animals, or flesh-eaters. With their long, sharp teeth or their sharp beak and claws, they tear apart the flesh of other animals. Most carnivores live in the woods or forests.

d. Animals That Eat Plants. *Herbivorous animals* (plant-eaters) are the opposites of carnivorous animals (flesh-eaters). Common herbivores are the cow, horse, deer, sheep, and pig. Their teeth cut and grind grass and other plants. The beaver, squirrel, rabbit, and chipmunk have sharp, chisel-shaped teeth for gnawing.

e. Animals That Hibernate. *Hibernate* means to spend the winter asleep. Hibernating animals like the frog, woodchuck, and snake lie in a continuous sleep in a safe, convenient shelter all winter. While inactive during hibernation, they expend only a small amount of energy. They obtain this energy from the food they stored as fat in their body during the summer months.

f. Animals With Protective Coloring. *Protective coloration* is an adaptation that enables many animals to escape their enemies, as the color of their feathers, fur, or skin blends in with their surroundings. The pheasant, quail, rabbit, snake, and many insects benefit from protective coloration. A curiosity is the chameleon, a reptile that can rapidly change its skin color with changes in lighting or temperature.

g. Animals With Special Protection. The turtle has an outer shell into which it can withdraw. The skunk is adapted to protect itself when in danger by giving off an evil-smelling substance. A few snakes in the United States (the rattlesnake, copperhead, water moccasin, coral snake) have specially adapted hollow teeth, called *fangs*. Through the fangs, these snakes inject a poison into their enemy.

5. ANIMALS WHOSE HABITAT IS THE AIR

The air is the habitat of some mammals and many species of birds and insects.

a. Adaptations of Mammals. The only mammal that can fly is the bat. It has wings made up of a membrane (skin) that stretches over the bones of its very long claws. One type of bat catches and feeds on insects. Another type eats fruits. Still another punctures the skin of another mammal and feeds on its blood.

b. Adaptations of Some Birds. Birds have feathers and wings that adapt them for flight. These structures aid a bird in obtaining food and escaping from its enemies. Some birds, such as the woodpecker, have long, sharp bills that are adapted to boring into the bark of trees in search of insects. Hawks and owls have sharp, hooked bills as well as talons (claws) which help them catch rats and mice. Ducks have webbed feet which help them swim. The great blue heron and stork have long legs which help them wade in shallow water in search for food. The kingfisher has a long, sharp, pointed bill which helps it catch fish.

c. Birds That Migrate. Certain northern birds leave their habitat in the fall when their food supply begins to diminish. These birds, called *transient visitors*, fly to a similar, southerly habitat and remain there until the spring. They then return northward. This flight from one climate to another is called *migration*. Some migratory birds are the scarlet tanager, goose, hummingbird, robin, and bobolink. The arctic tern flies from the Arctic to the Antarctic, a distance of about 11,000 miles, and then returns to the Arctic in time for its mating season.

d. Birds That Do Not Migrate. Some birds such as the woodpecker, chickadee, crow, bluejay, quail, and pheasant remain in the same habitat all year around. They can find food in all seasons. Such birds are called *permanent residents*.

e. Adaptations of Insects. Flying insects possess very thin, delicate wings. Flies and mosquitoes have one pair of wings. Butterflies and moths have two pairs.

Unlike other flying insects, but like some birds, the monarch butterfly is adapted to migrate. As cool weather sets in the butterflies gather in large groups and fly southward together. In the spring, they return north and mate.

6. ANIMALS THAT MAKE WATER THEIR HABITAT

a. Fish. These animals have a number of special structures that fit them to live in water. In most fish, the whole body, except the head and fins, is covered with overlapping scales. The scales not only protect the fish, but also allow them to move freely. Movement of the fish is also aided by a slimy substance covering the scales. The streamlined body of most fish permits the animal to move through the water easily. Large fins propel the fish rapidly.

Fish have gills by which they obtain oxygen from the water. In many fish is a small sac, called an *air bladder*, which helps the fish swim at particular levels.

The trout, perch, carp, sunfish, bullhead, and pike spend their entire lives in the fresh water of streams, ponds, and lakes. The flounder, mackerel, and sailfish live their entire lives in the salt water of oceans and bays. The eel and the salmon spend part of their lives in fresh water and part in salt water.

b. Other Animals. Amphibians, such as frogs, spend the early part of their life in water as fishlike animals called *tadpoles*. In this stage they are adapted to breathe through gills. Later in life, they develop lungs and can live on land. In the adult stage, frogs can also breathe through their moist skin while in water. Webbed feet adapt them to swimming. Their sticky, elastic tongue enables them to catch insects for food.

Some reptiles, such as alligators, spend part of their life on land and part in water. They hatch from eggs laid in nests on land. Having lungs, most breathe air. While in water they often feed on fish. On land, they feed on insects and small mammals.

Some mammals, such as the whale and porpoise, have special structures that enable them to live in water. Both of these animals have lungs and breathe through nostrils on the top of their head. Both have flippers for swimming.

7. PLANTS WHOSE HABITAT IS THE LAND

a. Sunny Habitat. Plants that live in abundant sunshine, as in fields and plains, have long roots that enable them to obtain water. Grasses have root systems that branch out and extend in many directions. The cactus, which lives in the dry, hot desert, has extremely long, deep roots. In some plants, such as the beet and the carrot, the large root systems not only absorb water, but also store food.

The stems of plants support the leaves, exposing them to the air and sunlight. Stems also act as pipelines: water rises from the roots to the leaves; dissolved food material flows from the leaves to the roots. The liquids in the stem make up the *sap* of the plant.

As trees grow, additional layers are added to their trunks. The number of layers, or *rings*, indicates the approximate age of the tree. Many trees, such as the sugar maple, are able to survive the cold winters by having the sap flow into the roots in the winter and return to the stem and branches in the spring. It is during this time, when the sap is flowing, that the sugar maple is tapped for the sugary sap we use as a flavoring.

The leaves are the "factories" where the food-making process of green plants takes place. The leaves are so arranged that they receive the most sunlight possible. In some plants, such as the dandelion and the lettuce, the leaves are arranged in the form of a cluster, called a *rosette*, near the ground.

b. Shady Habitat. Since shaded areas usually have damp, moist soil, the plants in this habitat do not have long roots. Examples are ferns and mosses. Ferns have short roots, whereas mosses have short, underground, hair-like projections. The skunk cabbage and pussy willow grow in soft, wet soil. The jack-in-the-pulpit thrives in dark, damp woods.

8. PLANTS WHOSE HABITAT IS WATER

Water plants, such as the pond lily, are supported (buoyed up) by water. Water plants lack the strong supporting stems found in most land plants. The pond lily has a long stem with roots that reach the bottom of the pond. The floating leaves enable the plant to receive abundant sunlight and carbon dioxide from the air for the food-making process.

9. PROTISTS WHOSE HABITAT IS THE LAND

Molds and mushrooms live in dark, damp places. They lack chlorophyll; they cannot make their own food. Their rootlike extensions enable them to absorb nourishment from dead, decaying matter.

10. PROTISTS WHOSE HABITAT IS A LIQUID ENVIRONMENT

Algae, bacteria, and protozoans all live in a liquid environment. Some species live in fresh water, some in salt water, and others in the body fluids of plants or animals. Algae possess chlorophyll and make their own food. Bacteria obtain food by living on other organisms (see *parasites*, section 7 on page 25), or by converting dead organic matter to food (see *bacteria of decay*, section 6-a on page 25). Some protozoans, such as the malarial parasite, live in the bloodstream of an animal. Other protozoans, such as the ameba, feed on other, smaller protists.

Multiple-Choice Questions

Write the number preceding the correct answer.

1. The region in which an organism normally makes its home is called its (1) adaptation (2) habitat (3) abode (4) burrow.
2. An animal that naturally enriches soil and enables air and water to enter it is the (1) chipmunk (2) earthworm (3) rabbit (4) woodchuck.
3. An animal that makes its home in the soil is the (1) bat (2) grasshopper (3) woodchuck (4) praying mantis.
4. The mole is considered useful to a farmer because it (1) tunnels underground (2) aerates the soil (3) builds mole hills (4) eats harmful insect larvae.
5. An animal that stores food for winter use is the (1) grasshopper (2) robin (3) squirrel (4) carp.
6. An animal that usually eats meat is called (1) herbivorous (2) carnivorous (3) a hibernator (4) colonial.
7. An adaptation of meat-eating animals that helps them catch their prey is (1) hoofs (2) fur-covered bodies (3) grinding teeth (4) sharp teeth.
8. An insect that migrates to a warmer climate before winter sets in is the (1) monarch butterfly (2) cricket (3) honeybee (4) grasshopper.
9. The gnawing teeth of the rabbit are an adaptation for (1) catching prey (2) cutting down trees (3) eating plant matter (4) burrowing.
10. An animal that hibernates through the winter is the (1) chickadee (2) field mouse (3) red fox (4) woodchuck.
11. An animal that is protected by its odor is the (1) rabbit (2) red squirrel (3) skunk (4) field mouse.
12. For protection, some snakes have a special adaptation called (1) claws (2) fangs (3) rattles (4) scales.
13. The bill of a hawk is (1) hooked (2) long and needle-shaped (3) short and stubby (4) long and flat.
14. The claws of an owl are an adaptation that helps it to (1) clean its feathers (2) fly (3) secure and hold its prey (4) walk.
15. A common bird that migrates south before the winter is the (1) pigeon (2) downy woodpecker (3) hummingbird (4) chickadee.
16. A bird that spends the winter in the north is the (1) hummingbird (2) bobolink (3) robin (4) crow.
17. A fish that spends part of its life in salt water and part in fresh water is the (1) brook trout (2) salmon (3) shark (4) sunfish.
18. The part of a frog adapted to catching insects is its (1) webbed feet (2) claws (3) sticky tongue (4) throat pouch.
19. In order to live, a desert cactus must have (1) a very damp climate (2) abundant parasites (3) hot nights (4) some water.

20. A tree whose sap is used by man for food is the (1) elm (2) hemlock (3) oak (4) sugar maple.
21. The dandelion has (1) rosette leaves (2) a single leaf (3) opposite leaves (4) alternate leaves.
22. The age of a maple tree can be estimated by counting its (1) bark (2) buds (3) leaves (4) rings.
23. Molds and mushrooms grow best in an environment that is (1) warm and dry (2) sunny and moist (3) dark and moist (4) cold and moist.
24. An organism that lives in the body fluid of an animal is the (1) poisonous mushroom (2) one that causes malaria (3) alga (4) bread mold.
25. A plant usually found growing in damp, dark woods is the (1) buttercup (2) daisy (3) dandelion (4) jack-in-the-pulpit.

Completion Questions

Write the word or expression that correctly completes the statement.

1. Ant hills are usually found in _____ areas.
2. A special trait of an organism that enables it to live in a particular habitat is called a (an) _____.
3. A special trait of the mole that permits it to burrow underground is its _____.
4. One adaptation of land animals is _____ for breathing.
5. Insects that store food for the winter are the bee and the _____.
6. Animals that eat only plants are called _____.
7. The special adaptation of the cow and the horse that permits them to eat plants is their _____ teeth.
8. When an animal sleeps through a winter in a shelter, it is said to be _____.
9. Pheasants and quail have a good chance to survive because their _____ permits them to blend in with their surroundings.
10. An adaptation of the duck that enables it to swim is its _____ feet.
11. The porpoise and the _____ are water-living mammals.
12. The root system of the beet and the carrot stores _____.
13. The usual habitat of skunk cabbage is _____.
14. A good place to look for a fern is in a (an) _____ area.
15. The _____ is an example of a water-living plant.

Chapter 4. Humans in Relation to Other Living Things

1. HUMANS CAN ADJUST TO MOST ENVIRONMENTS

Having a highly developed brain, we humans can reason, think, create, invent, and communicate with one another. Our dominance over other organisms can be attributed, in part, to our *opposable* thumbs. A thumb can be placed opposite each of our other fingers, enabling us to hold tools and other objects. We have adapted to almost every environment without seasonal migration in search of food and shelter, as lower forms of life must do.

We have been able to change our immediate environment to suit our life needs. Thus, we have built homes in which the temperature and humidity can be controlled. We have made clothing to suit different climates. We have devised methods of purifying water and disposing of sewage and other wastes. And we have learned to use a multitude of other living things to achieve a high living standard.

2. HUMANS USE OTHER ORGANISMS IN THE ENVIRONMENT

Ancient humans met their needs for food by hunting wild animals and gathering wild plants. In time, humans learned to domesticate the animals and plants that were useful to them. Today, for food, we depend mainly on domesticated animals such as sheep, cattle, and poultry and on domesticated plants such as wheat, potatoes, and sugar cane. Animals, such as horses and camels, are used for transportation and other work. Plants, such as the digitalis, are a source of medicines; others such as maple and oak trees, are a source of lumber; still others, such as pines, are used for making paper.

3. HUMANS IMPROVE USEFUL ORGANISMS

Through scientific research, we have improved plants and animals upon which we depend, as follows:

   a. By providing better shelter and better types of food, scientists have improved the animals we raise. Examples: hogs, beef cattle, milk cows.
   b. By using better methods of farming, farmers have improved the quality and increased the quantity of food crops. Examples: wheat, peas.

c. By the crossbreeding of plants and of animals, scientists have improved certain species and produced new breeds. Example: corn, disease-resistant cattle.

4. THERE IS A BALANCE IN NATURE

In nature, where humans have not intruded, the number of organisms of different kinds (protists, plants, animals) in any community (pond, forest, or seashore) tends to remain unchanged from year to year. This tendency is known as the *balance of nature*.

5. UPSETTING THE BALANCE OF NATURE

Since conditions are always changing, the balance of nature is never really permanent. The balance in a region is upset whenever (*a*) its climate changes drastically or a severe natural disturbance strikes, such as an earthquake; (*b*) a new plant or animal is introduced into the region; (*c*) an established plant or animal is removed from the region; or (*d*) humans spoil the environment. Under any such condition, the balance of nature is changed because the new condition in the area may be favorable to some living things but unfavorable to others.

For example, as the result of an earthquake, the course of a river feeding a lake was changed so that the river no longer fed the lake. The lake dried up and all the plants and animals living in the lake died. The lake bottom was then inhabited by land plants and animals. After a period of time, a balance of nature developed among the new plants and animals living in the area.

6. THE BALANCE OF NATURE CONTROLS LIFE

All living things tend to produce more young than can possibly survive in a given environment. This is because natural conditions prevent living things from multiplying too greatly. Poor climatic conditions, natural enemies, and shortages of food and water are some of the natural factors that help continuously to maintain a balance among living things.

7. HUMANS CHANGE THE BALANCE OF NATURE

When we alter the environment to accommodate our needs, we upset the balance of nature more frequently and more seriously than does any other living thing.

a. Destruction of the Homes of Wildlife. By cutting and burning down forests to establish farms, by causing forest fires, and by damming streams, humans have destroyed the homes of other living things.

b. Destruction of Wildlife. As the result of hunting, sometimes only for sport, people have almost completely wiped out some species of animals. For example, only a few buffalo and whooping cranes remain of the countless number that once inhabited the United States. The passenger pigeon of the United States, once present in the millions, is now extinct.

c. Introduction of New Organisms. Plants and animals that were not destructive in their original environment became destructive when humans introduced them into a new region. In the new environment, the species had few or no natural enemies and found an abundance of food. As a result, they increased in number so rapidly that they became destructive pests. For example, the starling was originally introduced into this country to destroy harmful insects. Lacking natural enemies, the starling has rapidly spread over the entire country and is driving out our native birds.

d. Air Pollution. As our population increases, we burn more and more fuel to provide our people with transportation, to run factories and power plants, and to heat buildings. All of these uses of fuel produce *air pollution*. When coal, fuel oil, gasoline, and natural gas are burned, they release smoke, carbon dioxide, carbon monoxide, sulfur dioxide, nitrogen oxides, and other poisonous gases. Such pollutants are responsible for *acid rain* and the thinning of the *ozone layer*.

(1) *Acid Rain.* Sulfur dioxide and nitrogen oxides pollute land areas not only near where the pollutants are produced, but also distant land areas and bodies of water. *Acid rain* occurs because falling rain dissolves the oxides in the atmosphere and forms solutions of acids. As acid rain falls upon ponds and lakes, the water becomes so acid that no life can exist in it. Also affected by excessive acid in the environment are trees and other plant life, and even buildings.

(2) *Ozone Problems.* Ozone is a component of the ozone layer of the stratosphere. Normally, this layer protects us and all other living things against the harmful effects of the ultraviolet rays in sunlight by absorbing most of the rays before they reach us. In humans, the ultraviolet rays can cause severe sunburn and even skin cancer. In the lower atmosphere, near the earth's surface, where ozone results from air pollution, ozone itself is harmful. Related to smog, it irritates the respiratory system and damages plants.

The ozone layer of the stratosphere is harmed by freon and related substances that are used in refrigerators, air conditioners and aerosol propellants. These chemicals are also present in the engine exhaust of jet airplanes and automobiles; and in some products, such as household cleaners. Regardless of their source, anywhere in the world, such chemicals eventually reach the ozone layer and destroy it. Unless all nations cooperate in reducing the use of such chemicals, the ozone layer in time will no longer protect us.

e. Water Pollution. Our people, factories, and farms produce huge amounts of many types of wastes. These wastes, which include sewage, garbage, and chemicals, are often dumped into nearby bodies of water and pollute them. Such severely polluted water, as well as oil spills and acid rain, often kill many desirable species of water-dwelling organisms. As this happens, the natural balance of organisms in a body of water is upset. Only undesirable types may survive. Thus, desirable food fish may be replaced by undesirable types.

For more on the pollution of water, read section 6 on page 52.

f. Soil Destruction. *Topsoil* contains many minerals that are essential for the growth of crops. When soil loses its topsoil, rich farmland becomes barren wasteland. Agents of destruction are (1) wind and runoff of rainfall that carry away the topsoil, and (2) improper methods of farming.

Coal, oil, and metals—natural resources that cannot be renewed—are constantly being removed from the earth for use in homes and industries. Mining has been responsible for destroying soil not only by scarring the land, but also by polluting other nearby land.

For a further study of soil destruction, read section 4 on page 44.

8. WHAT OF THE NATURAL BALANCE OF THE FUTURE?

From now on, if living things as they exist today are to continue surviving on our planet, we humans must become increasingly aware of how we upset the balance of nature and cause ecological damage. We must also take steps to improve the present environment as well as to prevent future damage. (You will learn about preserving our natural resources when you study Chapter 7, Conservation, beginning on page 54.)

Multiple-Choice Questions

Write the number preceding the correct answer.

1. One of the main reasons why humans are adapted to practically every environment is that they (1) live in groups (2) have a highly developed brain (3) have good means of transportation (4) have two eyes.
2. Humans (1) can change their adaptations (2) can change parts of the environment to suit their needs (3) cannot change the balance of nature (4) cannot adapt to environmental changes.
3. Conditions in an environment are most frequently upset by (1) disease (2) erosion (3) humans (4) storms.
4. A new animal introduced into a region may increase in numbers because of (1) abundant sunshine (2) good hiding places (3) plentiful water (4) the absence of natural enemies.
5. One way by which humans have improved some animals in the environment is by (1) improving their shelters (2) introducing new enemies (3) eliminating weeds (4) passing laws.
6. An animal used for work is the (1) sheep (2) wolf (3) camel (4) duck.
7. A valuable drug obtained from a plant is (1) kale (2) arrowroot (3) barley (4) digitalis.
8. A grain used as food for humans is (1) cabbage (2) spinach (3) wheat (4) carrot.
9. A very long spell of dry weather may (1) result in the appearance of new types of plants or animals (2) cause plants in a region to increase in number (3) not affect the balance of nature (4) affect plants but not animals.
10. When large amounts of sewage reach a freshwater stream, we can expect damage to (1) water-dwelling plants, only (2) water-dwelling animals, only (3) both water-dwelling plants and animals (4) nearby land trees.

Completion Questions

Write the word or expression that correctly completes the statement.

1. The human _____ is a structural adaptation for grasping objects.
2. Another adaptation that gives humans superiority over all other organisms is the highly developed _____.
3. Improper farming may result in the removal of _____ by the wind.
4. As humans advanced in scientific knowledge, they became _____ (*more, less*) dependent on the environment.
5. By applying the method of _____, scientists have not only improved useful plants, but have also produced new breeds.

6. The extraction of oil from the earth, refining the oil, and using the refined product usually _____ the environment.
7. The layer of the atmosphere that helps protect us against skin cancer is the _____ layer.
8. Gases released by burning fuels that are responsible for the formation of acid rain are _____ and nitrogen oxides.
9. When the numbers of different kinds of organisms in a community stay about the same from year to year, the community is said to be in _____.
10. Excessive amounts of carbon dioxide and other gases added to the atmosphere may, in time, result in _____ the entire world.

Thought Questions

1. At one time, cattle raised in Texas had good beef but often died from the disease called tick fever. Then, an Indian cattle breed that had poor beef but was immune to tick fever was imported. Modern Texas cattle have good beef and are immune to tick fever. How could this improvement have been accomplished?
2. How might an oil spill off the coast of Alaska affect the price of salmon in California?
3. In the upper atmosphere, ozone is beneficial for us; in the lower atmosphere, ozone is harmful. Explain.

Chapter 5. Soil and Its Problems

Because soil supports the growth of plants, which is the source of food for most other living things, the soil is our most important natural resource.

1. WHAT IS SOIL?

The loose surface material that covers the earth is called *soil*. Soil is a mixture of broken rock and minerals, and decaying matter. The soil we have today was formed after millions of years of weathering and erosion of the solid rock of the earth's crust, called the *bedrock*.

Digging into the soil reveals that it consists of two distinct layers, *topsoil* and *subsoil*, resting over the bedrock. It is the breaking of bedrock that produces the particles making up topsoil and subsoil (Figure 5-1).

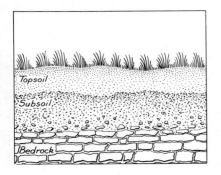

Fig. 5-1. The covering material of the earth. Although the layer of topsoil on the earth is extremely thin, it is essential to the survival of all living things.

a. Topsoil. The dark, loose surface layer of soil is the *topsoil*. Plants grow in this layer. Topsoil is not evenly distributed over the earth. It is an inch or two deep in rocky areas and up to a few feet thick in rich farmlands. Topsoil is made up of sand, clay, silt, minerals, and decaying plant and animal matter.

b. Subsoil. The layer of tightly packed soil just below the topsoil is the *subsoil*. Subsoil is similar in composition to topsoil, except that it lacks decaying matter, and may sometimes contain gravel (pebbles and small pieces of rock). It may extend many feet down where it is mixed with rock fragments produced by the weathering of the bedrock below it. Plants cannot thrive in subsoil.

2. IMPORTANCE OF TOPSOIL

In areas having rich topsoil, vegetation and animal life abound. Such areas also make fertile farmland. Areas such as mountains, deserts, and wastelands are marked by poor surface soils that cannot support edible plant and animal life.

Rich topsoil is the most suitable environment for plant growth because of its mineral and humus content, and its porosity (possessing tiny openings). *Humus* consists of decaying plant and animal matter. Humus not only provides the topsoil with minerals, but also helps the soil retain moisture. Because of the *porous* nature of topsoil, air and water can easily enter the soil and then be taken in by plants. The porosity and fertility of the topsoil are aided by earthworms, certain insects, and bacteria, which flourish in topsoil.

3. TYPES OF SOIL

Not all surface soils are favorable for agriculture. Sandy and clay soils will not support plants. Loam soil is the most fertile type. The composition and properties of these soils are outlined in the Table below.

Major Types of Soil

Soil	Composition	Properties
Sandy	Consists mostly of large grains of sand and a small amount of clay.	Does not retain water because water readily drains out of it through the large spaces between the sand grains. Consequently, sandy soil is a dry soil and therefore not suitable for plant life.
Clay	Consists of fine particles of feldspar (a mineral).	Absorbs water slowly and retains it for a long time because the particles bind together. Clay soil becomes hard-packed when dry and therefore is unfavorable for vegetation.
Loam	Consists of a mixture of sand, clay, and humus.	Loam soil is loose, retains water, does not become hard-packed, and contains minerals. Therefore, it is the best plant environment.

4. SOIL EROSION PROBLEMS

Various agents (conditions) are constantly at work eroding the earth's crust. These agents affect valuable topsoil much more rapidly than they affect rock. The removal of topsoil by the agents of erosion is called *soil erosion*. The agents chiefly responsible for eroding soil are wind, running water, and some human activities. Wind and running water together remove about three billion tons of topsoil from the United States each year. Much of this is lost because it is deposited in the oceans and elsewhere.

a. Erosion by Wind. In moist regions, soil is held together by moisture and the roots of plants, and cannot be blown away by the wind. In other regions, however, valuable topsoil, lacking moisture, becomes dry. It is then easily picked up by the wind and carried away.

In many of our Midwestern states, from North Dakota down to Texas, millions of acres of valuable farmland have been rendered useless by the removal of topsoil by the wind.

b. Erosion by Running Water. In cultivated areas, or other regions rich in plant life, such as forests, humus and the roots of plants serve not only to slow runoff rainfall, but also, like sponges, to absorb the runoff. In addition, the soil is held together by a network of branch roots. In plantless areas, during a heavy rainfall, running water picks up and removes a good deal of loose topsoil.

If flowing water runs into a slight depression in the earth, such as a plow furrow, the water will flow through this path and deepen it. Frequently, running water deepens the path sufficiently to produce a channel, called a *gully*. Water running along a gully not only removes topsoil, but also cuts up the land, making it useless for agriculture.

c. Erosion by Humans. In the "dust bowl" of the 1930's, the removal of topsoil by the wind in the Midwestern states was due mainly to improper methods of agriculture over many years. The soil had been robbed of much of its fertility, and planting steadily declined. When the area suffered a severe drought, the dry, plantless soil was blown away by strong winds.

In other areas, topsoil is destroyed by the *strip mining* of minerals, such as coal. In this mining method, strips of soil are bulldozed away and the coal under the soil is removed. As a result, the topsoil and the natural environment of plants and animals are destroyed and the landscape is made ugly. In addition, the wastes of other types of mining as well as wastes from extracting metals from the earth have polluted nearby land.

5. PREVENTING SOIL EROSION

Erosion of life-supporting topsoil must be prevented in order to assure a continuous supply of food for all living things. Some common practices to prevent soil erosion are the following:

a. Adding Humus. Humus on the ground helps stop rapid runoff and reduces the possibility of floods. When added to soil, humus not only enriches the soil, but also holds the soil together and thus prevents erosion of the fertile topsoil.

b. Planting Cover Crops. Fertile lands are kept covered with vegetation. So, after a crop is harvested, a different crop is planted to cover bare soil and prevent erosion. Alfalfa is often used as a cover crop.

c. Planting Windbreaks. Planting trees and shrubs around farms can reduce the force of winds that otherwise would be strong enough to pick up and blow away exposed soil (Figure 5-2).

Fig. 5-2. Windbreaks.

d. Contour Plowing. In contour plowing, hilly land is plowed in a circular pattern; that is, across slopes rather than up and down the slope (Figure 5-3). As the water flows into the circular furrows, it is trapped and absorbed instead of flowing directly downhill and washing away the topsoil.

Fig. 5-3. Contour plowing.

e. Terracing. Hilly farmland is sometimes planted on steps, called *terraces*, cut into a hill (Figure 5-4). Since each terrace holds back some water, the rapid downhill flow of rainwater is checked and soil erosion prevented.

Fig. 5-4. Terracing.

f. Strip Cropping. On some farms, crops are grown in rows with bare strips between them. To prevent erosion of the bare strips, a second crop is planted in them. For example, rows of corn or cotton are alternated with rows of thick-growing cover crops, such as alfalfa or clover (Figure 5-5). The thick-growing crops hold the soil together, absorb water, and prevent erosion from occurring in what would have been uncovered soil.

Fig. 5-5. Strip cropping.

6. LOSS OF SOIL FERTILITY

As you are aware, certain minerals are needed in the soil for proper plant growth. Plants do not grow well in soil that lacks potassium, nitrogen, and phosphorus. Small amounts of sulfur, iron, calcium, and some other minerals are also necessary. If a farmer plants the same crop year after year, the crop will gradually remove the same minerals from the soil. When the soil becomes exhausted of these minerals, the same crop will no longer grow in the soil. Certain crops, such as cotton and tobacco, rob the soil of its minerals rapidly.

7. HOW SOIL FERTILITY IS RESTORED

Minerals can be returned to the soil in a number of ways.

a. Rotating Crops. The planting of different crops on the same plot of land from time to time is called *crop rotation*. For example, a farmer may grow wheat, or corn, or cotton in the same field for three to five years. These plants remove nitrogen from the soil. Then for a period of two years he would plant alfalfa, clover, beans, or other legumes. As we discussed on page 25 (section 5-a), the bacteria that live in the roots of such plants take nitrogen from the air and put it into the soil in a form that plants can use.

b. Adding Fertilizers. A *fertilizer* is a substance that contains the minerals needed for proper plant growth. Fertilizers may be manure, specially prepared chemical mixtures, or humus. Fertilizers rich in phosphorus, nitrogen, potassium, and other minerals may be added periodically to the soil by farmers to restore one or more of these minerals to the soil.

c. "Resting" the Soil. Frequently, a farmer does not plant a part of his land, but allows the soil to remain idle, or *fallow*, for a year or more. During this time, some of the fertility to the soil is restored by soil bacteria, by aeration, and by the weathering of some soil minerals.

d. "Sweetening" the Soil. Plants will not grow in soil that contains too much acid. Small quantities of lime may be periodically added to soil by farmers to neutralize the acid, or "sweeten" the soil.

e. Draining and Irrigating. Plants will not grow in soil containing too much water. By drawing off water from, or *draining*, swamps and marshes, much rich farmland is reclaimed for agriculture.

Plants also will not grow when drought occurs or in soil that is too dry. Such regions can be made fertile by bringing water into them, or *irrigating* them. At present, many millions of acres of farmland in the United States are under irrigation by water that reaches them from distant dams that trap river water and store it for future use.

f. "Healing the Soil's Wounds." As we noted before in this chapter, strip mining has harmed what would have been fertile land. To remedy this type of damage, attempts are made to cover exhausted strip mines with the topsoil that had been removed and to reseed the land with grass, clover, and other plants. Thus, in time, the fertility of the soil should be restored.

Multiple-Choice Questions

Write the number preceding the correct answer.

1. The two layers making up soil are (1) topsoil and sand (2) subsoil and silt (3) topsoil and subsoil (4) clay and sand.
2. Plants grow best in (1) bedrock (2) subsoil (3) rocky soil (4) topsoil.
3. Decaying plant and animal matter is usually found in (1) topsoil (2) sand (3) subsoil (4) clay.
4. A material that makes soil more porous, moist, and fertile is (1) fertilizer (2) humus (3) lime (4) sand.
5. Most of the humus so necessary for good garden soil comes from (1) air and rain (2) commercial fertilizer (3) decayed plant material (4) erosion of rock material.
6. Earthworms are desirable animals because they (1) destroy harmful insects (2) help keep the soil loose (3) kill weeds by eating roots (4) produce nitrates from nitrogen in the air.
7. Sandy soil is composed principally of (1) insects (2) decayed plants and animals (3) fertilizers (4) rock particles.
8. The type of soil that absorbs water most slowly is (1) clay (2) humus (3) loam (4) sand.
9. The principal harm done by soil erosion is (1) clogging up streams (2) killing fish in rivers (3) making rivers dirty (4) washing away soil.
10. The chief agent of soil erosion in dry regions is (1) running water (2) people (3) wind (4) ground water.
11. Running water is not an effective agent of erosion in (1) plantless areas (2) cultivated regions (3) moist areas (4) hilly regions.
12. Loss of soil can best be prevented by (1) covering the soil with a layer of fertilizer and sand (2) digging deep trenches so water can run off quickly (3) planting trees and grass (4) plowing the soil.
13. Contour plowing is done in an effort to (1) beautify a farm (2) control weeds (3) kill insects (4) save topsoil.
14. If a farmer plants rows of alfalfa between rows of cotton, he is using a method of farming known as (1) contour plowing (2) reforestation (3) terracing (4) strip cropping.
15. A method used by farmers to restore the fertility of the soil is (1) crop rotation (2) weathering (3) gullying (4) cutting down forests.
16. Clover is planted in crop rotation because it (1) makes the soil porous for better moisture distribution (2) prevents dust from being blown away from the surface (3) prevents the soil from becoming sour (4) supports growth of nitrogen-fixing bacteria.
17. A substance supplied to soil by fertilizer is (1) iron (2) copper compounds (3) phosphorus (4) mercury.

18. A substance added to soil to make the soil less acid is (1) salt (2) commercial fertilizer (3) lime (4) manure.
19. Much rich farmland that is covered with water can be reclaimed by the process of (1) draining (2) contour farming (3) terracing (4) adding fertilizers.
20. A method that is being employed to make land in dry regions productive is (1) strip cropping (2) reforestation (3) irrigation (4) planting clover.
21. The extraction of coal located under topsoil is accomplished by (1) terracing (2) contour plowing (3) strip mining (4) strip cropping.

Completion Questions

Write the word or expression that correctly completes the statement.

1. _____ is the loose portion of the material covering the earth.
2. The solid material from which both subsoil and topsoil are formed is the _____.
3. The layer of soil beneath the topsoil is known as _____.
4. A type of soil that becomes hard-packed when it loses its water is _____.
5. The process in which various agents remove much of our valuable topsoil is known as _____.
6. The chief agent of erosion in dry regions is the _____.
7. A deep channel cut into a hillside by water running down the hill is known as a (an) _____.
8. The humus of the forest floor helps to prevent soil erosion by absorbing _____.
9. _____ is the method used by a farmer when he plows around a hill.
10. Planting in steps on hilly land is known as _____.
11. _____ is the alternating of different crops in the same fields.
12. Legumes are planted because certain bacteria living in their roots restore compounds of _____ to the soil.
13. Substances added to the soil to restore various minerals are called _____.
14. Allowing a field to remain fallow in order to restore its fertility is called _____.
15. _____ is the process of bringing in water to dry areas.

Thought Questions

1. Explain what is meant by a cover crop and tell how it prevents soil erosion.
2. When subsoil is dug up and spread on the surface of the ground, plants do not thrive in it. Why?

Chapter 6. Water in the Soil

1. SURFACE AND UNDERGROUND WATER

Water that falls to the ground surface may do different things. Some of the water may run off into another body of water. In doing so, as we learned in Chapter 5, running water may erode valuable topsoil and deposit it elsewhere. The running water may also aid in making new soil by breaking rock down into small particles. Water that does not run off may cling to particles of topsoil, or may evaporate. Such water may be absorbed by plants or may seep down through pores and channels in topsoil and subsoil. The seepage stops where the water meets a solid layer of rock, such as bedrock. When all the soil spaces are filled with water, the soil is said to be *saturated*, and the water is called *ground water*.

Few people realize that there is more fresh water under the ground than there is in all our lakes, streams, and reservoirs. Like soil, water, wherever it is present, is a most important natural resource because no living thing can survive long without it. Thus, water should never be wasted.

2. THE WATER TABLE

The top level of ground water is called the *water table* (Figure 6-1). Although ground water is found practically everywhere, it lies deeper underground in some places than in others.

In valleys, the water table may be at the surface. Where this occurs, lakes and swamplands are formed. In some hilly areas, the water table may be a great distance below the surface. In other areas the water table may be higher on a hill than in the valley. Where this happens, water gushes out as a *spring*.

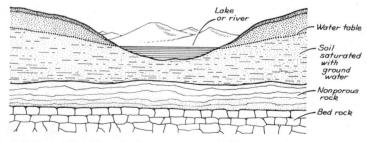

Fig. 6-1. The water table. The top level of ground water is called the water table. Beneath the water-table region lies soil saturated with ground water.

3. CONDITIONS THAT DETERMINE THE AMOUNT OF WATER HELD IN THE SOIL

The ground holds more water

  a. where rainfall is plentiful and the soil is porous.
  b. where the land is flat and there is little runoff.
  c. where vegetation is abundant enough to absorb water before it runs off.
  d. where the soil is porous. The porosity of the soil depends on the number and size of the air spaces between soil particles. The greater the number of air spaces and the larger their size, the more porous is the soil.

4. USES OF GROUND WATER

Ground water is useful in several ways:

  a. It furnishes plants with the water they need for survival.
  b. In many regions, it provides us with a supply of water for drinking and irrigation. In such places the water comes to the surface as springs and artesian wells.
  c. It furnishes water to rivers and springs during periods when they receive no rainwater.
  d. Where ground water comes close to hot rocks, the water boils and gushes into the air at intervals. Such is the action of a *geyser.*

5. USES OF SURFACE WATER

Surface water is important in numerous ways:

  a. In regions where surface water flows over falls, such as Niagara Falls, running water is useful in the production of electrical energy. For the same purpose, water is held behind dams and is released in a controlled fashion.
  b. Rivers, lakes, and oceans serve as avenues of transportation.
  c. Bodies of water provide recreation for fishing, boating, and swimming.
  d. In many regions, surface water is collected and stored in reservoirs as a source of water for home, industry, and irrigation.
  e. Surface water is an important contributor to the *water cycle* (Fig. 15-6 on page 147). Water evaporates, enters the atmosphere, and eventually returns to the surface as rain or snow.
  f. The water in our oceans moderates the climate of nearby regions. It makes coastal regions warmer in winter and cooler in summer. It also provides land breezes at night and sea breezes during the day.

6. POLLUTION OF WATER

Ground water and surface water become polluted in the following ways:

a. Untreated sewage is allowed to enter the water. Such water often carries disease germs.

b. Garbage is dumped into the ocean and in unpopulated areas of watersheds. In oceans, garbage is dangerous to all forms of oceanic life, including people who swim in the water. *Watersheds* are elevated regions from which rainfall drains into streams and other bodies of water. Garbage in watersheds can enter the water supply of nearby communities.

c. Chemicals, medical wastes, radioactive materials, and factory wastes are discharged into streams, other bodies of water, and storage ponds. Such wastes are usually *toxic* (poisonous) to humans and other organisms. Toxic wastes may seep down and pollute ground water.

d. Oil, from oil wells, storage tanks, and tanker ships, leaks into water. There, the oil can kill many forms of wildlife, including aquatic birds.

e. After rains, insecticides and fertilizers used on farms run off into nearby water sources. There, they interfere with organisms that inhabit the water.

f. As explained on page 38, section d(1), acid rain falling into quiet bodies of fresh water destroys organisms living in the polluted water.

Multiple-Choice Questions

Write the number preceding the correct answer.

1. Water that sinks into the soil is known as (1) the water table (2) ground water (3) a solution (4) a river.

2. The upper level of the saturated portion of the soil is called (1) underground water (2) a well (3) the water table (4) a reservoir.

3. In swampland there is (1) no water table (2) a low water table (3) a high water table (4) no rainfall.

4. Springs gush out from (1) valleys (2) bare rocks (3) swamps (4) soil-covered hillsides.

5. Ground water can flow most rapidly through (1) sandy soil (2) loam (3) humus (4) clay soil.

6. Ground water is an important source of (1) ocean water (2) drinking water (3) water power (4) fish life.

7. Ground water may be used (1) to produce electricity (2) as a means of travel (3) for fishing (4) by plants as a source of water.

8. Water that flows over the face of the earth is called (1) ground water (2) the water table (3) surface water (4) sub-surface water.

9. Ground and surface water containing waste detergents and insecticides are considered to be (1) harmless for irrigation (2) safe to drink (3) harmless to fish (4) polluted for most living things.
10. Underground water that reaches the surface after coming in contact with heated rocks can form a (1) geyser (2) swamp (3) valley (4) watershed.

Completion Questions

Write the word or expression that correctly completes the statement.

1. Ground water is found _____ (*above, below*) the water table.
2. The water table is usually _____ (*higher, lower*) on a hill than in a valley.
3. The water table is _____ (*higher, lower*) after a rainfall.
4. The water table is deepest in the earth in _____ regions.
5. The size and number of air spaces in the soil determine its _____.
6. The larger the air spaces in the soil, the _____ (*greater, smaller*) the amount of water absorbed by that soil.
7. Much ground water is found in areas that have a _____ (*small amount, great deal*) of plant life.
8. The source from which rivers obtain water during intervals of slight rainfall is the _____.
9. Elevated regions where rainfall drains into rivers are called _____.
10. Rainfall that harms fish in freshwater lakes is known as _____.

Thought Questions

1. On land, fertilizers help plants grow. When washed into a lake, fertilizers interfere with animal life there. Explain.
2. What is the relationship between drought in a region and the water table there?

Chapter 7. Conservation of Natural Resources

1. THE MEANING OF CONSERVATION

Our earth provides us with our daily needs which are frequently referred to as *natural resources*. These resources include not only plant and animal life, but also soil, water, air, and minerals. The wise use and preservation of natural resources is called *conservation* (keeping from loss, waste, etc.). To supply us and future generations with the necessities of life, we must keep our natural resources from being damaged, lost, or wasted.

2. THE IMPORTANCE OF FORESTS

In addition to lumber and other products they provide, forests are important because the forest floor absorbs and holds large quantities of water. By giving up this water slowly, rapid runoff does not occur, thereby reducing soil erosion and preventing floods. Forests remove excess carbon dioxide from the air and release essential oxygen. Forests also provide homes and food for many valuable animals; and recreational activities, such as camping and hiking, for humans.

3. ENEMIES OF THE FOREST

Agents that tend to destroy forests are:

a. People. The destruction of most of our forests is the result of our need for fuel, farmland, and lumber. Careless and wasteful lumbering practices, for example, have leveled off millions of acres of timberland despite the consequences to generations to come and to the balance of nature.

b. Fire. Many thousands of acres of valuable forest land are destroyed each year by fire. Although forest fires result from human carelessness, others are caused by lightning and volcanic eruptions.

c. Disease. Some diseases that ruin trees are chestnut blight, white-pine blister rust, and Dutch elm disease.

d. Insects. Trees are the prey of many insects. Some varieties of beetles, such as the wood-borer beetle and bark beetle, bore into the bark and wood of a tree, eventually killing the tree. Certain caterpillars, such as the gypsy moth, destroy oak trees by feeding on their leaves.

54

e. Drought. From time to time, some regions suffer from an extended period of little or no rain. This condition can affect a forest in two ways:

(1) Dry leaves and other debris on a forest floor become excellent fuel once a fire has started. Then, the fire continues to spread until an entire area is aflame or until extinguished by rainfall or human firefighting efforts.

(2) Young trees, which require an abundant supply of water, die off in large numbers during a drought.

4. FOREST CONSERVATION

Federal and state governments have developed programs of forest conservation to reduce further damage and thus insure a constant future supply of trees. Some conservation practices are:

a. Requiring lumber companies to cut down only those trees that are fully mature.

b. Replacing cut-down trees by planting new trees.

c. Fire control and prevention. Ranger lookout towers have been built and new techniques of firefighting have been devised. The public is being educated in fire prevention.

d. Insect control. The best method of controlling harmful insects in forest areas is to use *biological controls.* One such control is introducing birds or other natural enemies that feed on the harmful insects. Another control is spraying the area with certain bacteria that kill harmful insects without endangering other forms of life.

e. Some tree diseases are controlled by spraying or by dusting the trees with various chemicals.

f. Many acres of timberland have been taken over by the Federal and state governments. These areas have been made *forest preserves* or *national parks* where laws forbid the uncontrolled cutting of timber as well as other destructive activities.

5. WILDLIFE CONSERVATION

Another resource in which diminishing numbers are causing alarm is *wildlife.* Wildlife includes all animals that can live without depending on humans. The conservation of wildlife is important for several reasons. Conserving wildlife can prevent the extinction of animals that are becoming rare. Conservation also helps maintain the balance of nature. Conservation practices will assure us of a continual supply of those wild animals that are valuable for food, fur, or sport.

a. Fish. Fish are a source of food, chemicals, and sport. Some laws enacted to conserve freshwater fish are:

(1) Fish may not be caught during their breeding season. This is known as the *closed season.*

(2) The size and number of fish that may be caught are limited.

(3) In many localities, it is forbidden to empty sewage or industrial wastes into rivers or streams. Many of these wastes would pollute the waters and destroy the fish.

In addition to preventing the destruction of fish, Federal and state agencies attempt to maintain their numbers. Young fish are raised in Government hatcheries until the fish are large enough to care for themselves. These fish are then used to restock rivers and lakes.

b. Birds. Birds are important to us because they destroy harmful insects and rodents, and eat weed seeds. Some conservation practices are:

(1) By law, non-game birds and their eggs may not be destroyed at any time.

(2) Spraying insecticides, such as DDT, is prohibited because they can interfere with the ability of birds to reproduce.

(3) Game birds may be hunted only during certain times of the year, known as the *open season.* Even during open season, the number of birds that may be killed is limited.

(4) Bird sanctuaries are maintained by the Government so that birds may live and breed safely.

(5) Certain scarce birds, such as the egret and whooping crane, may not be hunted at any time nor may their breeding places be destroyed.

c. Other Animals

(1) Laws forbid the hunting and trapping of many valuable fur-bearing animals. These may be hunted only during certain designated seasons, and the size and number that may be taken are limited.

(2) Game preserves and national parks are maintained by the Government. The animals living in these preserves are provided with food and are otherwise protected. As a result, the animals breed and increase in number.

6. CONSERVING WILD FLOWERS

Many types of wild flowers have become extinct; others are threatened. Excessive flower picking and the clearing of land are the main causes. Many states have passed laws to protect the flowering dogwood, mountain laurel, trailing arbutus, and rhododendron.

7. CONSERVING OTHER NATURAL RESOURCES

Some good conservation practices have been adopted to protect our nonliving natural resources. We have already studied some of the methods used to conserve soil (pages 45–46, section 5; and page 47, section 7). In the following sections we shall learn the procedures to conserve *water, air, minerals,* and *energy.*

a. Water Conservation. Many heavily populated sections of our country find themselves in danger of polluting or exhausting underground water, lakes, and streams. Some practices employed to conserve water are:

(1) Reservoirs are constructed to store excess water resulting from heavy rains or the melting of snow in the spring.

(2) Dams are constructed to control the flow of river water.

(3) Forests have been planted to absorb water and release it slowly.

(4) Many industries have devised methods to reuse water.

(5) Laws have been enacted to prevent pollution of rivers and streams.

(6) The Federal government provides assistance in cleaning up areas that have been contaminated with toxic wastes.

(7) Some nations are beginning to cooperate in reducing acid rain.

b. Air Conservation. Polluted air can cause illness and, in certain cases, death. Steps are now being taken to reduce air pollution levels and to prevent increasing pollution in the future. Some of these steps are:

(1) Elimination of faulty incinerators.

(2) Reducing harmful automobile exhausts by adjusting engines and by attaching to them special chemical devices (catalytic converters).

(3) Using fuels that produce less sulfur dioxide and other harmful gases.

(4) Providing factory chimneys with devices that reduce the emission of smoke.

THE ENVIRONMENTAL PROTECTION AGENCY

The Environmental Protection Agency (EPA) is a branch of our Federal government. It is concerned with establishing and maintaining a healthy environment. The EPA works together with state and local governments and manufacturers. It sets the standards for clean air, water, and soil. It also sets up regulations and guidelines for cleanup work, and provides advice and assistance for solving special environmental problems. The EPA brings offenders to trial.

c. Mineral Conservation. Increased use of coal and oil has created the danger that the supply of these valuable energy sources may not keep up with the demand. The same is true of the supply of other minerals, especially metals. The use of substitutes for some materials and recycling of others are helpful in providing for our present and future needs. *Hydroelectric* and *nuclear power* plants have been built as substitutes for coal and oil in producing energy.

d. Energy Conservation. The United States and other nations are facing an energy crisis. That is, the human population is demanding more energy from nonrenewable sources than new resources can be found and developed for use. Eventually, our resources of petroleum, coal, and natural gas may be exhausted.

Although we do use some nuclear energy for our energy needs, this source is not yet sufficient to meet our needs safely. Other safe methods of providing energy are still being developed. Among these methods are using heat energy from deep within the earth, constructing solar furnaces, harnessing the energy of the wind, and expanding the use of solar batteries. Until such energy sources become practical, we must conserve our nonrenewable resources in every way we can.

Conservation is the responsibility of everyone. Each of us must use natural resources wisely and sparingly so that future generations may not find themselves in want.

Multiple-Choice Questions

Write the number preceding the correct answer.

1. The practice of providing resources for future human use is known as (1) reforestation (2) conservation (3) irrigation (4) contour farming.
2. One of the major reasons for forest conservation is that forests (1) provide beauty (2) provide recreation (3) prevent floods (4) serve as national boundaries.
3. Most forest destruction has been caused by (1) lightning (2) disease (3) insects (4) human actions.
4. One of the best ways of reducing the number of harmful insects in an area is by (1) starting fires (2) increasing the number of forest rangers (3) making forest preserves (4) introducing insect-feeding birds.
5. Timberlands in which the Government forbids the cutting down of trees are known as (1) sanctuaries (2) forest preserves (3) reservations (4) forest rangers.
6. The name given to animals that are not raised by humans is (1) fur bearers (2) game animals (3) wildlife (4) animals of prey.

7. Rivers in which fish have been destroyed by industrial wastes are said to be (1) pure (2) polluted (3) sterilized (4) muddy.
8. The only kind of bird that the law permits to be hunted in open season is called a (1) song bird (2) sparrow (3) game bird (4) bird of prey.
9. A bird that cannot be hunted at any time is the (1) blue jay (2) starling (3) parakeet (4) whooping crane.
10. A wild flower that cannot be picked is the (1) mountain laurel (2) morning glory (3) dandelion (4) rose.
11. One thing we can do to conserve air is to (1) breathe slowly (2) prohibit all transportation (3) reduce factory and automobile exhausts (4) stop all burning.

Completion Questions

Write the word or expression that correctly completes the statement.

1. Conservation involves the use and _____ of resources for the future.
2. In the United States, elms have been destroyed by the disease known as _____.
3. Many streams and lakes are restocked by fish raised in Government _____.
4. The time of the year when a bird may not be hunted is called the _____ season.
5. To conserve water, the Government builds _____ to store excess water.
6. An air pollutant that can cause lung irritation is _____.

Thought Questions

1. In many parts of the world, forests have been and are still being cut down to provide lumber, fuel, and farmland. What effect has such forest destruction on (*a*) soil erosion, and (*b*) the carbon dioxide content of the air?
2. Why must the reduction of acid rain depend on the cooperation of all nations?

REVIEW OF UNIT I

1. Column A is a list of common animals. Column B is a list of the groups to which they belong. Match each animal's name in column A with the number of the group in column B to which it belongs.

Column A   Column B
a. chicken   1. mammal
b. cow   2. bird
c. eel   3. reptile
d. salamander   4. amphibian
e. turtle   5. fish

2. Give an example of each of the following.
   a. an animal that has four pairs of legs
   b. an animal with bones but no legs
   c. a bird that eats seeds
   d. a bird that lays eggs on the ground
   e. a bird that helps protect our trees
   f. a plant that is dangerous to handle
   g. a grass used as food by man
   h. an animal with four wings
   i. an animal that dams up streams
   j. an insect that is useful
   k. a plantlike protist that cannot make its own food
   l. an evergreen tree other than a pine
   m. a plant that never has seeds
   n. a water mammal with valuable fur
   o. an animal that has six legs
   p. a cold-blooded animal
   q. a mouse-eating bird
   r. a mammal that can fly
   s. a tree that loses its leaves in winter
   t. a bird that nests in birdhouses

3. Identify each of the leaves below, choosing your answers from the following
   list: maple, oak, pine, willow, poison ivy.

4. The birds represented by the pictures below are: crow, chickadee, sea gull, woodpecker, blue jay, kingfisher, hummingbird, robin, lark. Identify each bird.

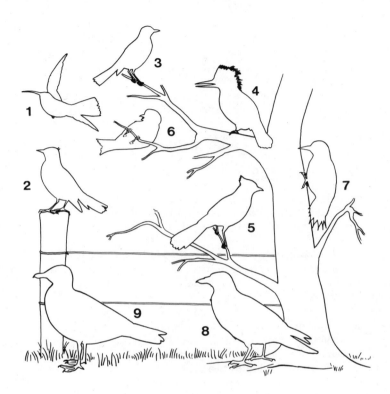

5. Plants and animals live under widely different conditions.
   a. Select an animal that lives in a cold climate and tell how it is fitted to live there.
   b. Select an animal that lives in water and tell how it is fitted to live there.
   c. State two ways in which a maple tree is fitted to live through the winter.

6. Give two examples of each of the following.
   a. animals that eat plants   c. animals with special methods of protection
   b. birds that eat fish   d. insects that store food for winter use

7. Column A is a list of the activities of some animals. Match each activity in column A with the number of the animal described in column B.

Column A	Column B
a. builds a dam	1. turtle
b. flies south in autumn	2. chipmunk
c. swallows particles of soil	3. mole
d. hibernates through most of the winter	4. heron
e. has feet adapted for burrowing	5. mink
f. stores food for winter use	6. chameleon
g. a mammal that kills animals for food	7. bobolink
h. changes the color of its skin	8. frog
i. catches food in shallow water	9. earthworm
j. protects itself in a shell	10. beaver

8. Give the meaning of each of the following terms.
   a. humus   *c.* strip-cropping
   b. fertilizer   *d.* contour plowing

9. The water from a steep hillside runs into a small lake.
   a. Does the water wear away the land faster where it runs rapidly or where it runs slowly?
   b. At what season of the year will most soil be carried away?
   c. How would planting trees on the hillside help to slow down erosion?
   d. Why does a stream on the hillside flow in a deep gully?

10. Explain each of the following.
   a. Topsoil is thicker in a valley than on a steep hillside.
   b. The wind sometimes destroys farmland.
   c. Loam soil is a better soil for gardens than sandy soil.
   d. Contour plowing is the best type of plowing for hillsides.

11. Tell where each can be found near your school.
   a. a pond being filled by sand from a stream
   b. a slope being gullied after each rain
   c. a place where soil conservation is being practiced

12. Explain how each of the following practices aids in the conservation of natural resources.
   a. building dams   *d.* reforesting
   b. contour plowing   *e.* rotating crops
   c. terracing   *f.* fertilizing the soil

13. Soil conservation is of great importance to us. Tell what harm may result from each of the following.
   a. plowing up and down a slope
   b. leaving land without plant cover in winter
   c. removing topsoil to mine copper

Unit II.
Our Body and Our Health

Chapter 8. The Nature of the Human Body

1. HOW OUR BODY IS ORGANIZED

The human body consists of billions of cells. A *cell* is a microscopic unit of living matter. It is the unit of structure and function of the body. All the work performed by the body is the result of the activities of the cells.

2. CELLS

A cell (Figure 8-1 on next page) is made up of the following:

a. The **cell membrane** is the boundary of a cell. The cell membrane controls the exchange of materials (food, oxygen, and wastes) between the cell and its surroundings.

b. The **nucleus** contains threadlike bodies called *chromosomes*. The chromosomes are made up of *genes*, which direct all cell activities and control heredity.

c. The **cytoplasm** is a jellylike fluid that carries out all the body activities as directed by the genes.

3. TISSUES

Cells are arranged in groups. A group of similar cells carrying out one specific activity is called a *tissue*. For example, nerve cells, grouped together, form nerve tissue; groups of muscle cells form muscle tissue (Figure 8-1 on next page).

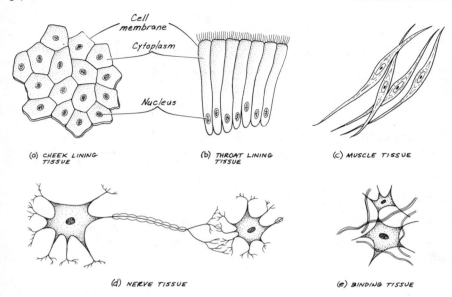

(a) CHEEK LINING TISSUE   (b) THROAT LINING TISSUE   (c) MUSCLE TISSUE

(d) NERVE TISSUE   (e) BINDING TISSUE

Fig. 8-1. Some types of tissues. (a) A flat-celled tissue forms the protective inner lining of the cheek.

(b) The hairlike projections of the cells of throat tissue trap dust and other foreign particles.

(c) The long cells of this type of muscle tissue produce movement in the walls of the small intestine.

(d) Messages travel through the chainlike connections of the cells of nerve tissue.

(e) The strong fibers of binding tissue connect body parts such as bones.

4. ORGANS

A group of tissues performing one particular function is called an *organ*. The heart is an organ. Some of the tissues making up the heart are muscle tissue and nerve tissue. Other organs are our sense organs. For other examples of organs, the major tissues in them, and their functions, see the Table on the next page.

5. ORGAN SYSTEMS

Organs that work together to perform one special function form an *organ system*. Some of the systems in the human are the digestive system, the circulatory system, the nervous system, and the skeleton-muscle system. The skeleton-muscle system is described in this chapter, beginning on page 66. Other systems are described in later chapters.

Some Organs of the Human

Organ	Major Tissue	Function
Heart	muscle blood nerve	Pumps blood through the body.
Skin	lining blood nerve	Acts as a sense organ. Helps eliminate wastes from the body. Line of defense against invasion by germs. Helps regulate the temperature of the body.
Stomach	lining muscle blood	Digests some food.
Liver	lining blood binding	Aids in the digestion of food.
Kidneys	lining blood binding	Eliminate liquid wastes from the body.
Small intestine	lining blood muscle	Completes the digestion of food.
Lungs	lining blood binding	Region where oxygen enters the bloodstream. Eliminate gaseous wastes from the body.
Sense organs (eyes, ears, nose, skin, tongue)	nerve blood binding lining	Detect changes in the environment. Send signals to the brain.

BONES AND MUSCLES

Without a skeleton, the human body and that of many other organisms would be nothing more than blobs. You may have seen such soft, shapeless masses in science-fiction movies. If the body were made up of such a blob, it could twitch and, perhaps, slither along. On the other hand, if the body were made up only of a collection of attached bones, a *skeleton*, it would not be able to move around at all.

Acting together as one system, the skeleton and the muscles attached to it enable the body to move as a whole, as when walking or running. Or, acting on a part of the body, such as a hand, the muscles attached to the bones in the hand enable the hand to move, as when writing.

Not all muscles are attached to bones. Some muscles make up a part of the walls of soft organs, such as the heart and stomach.

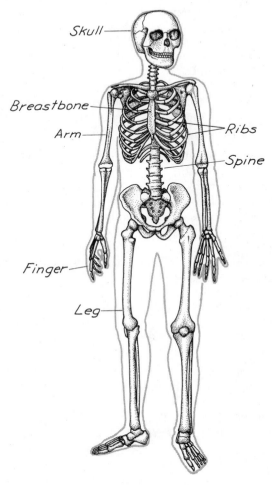

Skull

Breastbone

Arm

Ribs

Spine

Finger

Leg

Human skeleton

Fig. 8-2. The bones in the human skeleton. Bones perform special functions in supporting the body, giving it shape, allowing movement, providing protection for internal organs, and manufacturing blood cells. Minerals, such as calcium and phosphorus, obtained from certain foods, make the bones rigid and strong.

THE SKELETON-MUSCLE SYSTEM

6. THE HUMAN SKELETON

The framework of 206 bones making up the human body is called the *skeleton*. Since the skeleton is strong and rigid, it gives the body shape and provides support, just as a steel framework does for a tall building. The bones of the skeleton, with the aid of muscles, help produce body movement and provide protection for the internal organs. Long bones, such as those of the thighs, have hollow centers filled with *marrow*, a tissue that manufactures blood cells.

The divisions of the skeleton are the skull, spine, shoulders, hips, and limbs. (See Fig. 8-2.)

a. The Skull. The *skull* is a hollow, bony structure that encloses the brain, the eyes, and the sensitive parts of the ears. The skull is attached to the top of the spine.

b. The Spine. The column of bones that keeps the body erect is called the *spine*, or *backbone*. The spine is composed of many small bones, called *vertebrae*. A pad of binding tissue (*cartilage*) between adjoining vertebrae makes the spine flexible and absorbs some of the jarring caused by walking, running, or jumping. Attached to the spine are the ribs and hipbones.

c. The Ribs. Twelve pairs of *ribs* are attached to the spine in the chest region. Most rib bones curve and meet in the front of the body. The ribs and spine form a bony cage around the heart and lungs.

d. The Hipbones. These winglike structures are made of joined, basin-shaped bones that support the soft organs in the lower part of the body.

e. The Limbs. The *limbs* are set into sockets in special bones. The upper limbs, the arms, are set into the forward end of each shoulder blade. The lower limbs, the legs, are set into the side of each hipbone.

7. JOINTS

The region where two bones meet is called a *joint*. There are two types of joints in the skeleton: *movable* and *immovable*.

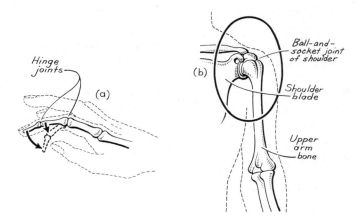

Fig. 8-3. Types of movable joints. The free and easy movement of the bones is aided by joints.

(a) The hinge joints in the fingers permit only up and down movement of the finger bones.

(b) The ball-and-socket joint in the shoulder allows movement of the arm in almost all directions.

a. Movable Joints. This type of joint is present in the limbs and much of the spine. Without such joints, it would be impossible for the bones of the body to move. The main types of movable joints are the *hinge* and the *ball-and-socket.* (See Fig. 8-3.)

(1) *The Hinge Joint.* This type of joint acts like a hinge, permitting movement in one direction only, such as up and down, or back and forth. The joints in your knees, elbows, fingers, and toes are hinge joints.

(2) *The Ball-and-Socket Joint.* This type of joint allows movement in almost all directions. Ball-and-socket joints are found in the shoulders and the hips.

b. Immovable Joints. This type of joint is present between the bones of the skull and the bones of the hips. In such joints, the edges of the bones interlock in a way that keeps the bones from moving.

Bones are held together at the joints by *ligaments.* These are bands of strong tissue that not only permit movement of the bones, but also prevent detachment of the bones from the joint.

Every movable joint is enclosed in a sac of fluid. By lubricating the joint, the fluid reduces the friction between the moving bones.

8. MUSCLES PRODUCE MOVEMENT

Movement of the bones is produced by the action of *muscles* that are attached to them. A muscle is fastened to a bone by a strong cord of binding tissue, called a *tendon*. Movement of organs inside the body, such as the stomach, is produced by the action of muscles that are not attached to bones. These muscles are different from those that move bones. The muscles attached to bones are called *voluntary muscles*. Those not attached to bones are called *involuntary muscles*.

a. Voluntary Muscles. These muscles are under your control. They are found mainly attached to bones in the arms, legs, face, neck, chest, and abdomen. Voluntary muscles operate in pairs. When one of the muscles attached to a bone contracts, or shortens, it pulls the bone in one direction. The other muscle of the pair attached to the opposite side of the bone relaxes, or lengthens. Contraction of the second muscle returns the bone to its original position. (See Fig. 8-4.)

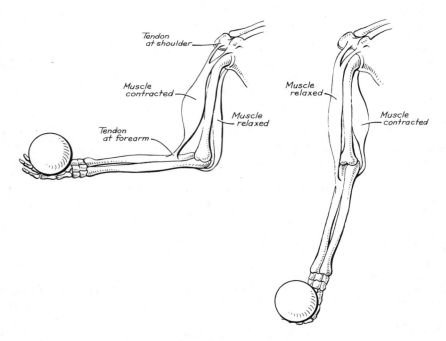

Fig. 8-4. Voluntary muscles in action

b. Involuntary Muscles. These muscles are not under your direct control. They are found in the walls of the food tube, in the walls of some blood vessels, and in other parts of the body. They move food through the food tube and blood through the blood vessels without your conscious direction or your awareness.

A type of involuntary muscle is also found in the heart. By contracting and relaxing, heart muscles force blood into the arteries leading out of the heart.

Multiple-Choice Questions

Write the number preceding the correct answer.

1. The tiny units of structure and function in the human body are the (1) tissues (2) organs (3) cells (4) bones.
2. Groups of tissues that carry on a specific task make up (1) a cell (2) a system (3) an organ (4) an individual.
3. The bones of which the spine is composed are the (1) skull (2) vertebrae (3) limbs (4) skeleton.
4. Bones are rigid because they contain (1) minerals (2) blood (3) muscles (4) skin.
5. The region where two bones meet is called a (1) limb (2) joint (3) tendon (4) cell.
6. The joint that allows bones to move in almost all directions is (1) the hinge (2) the ball-and-socket (3) partially immovable (4) immovable.
7. The bones of the hand are held together by (1) tendrils (2) filaments (3) ligaments (4) vertebrae.
8. The movement of the bones of the body is produced by the action of (1) ligaments (2) muscles (3) limbs (4) cartilage.
9. A structure that attaches muscle to bone is the (1) ligament (2) cartilage (3) blood (4) tendon.
10. The muscles that are under the direct control of a person are the (1) heart muscles (2) involuntary muscles (3) voluntary muscles (4) muscles in the blood vessels.
11. The special structures that inform us of a change in our environment are called the (1) nerves (2) brain (3) sense organs (4) skin.
12. In addition to protecting the body against disease germs, the skin also (1) acts as a sense organ (2) aids in digestion (3) supports the bones (4) produces movement of the bones.
13. The liver is an organ that (1) acts as a sense organ (2) regulates the body temperature (3) aids in digestion (4) pumps blood.
14. The kidneys, skin, and lungs of the body are similar because each (1) aids in breathing (2) aids in circulation of the blood (3) aids in digestion (4) gives off body wastes.
15. The part of a cell that contains the genes that control the cell's activities is the (1) cell membrane (2) cytoplasm (3) nucleus (4) cell wall.

Completion Questions

Write the word or expression that correctly completes the statement.

1. Groups of similar cells that perform a particular function are called _____.
2. Systems in the human are composed of _____ working together.
3. The body is supported by a framework of bones called the _____.
4. The _____ is the cavity that houses the brain.
5. The head and body are kept erect by the _____.
6. The arms and legs together are known as the _____.
7. Our body would be rigid if the bones were not set into _____.
8. The bones of the skull meet in a (an) _____ joint.
9. The type of joint found in the elbows is a (an) _____ joint.
10. Voluntary muscles always work _____ (*singly, in pairs*).

Thought Questions

1. Explain, with an example, the relationship between tissues and an organ.
2. How does the shape of the cells of nerve tissue suit these cells to their function of carrying messages?

Chapter 9. Foods and Health

1. WHY DO WE NEED FOOD?

To remain alive, all living things require food. The foods we eat contain substances that nourish our body.

a. Energy. *Energy* is the ability to do work. All our body activities—such as walking and talking, and writing and reading—require energy for their performance. The energy needed by the human is obtained from the substances that are present in foods.

Energy is released when foods are oxidized in the cells of the body. This process is called *oxidation*. Foods are the fuel that the body oxidizes, just as gasoline is the fuel that an automobile engine oxidizes.

Some energy released by the oxidation of foods is heat energy, which keeps the body warm, normally at a temperature of 98.6°F. For many people, a temperature a little below or a little above 98.6°F is considered normal.

b. Materials for Growth and Repair. As you grow taller and heavier, you are forming more and more cells. Foods furnish the body with the raw materials needed to make these new cells.

During the course of a day's activity, you are continually wearing out some cells. At times, cells are destroyed as a result of injury. The foods you eat supply the body with the materials it needs to repair and replace damaged cells.

c. Materials for Proper Body Activity. Certain chemicals, such as vitamins, are needed to regulate the activities of the cells of your body and to keep them functioning properly. These chemicals are supplied by the foods you eat.

2. WHAT ARE THE NUTRIENTS?

The materials in food that can be used by the body are called *nutrients*, namely: carbohydrates, fats and oils, proteins, mineral salts, vitamins, and water.

a. Carbohydrates. Starch and sugar are examples of carbohydrates. The body obtains most of its energy from these nutrients. They are also used by the body to make other needed substances.

Foods that provide us with starch are bread, potatoes, rice, cereals, spaghetti, and cake. Foods that furnish us with sugar are fruits, syrup, candy, and honey. When we eat more carbohydrates than our body can use, the excess carbohydrates are generally changed to fat, which is then stored in the body.

b. Fats and Oils. At room temperature, fats are solid and oils are liquid. Both are of similar chemical composition and are used as fuels to provide energy. When oxidized in the cells, fats and oils release about twice the energy of an equal weight of carbohydrates. However, fats and oils take longer to digest than do carbohydrates.

When eaten in excess, fats are readily stored in fat tissue. In some people, however, certain fatty substances, such as *cholesterol*, are deposited in blood vessels and block the flow of blood. (See "Cholesterol," below.) The substances associated with cholesterol are called *saturated fats*—which are hard fats present in butter and fatty meats. Healthy fats are *unsaturated*. These are liquid fats found in vegetable oils and fish.

CHOLESTEROL

Cholesterol is responsible for half the deaths in the United States. Yet, cholesterol is essential for the normal functioning of our cells.

The explanation for this contradiction is that, in many people, cholesterol is deposited inside blood vessels where the cholesterol hardens and clogs the blood vessels. In time, this condition can lead to a heart attack or a stroke. In both cases, the clogging of blood vessels prevents the flow of blood to heart muscle and brain tissue, and so injures them.

Physicians advise that we eat less fatty meats and more carbohydrates, fish, lean meats, skinned poultry, and vegetable oils.

---

c. Proteins. Some body energy is obtained from proteins, but proteins have two more important uses: (1) Supply the raw materials for the growth and repair of cells. (2) Manufacture many chemical compounds needed for normal functioning of the body. Excess proteins are not stored but are broken down into simpler substances that are expelled from the body in urine.

Foods that supply us plentifully with proteins are eggs, lean meats, fish, milk, nuts, beans, whole-grain cereals, and cheese.

d. Mineral Salts. Mineral salts are chemicals containing certain important elements. The body needs these elements to build various types of tissues and regulate important body activities. (See Table 9-1 on next page.)

Table 9-1. Important Mineral Elements in Mineral Salts

Mineral Element	Value to body	Foods providing the element
Calcium	Building strong bones and teeth. Clotting of blood. Normal functioning of muscles, nerves, and heart.	Milk and dairy products; egg yolk; leafy green and yellow vegetables, such as kale, turnip greens, and cabbage; canned salmon.
Phosphorus	Building strong bones and teeth. Formation of proteins and chemicals needed to release energy.	Milk and dairy products; leafy green and yellow vegetables; egg yolk.
Iron	Making hemoglobin, the chemical in red blood cells that carries oxygen to all body cells.	Liver; whole-grain cereals; egg yolk; beans; leafy green vegetables.
Iodine	Functioning of the thyroid gland, which produces a chemical essential to the body.	Saltwater fish; iodized salt; vegetables grown near seacoasts.
Sodium	Normal functioning of nerves and muscles. (Excess sodium may aggravate high blood pressure.)	Table salt.
Chlorine	Making hydrochloric acid, which is essential to digestion in the stomach.	Table salt.
Fluorine	Building strong bones and teeth.	Water, depending on content of fluorine in it; seafoods; toothpastes containing fluorides.
Potassium	Normal functioning of muscles, nerves, and heart.	Many foods, especially bananas, oranges, apricots.

e. Vitamins. Vitamins are chemicals the body must have to enjoy good health. Each vitamin serves the body in a particular way. A dietary *deficiency disease* may result if the body lacks one or more vitamins. (See Table 9-2.)

In preparing foods, vitamins may be lost. For example, foods containing vitamin C should not be boiled because boiling destroys the vitamin. Other vitamins, such as B_{12}, which are soluble in water, can be dissolved out of foods. Therefore, foods should be cooked with as little water as possible.

Food are often *enriched* by the addition of vitamins. Bread is enriched by the B vitamins, milk by vitamin D.

Table 9-2. Important Vitamins

Vitamin	Value to body	Foods providing the vitamin
Vitamin A	Normal growth and proper development of bones and teeth. Formation of normal skin. Normal vision, especially in dim light. (Deficiency may cause *night-blindness* and "dry eye.")	Milk; butter; cheese; egg yolk; fish-liver oils; liver; green and yellow vegetables.
Vitamin B_1	Helps oxidation of food. Promotes appetite. (Deficiency may cause *beriberi*, a nervous disorder.)	Lean meats; liver; wholegrain cereals; enriched bread; eggs; nuts; fruits; leafy green vegetables.
Vitamin B_2	Helps oxidation of food. For general good health and growth. Healthy eyes. (Deficiency contributes to *pellagra*, which affects nerves and skin.)	Lean meats; liver; wholegrain cereals; milk; nuts; eggs; cheese; yeast; leafy green vegetables.
Niacin	Proper functioning of the nervous system. Together with vitamin B_2, helps prevent pellagra.	Lean meats; liver; milk; eggs; green vegetables; whole wheat.

Vitamin	Value to body	Foods providing the vitamin
Vitamin B$_{12}$	Production of healthy red blood cells and hemoglobin. (Deficiency causes *anemia*—a lack of red blood cells or hemoglobin.)	Liver, eggs, fish, beef.
Vitamin C	Healthy bones, muscles, and gums. Keeps walls of blood vessels strong. Helps heal wounds. Prevents or cures *scurvy*. (This disease is marked by bleeding gums, loosened teeth, swollen joints, and poor wound healing.)	Citrus fruits (lemons, limes, oranges, grapefruits); cabbage; tomatoes; green peppers; strawberries.
Vitamin D	Helps calcium and phosphorus to form strong, healthy bones and teeth. Prevents *rickets*. (In this disease, the bones become soft and misshapen.)	Milk (to which vitamin D has been added); eggs; fish-liver oils. (In sunlight, vitamin D, the "sunshine vitamin," is formed in the skin.)
Vitamin E	Prevents oxidation of certain fats and vitamin A. Promotes ability of rats to reproduce.	Wheat germ; leafy green vegetables; meat; whole-grain cereals.
Vitamin K	Normal clotting of blood.	Leafy green vegetables; egg yolk; milk.

f. Water. All living things need water for survival. This is because all the chemical reactions that go on in living things can take place only in water. The living material of our body tissues is about 70 percent water. Water is used by the body in producing the juices that digest the nutrients. Our blood is chiefly water. The water in blood carries digested materials to all cells and removes their waste products. Water in sweat helps maintain normal body temperature.

The liquids we drink supply us with water. Many foods, such as fruits and vegetables, also provide water. Six to eight glasses of water should be drunk daily.

3. TESTS FOR THE NUTRIENTS

> **CAUTION:** When a test requires heat or a strong chemical, such as an acid, be sure to wear safety goggles. Also, point the mouth of a test tube away from yourself and others near you.

Students can test for the presence of nutrients in foods as follows:

a. Testing for Carbohydrates

(1) *Sugar.* The food being tested is boiled in a test tube for about a minute with some Benedict's or Fehling's solution. Sugar is present if the mixture turns an orange or brick-red color. Clinitest tablets and Clinistix are convenient methods of testing for sugar in liquid foods without boiling. The color changes are the same as those with Benedict's solution.

(2) *Starch.* A few drops of iodine solution are placed on the food being tested. If starch is present in the food, a blue-black color will appear.

b. Testing for Fats.
Some of the food is placed on a piece of unglazed paper, and the paper is then warmed gently. The appearance of a grease spot (which does not dry out in a few minutes) on the paper indicates the presence of fat.

c. Testing for Proteins.
A small amount of the food is placed in a test tube, and a few drops of nitric acid are added. The tube is heated gently until the acid boils. The nitric acid is carefully poured out of the tube, and the food is rinsed with water. Then a few drops of ammonium hydroxide are added. The appearance of a yellow or orange color indicates that a protein is present.

d. Testing for Water.
The food is heated in a dry test tube. If moisture appears on the inside of the cooler portion of the tube, it suggests that the food contains water.

e. Testing for Mineral Salts.
The food is heated in an iron spoon or pan until all the food has been burned. If a gray or white ash remains, the tested food contains mineral salts.

f. Testing for Vitamins. *Animal tests* can be used to determine the presence of a vitamin in foods. Such tests consist of two steps:

(1) A group of animals, such as rats, is fed an adequate diet.

(2) Another similar group is fed foods deficient in a single vitamin. The symptoms of the vitamin deficiency reveal the absence of the specific vitamin. For example, a diet lacking sufficient vitamin A produces the eye disease *xerophthalmia* ("dry eye").

Chemical tests are available for some vitamins, such as vitamin C. In the test for vitamin C, the food is mixed with a solution of indophenol. The color of this solution is blue, which becomes colorless in the presence of the vitamin.

Hospitals use instruments to test for the presence of food nutrients. The tests are quick and usually accurate. In general, all hospital tests are performed by electronic instruments, including computers.

4. EATING THE PROPER AMOUNT OF FOOD

When food is oxidized in the cells, energy is released. The amount of energy produced is measured in a unit called a calorie. A *calorie* is the amount of heat energy required to raise the temperature of one gram of water one Celsius degree. To express large amounts of heat energy more conveniently, the large calorie (Calorie) is used. The *Calorie* is the amount of heat energy needed to raise the temperature of 1,000 grams of water one Celsius degree.

People require different amounts of energy, according to:

a. Sex. Males may be more active than females and therefore may require more Calories.

b. Activity. Active people require more Calories than do those who are less active. For example, an athlete needs about 4,500 Calories a day, while a bookkeeper requires only about 2,500.

c. Age. Young people are usually more active than older people and therefore require more Calories. In addition, young people require more Calories during periods of rapid growth and development.

d. Temperature of the Region. To provide the body with warmth, people living in cold climates require more Calories than do people living in warm climates. Generally, people living in the colder regions eat more fats.

5. A BALANCED DIET AND DIETARY FIBER

If you eat too much of your favorite foods to the exclusion of other foods, you may be getting an abundance of certain nutrients and too little of others. For energy, for growth, for warmth, for proper body functioning, for protection against disease—in short, for your good health you must eat a varied, balanced diet. Such a diet is one that includes the right amount of dietary fiber and of every kind of nutrient.

Dietary fiber consists of carbohydrates present only in vegetables, fruits, and cereal grains from which the *bran*, or outer covering, has not been removed. Although fiber is not digestible, it is important because, by absorbing water and by swelling, it enables the large intestine to expel food wastes easily.

6. THE BASIC FOOD GROUPS

To be sure that people have a varied, balanced diet, nutrition experts have prepared a guide to good nutrition. This guide classifies foods into *four basic food groups*: the meat group; the vegetable and fruit group; the milk group; and the bread and cereal group. If, every day, you eat at least the suggested minimum servings from each group, you will be certain to get the greatest nutritional benefit from your meals. (See Table 9-3 below.)

Table 9-3. The Four Basic Food Groups

Food Group	Foods in the Group	Value
1. Meat Group	All kinds of meat, fish, and poultry; eggs; dried beans; peas; nuts; peanut butter.	Two or more servings supply mainly proteins, some fats, some mineral salts, and some vitamins.
2. Vegetable and Fruit Group	All kinds of vegetables and fruits: oranges, apples, green peppers, strawberries, potatoes, dark green vegetables, yellow vegetables, carrots, spinach, dark green leaves.	Four or more servings supply vitamins A and C, some mineral salts, and fiber.

Food Group	Foods in the Group	Value
3. Milk Group	Milk, cheese, ice cream, yogurt, buttermilk.	Ages 9-12: 3 or more servings. Teenagers: 4 or more servings. Adults: 2 or more servings. The group supplies salts of calcium and phosphorus; proteins; carbohydrates; some fat; and vitamins A and D.
4. Bread and Cereal Group	Breads: white, rye, and whole grain. Cereals: cooked or dry whole grain; rice; cornmeal. Macaroni; spaghetti.	Four or more servings supply carbohydrates, proteins, fiber, and B-vitamins.

7. ORGANIC FOODS

Foods, in general, tend to spoil on standing. Methods of preservation such as canning, refrigeration, and dehydration (removal of water) increase the shelf-life of foods considerably. These methods destroy bacteria that cause spoilage as well as those that may cause disease. For example, proper canning can prevent *botulism*— an often fatal bacterial disease that is characterized by difficulty in swallowing and by some paralysis.

Certain chemical preservatives and additives also reduce food spoilage. Other chemicals are added to the soil or to the diets of animals to increase food production. It is claimed that some of these substances may be harmful to the body and may be associated with the rising number of cases of cancer.

An increasingly large number of people have adopted diets containing *organic foods*. These foods are grown in the absence of additives and are packaged without preservatives. In general, organic foods are more expensive than those grown otherwise.

8. SOME GOOD EATING HABITS

For general good health and physical fitness, observe these simple eating habits:

a. Eat three meals a day at regular times.
b. Eat a varied, balanced diet.
c. Do not overeat.
d. Eat slowly and in pleasant surroundings.
e. Have a short rest after a meal.
f. Do not engage in stressful activities while you eat.

Multiple-Choice Questions

Write the number preceding the correct answer.

1. Starch and sugar are (1) carbohydrates (2) fats (3) proteins (4) minerals.
2. Carbohydrates are used chiefly in the body for (1) repairing tissues (2) releasing energy (3) growth (4) preventing scurvy.
3. Potatoes are a good source of (1) fat (2) protein (3) sugar (4) starch.
4. The nutrient that yields the greatest amount of energy when oxidized in the body is (1) vitamins (2) proteins (3) fats (4) carbohydrates.
5. A plant food that is rich in fat is the (1) cabbage (2) lettuce (3) peanut (4) potato.
6. In order to build body tissues, a person needs plenty of (1) fats (2) carbohydrates (3) proteins (4) iodine.
7. A food rich in protein is (1) fish (2) lettuce (3) potatoes (4) butter.
8. To have strong, healthy bones and teeth, it is necessary to eat foods rich in phosphorus and (1) mercury (2) calcium (3) iron (4) sodium.
9. Vitamin C (ascorbic acid) is found abundantly in (1) rice (2) ham (3) oranges (4) cake.
10. Fresh ripe tomatoes are valuable in our diet as a rich source of (1) proteins (2) oxygen (3) fats (4) vitamins.
11. An insufficient amount of vitamin D in the body may be due to a lack of (1) fats (2) proteins (3) sunlight (4) salt.
12. Fish oil such as cod-liver oil is given to young children because it contains large amounts of (1) vitamin B (2) vitamin D (3) minerals (4) vitamin E.
13. Rickets may be caused by (1) bacteria (2) a lack of vitamin D (3) overeating (4) overexercise.
14. A good source of vitamin A is (1) butter (2) egg white (3) salt (4) sugar.
15. Whole-wheat flour is usually more healthful than white-wheat flour because whole-wheat flour (1) contains more starch (2) contains more vitamin B_1 (3) is dark in color (4) can be digested more rapidly.

16. The best reason for including fruits and leafy vegetables in our diet is that they (1) have a very high water content (2) are the best source of protein (3) are the cheapest foods (4) are rich in minerals and vitamins.
17. A food that contains no vitamins or minerals is (1) butter (2) potatoes (3) fish (4) sugar.
18. Some foods such as lettuce, cabbage, and fruits should be eaten raw because cooking these foods destroys their (1) vitamin A (2) vitamin C (3) vitamin D (4) vitamin K.
19. Eating fish, poultry, and vegetable oils instead of fatty meats can help prevent (1) night-blindness (2) clogged arteries (3) pellagra and beri-beri (4) scurvy and rickets.
20. The largest part of the weight of the body is (1) bone (2) fat (3) water (4) protein.
21. A substance used to test for starch is (1) Fehling's or Benedict's solution (2) iodine (3) litmus paper (4) nitric acid.
22. To test a substance for sugar, we use (1) Fehling's or Benedict's solution (2) ammonium hydroxide (3) water (4) hydrochloric acid.
23. A substance used in a test for protein is (1) unglazed paper (2) nitric acid (3) iodine (4) Fehling's or Benedict's solution.
24. A boy burns a piece a bread over a gas flame until there is nothing left but a gray ash. He can conclude that the bread contains (1) fat (2) minerals (3) starch (4) vitamins.
25. The number of Calories in a food represents (1) the vitamin content in the food (2) the ease with which the food can be digested (3) the amount of energy that can be obtained from the food (4) the mineral content of the food.

Completion Questions

Write the word or expression that correctly completes the statement.

1. The process carried on by cells that releases energy from food is called _____.
2. The nutrient _____ gives off the greatest amount of heat when used in the body.
3. The nutrient needed to carry digested foods throughout the body is _____.
4. The lack of a certain vitamin may lead to a (an) _____ disease.
5. Active people must obtain more _____ from food than less active people.
6. A (An) _____ diet supplies the body with the proper amount of the right foods.
7. Liver supplies the _____ the body needs to make hemoglobin.
8. Enriched milk has the vitamins A and _____ added to it.
9. Foods that do not contain preservatives or additives are called _____.
10. After eating, it is advised that you take a short _____.

Chapter 10. Our Body Prepares and Uses Food

THE FATE OF FOOD

Have you ever wondered what happens to the food we eat? Special X-ray photographs can reveal the path of food inside the body, but photos cannot tell us about the changes the food undergoes. Early scientists who dissected bodies described the major organs of what we now call the *digestive system*. However, they could not tell us what went on inside each organ.

Our knowledge of the process of digestion in humans can be said to have begun with the research of Lazzaro Spallanzani, an Italian of the 18th century. In his early years, he studied for the priesthood. Then a relative, who was a physics professor, turned Spallanzani's mind to science and experimentation.

One of Spallanzani's major discoveries arose from his curiosity about what happened to meat after it was swallowed. To find out, he made a little bag of cloth and filled it with chopped meat. After tying a length of string to the bag and, while holding the string, he swallowed the bag—meat and all. Then, at different time intervals, on different days, he pulled up the bag and examined its contents. (It was all very uncomfortable.) The first time, after 15 minutes, he noted that the meat had changed color and had a bad odor. Another time, after one hour, he found that the meat was soft and mushy. Still another time, after three hours, the meat had been liquefied.

In modern times, juices have been extracted from the stomach and other digestive organs. The effects of the juices on different nutrients have been observed. The details of what happens to food during and after digestion are the subjects of this chapter.

THE DIGESTIVE SYSTEM

1. FUNCTION OF THE DIGESTIVE SYSTEM

Every cell in your body must have food. However, the food that cells can use is quite different from the food you take into your mouth. In order to reach the cells, the nutrients in the food you eat must be changed to soluble form. In soluble form, the nutrients can pass through cell membranes and nourish cells. The process of changing nutrients to soluble form is called *digestion*. It is the function of the *digestive system*.

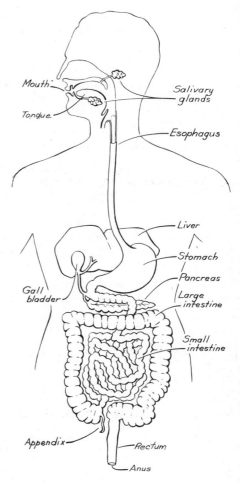

Fig. 10-1. Organs of the digestive system

2. WHERE DOES DIGESTION TAKE PLACE?

Foods are digested in organs that form a continuous tube, called the *food tube*, or *alimentary canal*. The food tube (Figure 10-1 on preceding page) starts with the mouth and ends with the *anus*, the lower opening of the food tube.

The innermost layer of the food tube is covered by the type of lining tissue that forms *glands*. Glands are organs that produce, or *secrete*, special juices. Some glands produce *mucus* and others produce *digestive juices*. Mucus is a slimy substance that lubricates the food tube and eases the passage of food through the tube. The digestive juices change the nutrients in food to soluble forms.

3. THE DIGESTIVE GLANDS AND JUICES

As foods pass through the organs of the food tube, the nutrients are acted upon by various digestive juices, each juice secreted by a different gland. From a gland, a juice passes into the food tube by way of a *duct*, or tube. Some digestive glands are present in the lining of the food tube. Others, the salivary glands, liver, and pancreas, lie outside the food tube.

The digestive juices contain water and special chemicals called *enzymes*. These chemicals break down the nutrients into simpler, soluble substances. In this liquid form, the nutrients are delivered to, and used by, all cells of the body.

ANSWER 2# LESSON 1#

4. HOW FOOD IS MOVED THROUGH THE FOOD TUBE

In the *mouth*, the movements of the tongue first mix the food with saliva, the juice secreted by the *salivary glands*. Then the tongue helps push the food down into the *esophagus*, or *gullet*. Wavelike motions of the esophagus then push the food into the *stomach*. Muscles in the walls of the stomach churn the food and mix it with *gastric juice*. When the stomach empties, the food passes into the *small intestine*. There, the squeezing movements of its muscular walls mixes the food with various enzymes and moves the food along the full length of the small intestine. While there, the digested nutrients enter the bloodstream. The remaining matter, mostly undigested wastes, is forced into the *large intestine*. Finally, the wastes are pushed to the lower end of the large intestine, where they are temporarily stored before leaving the body through the anus.

5. DIGESTION STARTS IN THE MOUTH

a. The Teeth. The mass of food you take into your mouth is first ground and crushed into smaller pieces by the teeth. All humans have two sets of teeth during their lifetime. The first set, called *baby teeth*, consists of 20 teeth which last until the child is 6 to 8 years old. The second set (Fig. 10-2) consists of 32 teeth, 16 in the lower jaw and 16 in the upper jaw. They are called *permanent teeth* because they cannot be replaced by the body.

The 32 permanent teeth are of four types, as follows:

8 *incisors* bite food
4 *canines* tear food
8 *premolars* grind food
12 *molars* grind and crush food

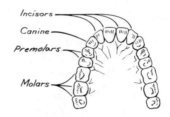

Fig. 10-2. The permanent teeth (lower jaw)

The center of a tooth is soft; it is called *pulp*. The pulp contains mostly blood vessels and nerves. Two layers of hard material cover the pulp: *dentine* and *enamel*. Enamel, a much harder layer, gives protection to the exposed part of the tooth above the gum (soft tissue around the base of the tooth). See Fig. 10-3.

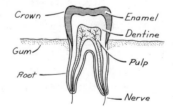

Fig. 10-3. A tooth. The exposed part of the tooth, which is about one-third of the whole tooth, is called the crown. The crown is covered with enamel, and the portion of the tooth that is not exposed is surrounded by the gum.

b. Saliva. While food is being chewed and mashed, it is also being mixed with *saliva* in the mouth. Saliva serves the digestive process in two ways: Because it is a slippery fluid, saliva softens and lubricates the food in preparation for swallowing. Saliva contains the enzyme *ptyalin*, which changes starch to a sugar.

6. DIGESTION IN THE STOMACH

The starch in swallowed food is only partially digested. By way of the esophagus, the food goes from the mouth to the *stomach*. Here, starch digestion stops, but gastric juice begins to digest proteins. Gastric juice contains hydrochloric acid, water, and two main enzymes, *rennin* and *pepsin*. Together, these substances begin to break down proteins.

The muscular walls of the stomach churn the food around and around, thoroughly mixing it with the gastric juice. After a few hours in the stomach, the partly digested food becomes soupy and passes into the small intestine.

7. DIGESTION IN THE SMALL INTESTINE

Most digestion occurs in the small intestine, which is a coiled tube more than twenty feet long and about one inch wide. In this organ, digestion is completed by three juices: *pancreatic juice*, *intestinal juice*, and *bile*.

a. Pancreatic juice is secreted by the pancreas. Enzymes in this juice digest fat, protein, and any carbohydrate not digested before.

b. Intestinal juice is secreted by glands present in the walls of the small intestine. It contains enzymes that complete the digestion of all the nutrients.

c. Bile is secreted by the *liver*, the largest gland in the body, and is temporarily stored in the *gall bladder*. Bile aids the digestion of fat by breaking it up into tiny droplets.

8. ABSORPTION IN THE SMALL INTESTINE

After digestion has been completed in the small intestine, all the nutrients are in a simple, dissolved form. They pass from the small intestine into the bloodstream through structures called *villi*. Villi are tiny hairlike projections in the cavity of the small intestine. Blood flowing through the minute blood vessels (*capillaries*) of the villi picks up the nutrients and delivers them to all cells of the body.

9. THE LARGE INTESTINE ELIMINATES WASTE PRODUCTS

The undigested parts of food and the wastes of the digestive process are forced from the small intestine into the large intestine. Here, water is extracted from the soupy mass, which then becomes semi-solid. This mass is stored in the *rectum* for a while and then is finally eliminated from the body through the anus.

THE CIRCULATORY SYSTEM

10. FUNCTION OF THE CIRCULATORY SYSTEM

After the digestive system has made foods soluble and the dissolved nutrients have passed into the bloodstream, the *circulatory system* then plays its part. It transports nutrients, oxygen, and other substances to all cells. It also carries away cellular wastes which, unless removed, would poison the cells.

The circulatory system consists of *blood*, the *heart*, and *blood vessels*.

11. THE BLOOD

Blood is present in blood vessels that branch to every part of the body. In the vessels, the blood is kept in constant motion by the pumping action of the heart. Blood is made up partly of microscopic cells and a liquid, called *plasma*, in about equal proportions. Blood cells are of two types, red and white, and are called *corpuscles* (Fig. 10-4).

Bacteria being engulfed

Red corpuscle   **White corpuscle**   **Platelets**

Fig. 10-4. Blood. Under a microscope, fresh blood stained with special dyes is seen to consist of red corpuscles, white corpuscles, platelets, and plasma. The clear area represents the plasma.

a. Red Corpuscles. These are disk-shaped cells that contain *hemoglobin*, a substance rich in iron. Hemoglobin transports oxygen from the lungs to all cells in the body. It is the substance that gives blood its red color.

b. White Corpuscles. These are colorless, irregularly shaped cells, much fewer in number than red cells. White corpuscles destroy germs that invade the blood and other tissues. Some white corpuscles destroy germs by surrounding and digesting them. Others produce *antibodies*, special chemicals that destroy some germs and the poisons released by others.

c. Platelets. When a blood vessel is cut and bleeding starts, the platelets release a substance that causes blood to *clot* (stop running out).

d. Plasma. This, the liquid part of blood, contains about 90 percent water. The red and white cells are suspended in the plasma. Plasma delivers dissolved foods to the cells and carries away wastes from the cells.

12. THE HEART

The heart is the hollow, muscular pump that forces blood to move around the body (Fig. 10-5). A wall of muscle tissue divides the heart into a right side and a left side. Each side is further divided into two *chambers*. An upper chamber is called an *auricle*; a lower chamber is called a *ventricle*.

Separating an auricle from a ventricle is a flap of tissue called a *valve*. This flap allows blood to flow in only one direction, from an auricle to a ventricle.

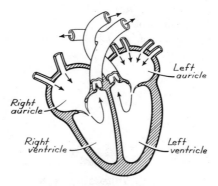

Fig. 10-5. The heart

13. THE BLOOD VESSELS

The tubes through which blood flows are called *blood vessels*. There are three types: *arteries*, *capillaries*, and *veins*.

a. Arteries. These are blood vessels through which blood flows away from the heart. Arteries have thick, elastic walls. The largest artery in the body is the *aorta*, the vessel that carries blood away from the left ventricle. As arteries go farther away from the heart, they branch out many times and become smaller and smaller. Finally, they become microscopic in size, and connect to capillaries.

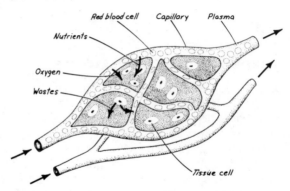

Fig. 10-6. The blood reaches the cells. Arteries subdivide and end in capillaries. Capillaries bring essential materials to the cells and take away wastes. The capillaries then recombine to form veins.

b. Capillaries. These are the tiniest blood vessels. They are present everywhere in the body, very close to every cell. There, they extend from the ends of arteries to the beginnings of veins. The transfer of food and oxygen from the blood to the cells and of wastes from the cells to the blood takes place through the extremely thin walls of the capillaries (Fig. 10-6).

c. Veins. Upon leaving the cells, the capillaries join together and connect to small veins. As small veins join together, these vessels grow larger and larger. Veins carry blood back to the heart. Veins from all parts of the body, except the lungs, empty the blood they carry into the right auricle. Veins from the lungs empty into the left auricle. Veins have valves all along their length that prevent the blood from flowing backward.

14. THE HEART IN ACTION

Blood from large veins flows into the auricles when they relax. The right auricle receives blood rich in waste carbon dioxide from all parts of the body except the lungs. The left auricle receives blood rich in oxygen that was picked up in the lungs. When the auricles contract, blood flows out of them into the ventricles.

The ventricles are relaxed when they receive blood from the auricles. When the ventricles contract, they pump blood out of the heart into the large arteries connected to it. Blood with carbon dioxide in the right ventricle is pumped to the lungs. Blood with oxygen in the left ventricle is pumped to all parts of the body except the lungs. (See Fig. 10-5, page 90.)

WONDERS OF THE CIRCULATORY SYSTEM

At one time, people believed that blood repeatedly moved up to the head and down to the toes, like the ebbing and flowing of the ocean tides. It was not until the 17th century that William Harvey, an Englishman, proved that blood was pumped in circular paths round and round the body. Since then, continuous research has led to many interesting facts about blood circulation. Here are some of them.

- For most people, depending on age and activity, the heart beats 70 or more times per minute.

- Depending on body size, most people have between 5 and 6 quarts of blood. This amount of blood circulates around the body as long as one lives.

- With every heartbeat, about two ounces of blood pass through the heart. Thus, in one hour, about 65 gallons of blood pass through.

- Although parts of the blood are constantly wearing out and being destroyed, they are constantly being re-formed from substances present in our food.

- If all the blood vessels were laid out end-to-end in a straight line, they would circle the earth, not once—but more than twice!

- Should the brain not receive a continuous supply of blood for more than 9 minutes, it would die. Before long, after that time, the rest of the body would die.

- Continuous research has led to such modern advances as heart transplants, artificial hearts, and electrical pacemakers, which regulate the heartbeat.

THE RESPIRATORY SYSTEM

Recall that during oxidation, cells use the oxygen and nutrients brought to them by the circulatory system. As a result of oxidation, the cells give off waste carbon dioxide and water, which the circulatory system removes from the cells.

15. FUNCTION OF THE RESPIRATORY SYSTEM

A lack of oxygen and an accumulation of carbon dioxide in body cells and the bloodstream can be fatal in a short time. Under normal conditions, the *respiratory system* prevents this from happening by removing from the blood excess carbon dioxide and replacing it with fresh oxygen.

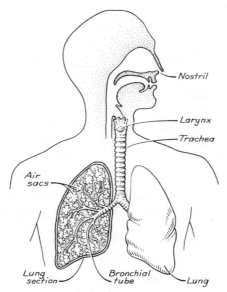

Fig. 10-7. The respiratory system. In the lungs, the exchange of gases between the blood and the air takes place in the capillaries surrounding each air sac.

16. THE PARTS OF THE RESPIRATORY SYSTEM

Two sets of organs make up the respiratory system: the organs of the air pathway and the organs that cause air to move into and out of the air pathway.

a. The Air Pathway. Before the oxygen of the air can enter the blood, the oxygen must pass through the following organs: the *nose, throat, voice box, windpipe,* and *lungs.*

(1) *The Nose.* When we breathe in, or inhale, air passes through the nostrils of the nose and enters the nasal passages. There, small hairs filter the dust out of the air, and the lining of the nasal passages warms and moistens the air. Before entering the throat, the air passes over the *adenoids,* which protect us against some germs that may be present in the air.

(2) *The Throat.* Air passing through the throat moves over the *tonsils,* which have the same function as the adenoids.

(3) *The Voice Box (Larynx).* From the throat, air passes through a slit in the upper part of the voice box. A flap, the *epiglottis,* above the slit, closes like a trapdoor when we swallow. This prevents food from entering the windpipe and causing choking.

(4) *The Windpipe (Trachea).* From the voice box, the air passes through the windpipe to its lower end, where it divides into two narrower tubes, each of which leads air to a lung.

(5) *The Lungs.* These two large organs fill most of the chest cavity. They consist of bronchial tubes, air sacs, and blood vessels. In the lungs, the oxygen of the inhaled air enters the bloodstream through the capillaries surrounding each air sac and is carried to the cells. At the same time, the wastes of oxidation pass from the blood into the air sacs. From there, the wastes leave the body as we exhale.

b. Movement of Air in the Air Pathway. When we inhale, air enters the air pathway; when we exhale, the opposite happens. Exhaled air contains more carbon dioxide and less oxygen than does inhaled air. The breathing movements that make these changes possible are performed by muscles attached to the ribs and by the diaphragm. The diaphragm is the sheet of muscle that extends across the body just below the lungs.

GETTING RID OF BODY WASTES

As cells carry on their life activities, they produce certain liquid wastes in addition to carbon dioxide and water. If allowed to accumulate, these wastes would kill the cells. The process by which the body and its cells get rid of liquid wastes is called *excretion*, which is the function of different excretory organs.

17. THE EXCRETORY ORGANS AND THEIR FUNCTIONS

a. Lungs. These eliminate carbon dioxide and water, as you already know.

b. Skin. Deep in the skin are over 2 million microscopic *sweat glands*. These glands have tiny openings, called *pores*, on the surface of the skin (Fig. 10-8). Through the pores, sweat glands give off *perspiration*, or sweat. This is a waste material containing chiefly water and salts. As the water in perspiration evaporates, it helps to keep the body cool.

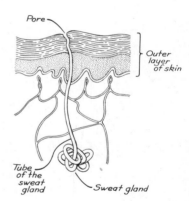

Fig. 10-8. A part of the skin (enlarged). A sweat gland removes wastes from capillaries around the gland. The wastes empty onto the surface of the skin.

c. Urinary System. This system consists of two kidneys, the urinary bladder, and special tubes. The kidneys are bean-shaped organs that are situated in the back of the body below the ribs. As blood flows through the kidneys (Fig. 10-9, on next page), nitrogen wastes (formed from the breakdown of proteins), water, and mineral salts are taken out of the blood. These substances make up the liquid waste called *urine*. The urine flows, by way of a tube from each kidney, to the *bladder* and from there to the outside of the body by way of a single tube.

KIDNEY REPLACEMENTS

The lives of some people are threatened when their kidneys fail to function properly. Some of these people are helped by kidney *dialysis*; and others, by kidney *transplants*.

In *dialysis*, a machine—an artificial kidney—is hooked up to the person's blood vessels. As blood moves through the machine, wastes are removed from the blood.

A *kidney transplant* involves the replacement of a faulty kidney by a healthy one that was donated by someone whose antibody types of tissue matched those of the patient.

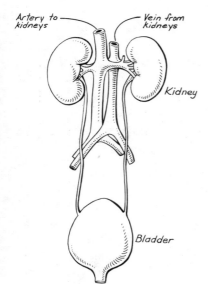

Artery to kidneys

Vein from kidneys

Kidney

Bladder

Fig. 10-9. The kidneys remove wastes.
Urine flows from the kidneys to the bladder and out of the body by way of tubes.

Note: The **large intestine** is not a part of the excretory system. Recall that the large intestine helps the body get rid of undigested food materials. These wastes, in semi-solid form, leave the body through the anus. (See section 4 on page 86.)

Multiple-Choice Questions

Write the number preceding the correct answer.

1. The process that changes food to a simple, soluble form is called (1) absorption (2) digestion (3) respiration (4) circulation.
2. Substances that cause chemical changes in foods are called (1) hormones (2) vitamins (3) red cells (4) enzymes.
3. Digestion starts in the (1) liver (2) mouth (3) small intestine (4) stomach.
4. The number of teeth in a full permanent set is (1) 12 (2) 22 (3) 32 (4) 42.
5. The special work done by the molars is (1) biting (2) cutting (3) grinding (4) tearing.
6. The inner portion of a tooth is made up of (1) enamel (2) pulp (3) dentine (4) mucus.
7. Gastric juice is secreted in the (1) mouth (2) stomach (3) small intestine (4) large intestine.
8. The stomach empties directly into the (1) large intestine (2) liver (3) heart (4) small intestine.
9. Most digestion in humans takes place in the (1) esophagus (2) mouth (3) small intestine (4) stomach.
10. An important substance that carries on digestion in the small intestine is (1) gastric juice (2) hydrochloric acid (3) pancreatic juice (4) pepsin.
11. Most food nutrients enter the bloodstream by absorption through the walls of the (1) liver (2) pancreas (3) small intestine (4) stomach.
12. The microscopic structure in the small intestine that absorbs digested food is called the (1) villus (2) pancreas (3) esophagus (4) gullet.
13. The secretion given off by the liver that helps in the digestion of fats is (1) ptyalin (2) pancreatic juice (3) bile (4) intestinal juice.
14. The liquid portion of the blood is the (1) red cells (2) white cells (3) plasma (4) hemoglobin.
15. The chief function of red corpuscles is to (1) carry food to cells (2) carry oxygen to cells (3) destroy disease germs (4) stop the loss of blood.
16. The most important function of the white corpuscles is to (1) carry oxygen to the cells (2) carry food to the cells (3) destroy harmful germs (4) store fat.
17. The receiving chambers of the heart are called (1) arteries (2) veins (3) auricles (4) ventricles.
18. The blood is pumped through the body by the action of the (1) heart (2) lungs (3) stomach (4) veins.
19. Blood vessels that carry blood away from the heart are (1) veins (2) arteries (3) capillaries (4) villi.
20. The blood is carried to the heart by (1) arteries (2) capillaries (3) veins (4) nerves.

21. The blood vessels seen in the back of the hand are (1) veins (2) tendons (3) arteries (4) ligaments.
22. The blood obtains oxygen in the (1) heart (2) liver (3) lungs (4) nostrils.
23. The process by which the body cells release energy from foods is called (1) circulation (2) oxidation (3) excretion (4) digestion.
24. The kidneys, skin, and lungs are similar because they each (1) aid in breathing (2) aid in circulation of the blood (3) aid in digestion (4) aid in removing body wastes.
25. In the human body, carbon dioxide is excreted mainly by the (1) kidneys (2) lungs (3) skin (4) large intestine.

Matching Questions

Match the items in column A with those in column B.

	Column A		Column B
1.	alimentary canal	*a.*	trachea
2.	stores urine	*b.*	small intestine
3.	windpipe	*c.*	food tube
4.	villi	*d.*	chamber of heart
5.	enzyme	*e.*	canines
6.	ventricle	*f.*	bladder
7.	allows exit of undigested food materials	*g.*	digests nutrients
8.	contains small hairs that filter dust out of air	*h.*	nose
9.	tear food	*i.*	anus
10.	transport oxygen	*j.*	red corpuscles

Completion Questions

Write the word or expression that correctly completes the statement.

1. The _____ is the muscle under the lungs that helps air enter and leave the air pathway in the body.
2. Another name for the esophagus is the _____ .
3. The hard material that protects the exposed part of a tooth is the _____ .
4. The digestive juice found in the mouth is _____ .
5. A chemical that must be present in gastric juice in order for pepsin to function is _____ .
6. The largest gland in the body is the _____ .

7. Attached to the liver is a small structure, called the _____, which stores bile.

8. The material found in red blood cells that unites with oxygen is _____.

9. The _____ are structures in the heart that prevent the flow of blood from ventricles to auricles.

10. The _____ is the largest artery in the body.

11. The life process by which wastes are eliminated from the body is called _____.

12. The _____ are the organs in which the wastes of oxidation are removed from the blood.

13. The _____ are the surface openings of the sweat glands.

14. In addition to helping the body get rid of wastes, _____ cools the body.

15. The two bean-shaped structures that extract nitrogen wastes from the blood are the _____.

Chapter 11. How the Body Controls Its Parts

1. TWO SETS OF CONTROLS

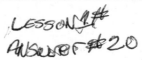

The human body is a highly complicated machine. It is composed of many billions of cells that form tissues, organs, and organ systems. Although each part of the human machine has its own special job to do, all the parts work together to make the body an efficient unit. This is made possible by the *nervous system* and the system of *ductless glands*. Together, both systems control all body activities.

2. THE NERVOUS SYSTEM COORDINATES ALL MUSCLE ACTIONS

All the muscles in your body work in harmony. Depending on their location, muscles move either bones or soft internal organs. For example, muscles in an arm move bones; those in the walls of the digestive tube move internal organs. The nervous system coordinates the muscles with the movements of your body.

In some situations requiring immediate action, the nervous system will perform a task without your thinking about the act. For example, should you touch a hot iron with a hand, your nervous system will cause muscles to withdraw the hand before it can be burned severely. Such an action is called a *reflex action*.

The muscular actions of the heart, blood vessels, and digestive tube are also performed without thought. These, too, are reflex actions.

3. THE PARTS OF THE CENTRAL NERVOUS SYSTEM

The main parts of the nervous system are the *brain*, the *spinal cord*, and bundles of cable-like nerve cells, called *nerves*. (See figure of a nerve cell on page 64.) Together, the brain and spinal cord make up the *central nervous system*. Nerves are present everywhere in the body. They transmit messages to and from the central nervous system and all parts of the body.

a. The Brain. The *brain* is the mass of nerve tissue located in the skull. The brain is divided into three major parts: the *cerebrum*, the *cerebellum*, and the *medulla* (Fig. 11-1 on next page).

(1) The Cerebrum. The largest part of the brain is the cerebrum. It occupies the upper region of the skull. The cerebrum controls our thinking and interprets sounds, sights, and other sensations for us. It also enables us to judge, make decisions, learn, and carry on all voluntary activities.

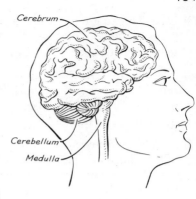

Cerebrum

Cerebellum

Medulla

Fig. 11-1. Parts of the brain

LESSON 11 ANSWER 11 16

(2) The Cerebellum. This part of the brain is smaller than the cerebrum. It is found in the lower rear portion of the skull. The cerebellum helps coordinate the movements of muscles under our control. It also helps maintain the proper balance of the body.

(3) The Medulla. Below the cerebellum is the medulla. It connects the brain with the spinal cord. The medulla controls many reflex actions, those actions over which we have no direct control. Some of these actions are the beating of the heart, breathing, sneezing, and coughing.

b. The Spinal Cord. This cord of nerve tissue extends downward from the medulla through the canal present in the backbone. Nerves branching out of the spinal cord connect the different parts of the body with the spinal cord. The spinal cord is the center of many reflex actions.

c. The Sense Organs. The eyes, ears, nose, tongue, and skin are the *sense organs.* They receive the sensations of light, sound, smell, taste, touch, pressure, pain, and temperature. As soon as a sense organ receives a sensation, the sensation is changed to signals (messages or *impulses*) that are similar to electricity. The signals then travel over nerves from the sense organ to the brain. There, the sensation is interpreted.

(1) Eyes. The eyes detect light coming from objects we see. The light sets up impulses in the eye. The impulses (messages) then travel to the brain, which interprets the impulses and tells us what we are viewing.

(2) Ears. The ears receive sound waves from objects. The waves set up impulses in the ear. These impulses travel to the brain, which interprets the impulses and tells us what we are hearing.

(3) Nose. The nose receives odors given off by objects. Nerves in the nose detect odors and send a message to the brain. The brain interprets the message and tells us what the odor is.

(4) Tongue. The tongue is the organ responsible for the sensation of taste. When something touches the tongue, special cells on the tongue, called *taste buds*, set up impulses that travel to the brain. The brain interprets the message and tells us what we are tasting.

(5) Skin. Scattered over the body and close to the surface of the skin are nerve cells of four different types, each of which detects a different sensation. They detect the sensations of heat, touch, pain, and pressure.

4. HOW WE LEARN

In our daily lives, we learn and use knowledge, understanding, and skills. All learning is centered in the cerebrum.

a. Trial-and-Error Learning. This type of learning involves making trials until we find the correct method of solving a problem. When we find the proper method, we not only have solved our problem, but we also have learned how to solve similar problems and make similar decisions.

b. Habits. A habit is an act that has been learned so completely that the act is performed automatically—without thinking about it. Habits are important to us because they make us more efficient in performing particular tasks, save us time and thought, and permit us to do several things at the same time.

(1) To form a desirable habit:

    a. Realize the values of the habit and have a desire to form it.
    b. Concentrate on the habit you want to form and practice it time and time again.
    c. Take pride in what you are achieving as the habit is being formed.

(2) To break an undesirable habit:

    a. Realize the disadvantages of the habit and have a sincere desire to break it.
    b. Replace the bad habit with a good habit.
    c. Constantly practice the good habit. Allow yourself *no exceptions*.

5. DUCTLESS GLANDS ASSIST THE NERVOUS SYSTEM

Body activities are regulated and coordinated not only by the nervous system but also by the *ductless glands* (Fig. 11-2). These glands are called ductless because they lack ducts, or tubes. They secrete (give off) chemicals, called *hormones*, directly into the blood. Hormones are carried by the bloodstream to different parts of the body. Some hormones regulate the rate of body growth and development, while other hormones regulate and coordinate the functioning of certain organs.

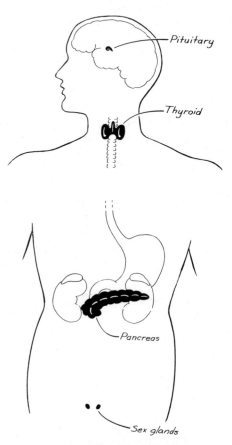

Fig. 11-2. Some ductless glands

6. SOME DUCTLESS GLANDS IN THE HUMAN

a. Thyroid Gland. This gland is at the base of the neck on the windpipe. It secretes the hormone *thyroxin*, which is rich in iodine. Thyroxin regulates the rate of oxidation of nutrients by the body cells. It also helps control mental and physical development.

Too much, or too little, secretion of thyroxin causes a swelling of the thyroid gland, a disease called *goiter*. Too much thyroxin greatly increases the rate of oxidation to the extent that extreme nervousness and loss of weight result. This condition can be treated by destroying a part of the thyroid gland, by using surgery or by other means. Too little thyroxin may result from a lack of iodine in the diet and can be treated by diet or injections of thyroxin. In a child, too little thyroxin hinders physical and mental development. In an adult, it may cause excessive gain of weight.

b. Pituitary Gland. This gland is at the base of the brain. It secretes many hormones, one of which is the *growth hormone*. This hormone regulates the growth of the body. Too little secretion in a child results in a *dwarf*; too much produces a *giant*.

c. Pancreas. This gland, just below the stomach, secretes the hormone *insulin* as well as pancreatic juice. Insulin regulates the rate of use of sugar by body cells. Insulin also regulates the storage of sugar by the liver. Too little secretion of insulin causes the disease *diabetes*. This condition may be treated by injections of insulin and by special diets. When untreated or unchecked, diabetes may cause severe circulatory ailments.

d. Adrenal Glands. An adrenal gland is located on the top of each kidney. The inner portion of each gland secretes the hormone *adrenaline* whenever a person is frightened or under some other kind of stress. In a way, adrenaline temporarily makes a person stronger by strengthening the heart action and increasing the breathing rate. (Read "Extraordinary Strength of a Parent" on next page.)

The outer portion of an adrenal gland secretes a few hormones, the most familiar of which is *cortisone*. This hormone is known for its ability to relieve inflammations, such as in allergies and in arthritis.

e. Sex Glands. The sex glands of females are the *ovaries*; of males, they are the *testes*. Besides producing the cells needed for reproduction, these glands secrete hormones that influence the body changes that occur as a person matures.

EXTRAORDINARY STRENGTH OF A PARENT

From time to time we hear of a parent whose baby is trapped inside a burning house and the doorway is blocked by two heavy beams. Ordinarily, moving one beam would take the combined efforts of at least two people. Yet, under these conditions, a frantic parent manages to move them, enter the house, and rescue the child. At such a time, what is the source of the person's extraordinary strength?

When a person is faced with such a situation—excitement, stress, fear—a message from the brain rapidly reaches the adrenal glands (section 6-d on previous page). Immediately, the glands secrete adrenaline into the blood. In seconds the adrenaline reaches many organs and causes them to react. The major body changes that occur are the following:

- Heart muscle contracts more strongly and more rapidly.
- Blood pressure rises.
- The liver sends extra glucose into the bloodstream.
- The glucose, upon reaching body cells, releases extra energy as it is oxidized.
- The breathing rate increases, enabling more oxygen to enter the body.
- The blood is ready to clot more quickly than usual.
- The muscles of the food tube stop contracting.
- The muscles attached to the skeleton contract more forcefully.
- Pain, if present, is either dulled or not felt until afterward.

All in all—under the influence of adrenaline—the body is mobilized for action.

Multiple-Choice Questions

Write the number preceding the correct answer.

1. All body functions of an individual are coordinated by the ductless glands and the (1) brain (2) nervous system (3) heart (4) circulatory system.
2. An example of an action controlled by the nervous system but performed without thought is (1) solving a problem (2) selecting a hat (3) beating of the heart (4) changing a TV program.
3. The largest part of the brain is the (1) spinal cord (2) medulla (3) cerebellum (4) cerebrum.
4. One of the functions controlled by the medulla is (1) thinking (2) heartbeat (3) body balance (4) judgment.
5. As soon as an eye receives the sensation of light, the sensation is changed into (1) a sound (2) a signal similar to electricity (3) a ductless hormone (4) an enzyme.
6. An organ in our body that detects changes in our surroundings is called (1) a sense organ (2) the brain (3) a nerve cell (4) the spinal cord.
7. Special structures in the human that help regulate many activities are the (1) sense organs (2) nerve cells (3) ductless glands (4) excretory organs.
8. The structures mentioned in question 7 produce chemicals called (1) enzymes (2) salivary juice (3) bile (4) hormones.
9. The gland that helps control physical and mental development is the (1) thyroid (2) pancreas (3) intestinal gland (4) liver.
10. Insulin is a substance used to treat people having the disease known as (1) cancer (2) diabetes (3) polio (4) malaria.
11. Of the following, the gland whose improper functioning may result in dwarfism is the (1) pancreas (2) gastric (3) intestinal (4) pituitary.
12. A type of learning that results from repetition of an act is known as (1) a habit (2) a simple reflex (3) trial and error (4) a stimulus.
13. A condition necessary to the breaking of an unpleasant habit is (1) a half-hearted attempt (2) a sincere desire to get rid of the habit (3) trial and error (4) medical attention.
14. Taste buds are located in the (1) esophagus (2) tongue (3) cerebrum (4) trachea.
15. The part of the brain involved in learning new definitions is the (1) medulla (2) cerebrum (3) cerebellum (4) spinal cord.

Completion Questions

Write the word or expression that correctly completes the statement.

1. The nervous system is composed of special cells called _____.
2. The central nervous system is made up of the spinal cord and the _____.
3. The part of the brain which helps control the balance of our body is the _____.
4. The brain and the spinal cord are joined together at a structure known as the _____.
5. The spinal cord is situated in the _____.
6. _____ are rapid actions in which the brain is not involved.
7. The eyes and ears are examples of _____ organs.
8. All sensations are interpreted by the _____.
9. Hormones are carried to the various parts of the body by the _____.
10. The _____ gland is located at the base of the brain.

Modified True-False Questions

If a statement is true, write the word true. *If a statement is false, write the word or expression that must be substituted for the italicized expression to make the statement true.*

1. The coordination of some body activities is the function of the *digestive* glands.
2. The brain consists mainly of the cerebrum, the cerebellum, and the *spinal cord*.
3. The lower rear part of the skull houses the *cerebellum*.
4. Ductless glands secrete *enzymes*.
5. Insulin is secreted by the *pituitary gland*.

Thought Questions

1. A horror movie may frighten you and make your heart beat faster. The increased rate of the heartbeat comes about because what you see and think about as you watch the movie cause messages in your body to move over certain pathways.

    Arrange the following body parts in proper order to show the pathways of the messages.

    cerebrum, heart muscle, medulla, eye, nerve cells of eye, nerve
2. How would you apply the three steps in habit formation in learning to become a good typist.

Chapter 12. Protists in Relation to Humans

Even very tiny protists play an important part in our daily lives.

1. IMPORTANT ANIMALLIKE PROTISTS

A drop of water from a stagnant pond or lake examined under the microscope reveals many animallike protists moving around. These organisms are called *protozoa* (Fig. 12-1). A protozoan consists of a single cell and carries on all the life activities that a many-celled animal, such as a dog, does. Protozoa feed, move about, reproduce, and respond to changes in their environment. They feed on smaller microscopic organisms and on particles of decaying matter. Many types of protozoa are important to us *indirectly* in that they serve as food for larger water-dwellers that we use as food. A few types of protozoa are important to us *directly* because they are responsible for diseases, such as malaria and African sleeping sickness.

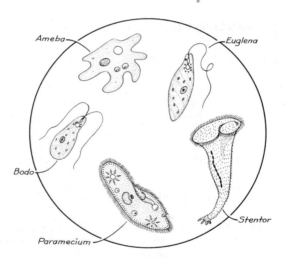

Fig. 12-1. Examples of protozoa (under the microscope)

2. IMPORTANT PLANTLIKE PROTISTS

The smallest plantlike protists are *bacteria*. They are one-celled, do not contain chlorophyll, and therefore cannot make their own food. Bacteria are found everywhere—in water, in the air, in the soil, on our bodies, and in the food we eat.

108

Bacteria perform most of the life activities that are carried on by more complex organisms.

There are three types of bacteria, according to their shape (Fig. 12-2):

    a. The *coccus* is ball-shaped.
    b. The *bacillus* is rod-shaped.
    c. The *spirillum* is spiral-shaped.

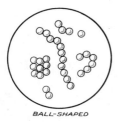  

BALL-SHAPED   ROD-SHAPED   SPIRAL-SHAPED

Fig. 12-2. Types of bacteria (under the microscope)

Of the many species of bacteria, most are harmless; many are beneficial; and some are harmful.

3. HELPFUL BACTERIA

Among the useful bacteria are those that:

    a. Restore soil minerals.
    b. Give flavor to butter and cheese.
    c. Aid in obtaining linen from the flax plant.
    d. Tenderize meat.
    e. Carry on decay.

Certain species of bacteria cause the decay, or *decomposition*, of animal wastes and dead bodies of plants and animals. In this way, they not only rid the world of dead bodies, but also return to the soil many of the minerals that had been taken out of the soil by green plants as they made their food. Other species of bacteria, called *nitrogen-fixing bacteria*, return valuable nitrogen compounds to the soil.

4. HARMFUL BACTERIA

Many diseases of humans and other organisms are caused by certain bacteria known as *germs*. (Harmful protozoa and viruses are also called germs.) Germ diseases are said to be *contagious* because they can be spread from one organism to another.

5. VIRUSES

All viruses are harmful. They are even tinier than the microscopic protozoa and bacteria. Viruses can be seen only with the aid of special powerful microscopes, such as the electron microscope. Viruses carry on only one life activity—reproduction. They reproduce only when they infect and destroy cells in the bodies of living things. Some diseases caused by viruses are the common cold, measles, mumps, smallpox, chicken pox, influenza, poliomyelitis, and AIDS.

6. HOW CONTAGIOUS DISEASES ARE SPREAD

A contagious disease may be spread in any one of the following ways:

a. Contact. Touching an infected person or some article used by the sick person may spread disease. Ringworm, athlete's foot, and tuberculosis are *transmitted*, or spread, by contact. AIDS is not transmitted by simple contact, but only by close contact with a body fluid of an infected person.

b. Inhaling Germs. As a sick person talks, sneezes, or coughs, that person releases into the air a fine mist containing germs. Upon inhaling these germs, another person may *contract*, or catch, the disease. Some of the common diseases transmitted in this way are the common cold, measles, whooping cough, and chicken pox.

c. Insects and Other Animals

(1) Insects. Certain species of mosquitoes transfer the germs that cause malaria and yellow fever. Flies transfer many germs, chiefly those causing typhoid fever. Fleas carried by rats transfer bubonic plague. Lice living on humans transfer typhus fever.

(2) Other Animals. If a dog infected with hydrophobia (rabies) bites a person, the dog will transmit the virus that causes this disease to the bitten person, who may then contract rabies.

d. Contaminated Food or Drink. Many disease germs are transferred by contaminated foods or beverages. Typhoid fever may be contracted by eating oysters grown in polluted water or by drinking polluted water. Food poisoning and some other intestinal diseases can be spread by contaminated milk.

7. PROTECTING OURSELVES AGAINST DISEASE GERMS

The following common methods are employed to destroy disease germs before they can enter the human body.

a. Sterilization. Utensils and surgical instruments are kept in boiling water or steam for at least 20 minutes, which is sufficient to kill all harmful germs.

b. Pasteurization. Most of the harmful germs in milk are destroyed by heating the milk to a temperature of approximately 145°F for about half an hour and then cooling it rapidly.

c. Cooking. Thorough cooking of pork and pork products kills the parasitic microorganism *trichina*, which may be present in the meat. (Trichina is a microscopic worm, not a protist.) Should the infected meat be eaten, the disease known as *trichinosis* may result.

d. Boiling Water. Since polluted water may carry the germs that cause typhoid fever, water from an unknown source should be boiled before using.

8. HOW THE BODY DEFENDS ITSELF AGAINST GERMS

The human body has many ways of defending itself against invading germs. Some body defenses are:

a. The Skin. The first defense of the body against disease-causing germs is an unbroken skin. A broken area of the skin, such as a cut, may permit germs to enter the body.

b. Lining of the Nose, Throat, and Windpipe. The internal lining of these organs produces a thick, slimy liquid called *mucus*. Many of the germs that enter through the nose and mouth are trapped by the mucus and prevented from passing further into the body. Also, the cells of the lining have millions of tiny hairs that project into the air passages. The hairs sweep foreign particles upward, away from the lungs.

c. White Blood Cells. One type of white blood cell in the body can surround germs and destroy them. Another type produces special chemicals called *antibodies*. Some antibodies directly destroy some invading germs. Other antibodies check or fight off poisons given off by germs.

9. WHAT IS IMMUNITY?

When a person does not contract a particular disease to which he or she has been exposed, the person is said to be *immune* to that disease. Immunity may develop as a result of:

a. Recovering From an Attack of a Disease. For example, a person who recovers from measles will not usually contract measles again.

b. Receiving Injections. For example, people are *vaccinated* to develop an immunity against smallpox. Similarly, people receive injections to build up an immunity to poliomyelitis (polio), diphtheria, tetanus, and other diseases.

Because immunity to certain diseases may not be permanent, "booster shots" are given to maintain immunity.

The disease called AIDS stands for Acquired Immune Deficiency Syndrome. It is caused by a virus that destroys the white blood cells. Thus, these cells can no longer kill germs or produce antibodies. As a result, AIDS victims **lack immunity—they cannot fight off this virus or other germs.**

10. SOME HUMAN DISEASES

Most of the common contagious diseases are caused by bacteria, protozoa, fungi, and viruses. The following tables summarize how these diseases are spread and how they can be prevented.

Table 12-1. Diseases Caused by Bacteria

Disease	*How spread*	*How prevented*
Diphtheria	Contact with infected persons or contaminated articles. Infected milk.	Injections are given to people before they have contracted the disease. Pasteurizing milk.
Scarlet fever	Contact with infected persons, contaminated articles, or people recovering from the disease. Infected milk.	Isolating sick people. Injections to build up immunity.
Tetanus (Lockjaw)	Deep puncture wounds, such as produced by a bullet or by a nail.	Injections to build up immunity. Prompt treatment of deep wounds.

Disease	How spread	How prevented
Tuberculosis	Contact with infected persons or contaminated articles. Infected milk or infected food products.	Isolating sick people. Maintaining body resistance. Periodic chest X-rays or skin tests.
Typhoid fever	Impure water. Contaminated shellfish. Flies carrying the germs. Contact with infected persons (carriers).	Sanitary sewage disposal. Control of water and food supplies. Injections to build up immunity.

Table 12-2. Diseases Caused by Protozoa

African sleeping sickness	The bite of the *tsetse fly*, which carries the protozoan causing the disease.	Fly control. Spraying insecticides.
Malaria	The bite of the female *Anopheles mosquito*, which carries the protozoan causing the disease.	Control of mosquitoes by: draining swamps, spraying swamps with oil, using insecticides, screening windows. Taking anti-malarial drugs such as quinine.

Table 12-3. Diseases Caused by Fungi

Ringworm	Contact with infected persons or using a towel handled by an infected person.	Avoid contact. Use fresh towel. Personal cleanliness.
Athlete's foot	Walking barefoot in public places such as gymnasiums, shower rooms, or swimming pools.	Wear bathing shoes. In public pools, the use of special pans containing chemicals that destroy the fungus. Thorough drying of feet with a clean towel.

Table 12-4. Diseases Caused by Viruses

Disease	How spread	How prevented
AIDS	Blood transfusions from infected donors. Sharing drug needles and syringes with infected persons. Sexual contact with infected persons.	Testing of all blood before transfusions. Say "no" to drugs. Avoid sexual contact.
Common cold	Contact with infected persons. Inhaling discharges from nose or mouth of infected persons.	Stay away from crowds and people with colds. Maintain body resistance.
Poliomyelitis	Contact with infected persons. Inhaling discharges.	Immunization with Salk or Sabin vaccine.
Smallpox	Contact with infected persons. Inhaling discharges.	Smallpox vaccination.

Multiple-Choice Questions

Write the number preceding the correct answer.

1. Microscopic one-celled animallike protists found in water are called (1) algae (2) fungi (3) protozoa (4) insects.
2. The smallest plantlike organisms on the earth are the (1) seed plants (2) mosses (3) ferns (4) bacteria.
3. Rod-shaped bacteria are called (1) cocci (2) spirilla (3) bacilli (4) algae.
4. Butter has its flavor because (1) of the action of certain bacteria (2) the milk from which it was made has been pasteurized (3) the milk has been shaken vigorously (4) the cream was removed first.
5. When camping and obtaining water from a brook, the water can be made safe to drink by (1) pasteurization (2) thorough shaking (3) letting it stand for an hour (4) boiling it for 20 minutes.
6. The general term applied to tiny living things that cause disease in humans is (1) alga (2) fungus (3) germ (4) protozoan.
7. The smallest thing which can cause disease in the human is a (1) protozoan (2) virus (3) flea (4) bacterium.

8. Bubonic plague may be spread by the (1) mosquito (2) flea (3) louse (4) dog.
9. White blood cells, the skin, and antibodies are similar in that they (1) control certain glands (2) give off body wastes (3) protect the body against harmful organisms (4) supply oxygen to the body cells.
10. Many disease germs that enter our body are destroyed by (1) red corpuscles (2) white corpuscles (3) the heart (4) the teeth.
11. If a child does not become infected with a contagious disease after being exposed to it, he is considered to be (1) disinfected (2) immune (3) intoxicated (4) sterilized.
12. A dreaded disease that can be entirely prevented by vaccination is (1) smallpox (2) cancer (3) anemia (4) malaria.
13. The best method of killing some of the dangerous disease germs in milk is (1) homogenization (2) pasteurization (3) refrigeration (4) separation.
14. Raw pork is not safe to eat because it (1) is hard to digest (2) may contain disease-producing worms (3) contains no vitamins (4) contains no carbohydrates.
15. People in flooded areas are warned to boil all drinking water. This is an aid in preventing (1) scarlet fever (2) smallpox (3) typhoid fever (4) yellow fever.
16. A disease that may develop if you puncture your foot by stepping on a nail is (1) scarlet fever (2) lockjaw (3) influenza (4) malaria.
17. A disease that is caused by a protozoan and is carried by a mosquito is (1) yellow fever (2) ringworm (3) tuberculosis (4) malaria.
18. An example of helpful bacteria are those that (1) cause colds (2) return nitrogen to the soil (3) destroy viruses (4) are infectious.
19. A disease that dogs can transmit to people is (1) rabies (2) AIDS (3) poliomyelitis (4) smallpox.
20. The virus that causes AIDS may be spread by (1) unclean food (2) transfusions of infected blood (3) walking barefoot (4) houseflies.

Completion Questions

Write the word or expression that correctly completes the statement.

1. The number of cells in a protozoan is _____.
2. Bacteria are one-celled organisms that _____ (*can, cannot*) make their own food.
3. Ball-shaped bacteria are called _____.
4. Most bacteria are _____ (*harmful, harmless*) to humans.
5. A disease which one person can contract from another person is called a (an) _____ disease.
6. Oysters from polluted water may transmit the disease _____.
7. Athlete's foot may be spread by a method known as _____.
8. The body's first line of defense against germs is an unbroken _____.
9. Chemicals called _____ are made by the body to fight germs.
10. The best method of protecting a person against polio is by _____.

Thought Questions

1. When in a crowded room, we cannot help breathing in some germs, such as the cold virus, that are exhaled by other people. Although a nearby person has a cold and sneezes in our direction, it is possible to escape becoming ill with a cold. Explain how the body protects us in such a case.

2. Explain why saying "No!" to drugs can prevent catching AIDS.

Chapter 13. Keeping Healthy

1. GOOD HEALTH

Good health means more than the absence of disease. *Good health* means having your body and mind in a condition that enables you to carry on your daily tasks efficiently and enjoyably.

Although we often speak of mind and body as though they were separate from each other, the two are really one—you—the whole person. For convenience in studying health, we usually consider mind and body separately. *Mental health* refers to health of the mind, and *physical health* refers to health of the body organs.

2. MENTAL HEALTH

Mental health is the state of mind that enables you to work, study, play, relax, adjust to your environment, and get along with people. In general, your behavior reflects your mental health. In our society there is a wide range in what is considered normal or acceptable behavior. This makes it difficult to define mental health. It is agreed by most people that proper mental health depends on factors such as:

a. Control of the Emotions. Your *emotions* are your feelings. Examples of some familiar emotions are fear, anger, worry, love, and hate. Emotions often make you act unconsciously in some way. How do you act toward your family when you are worried? How well can you study when you are frightened?

For good mental health, we must control our emotions and not let them control us. We can learn this control by constant practice in following the rules for making and breaking habits, as explained on page 102, section 4-b.

b. Having a Pleasant Personality. *Personality* means "you as a person." It includes the ways in which you behave under different conditions. Your personality can be considered pleasant if you

—get along well with yourself and with others.
—try to adjust to conditions around you.
—use your abilities to do worthwhile things.
—show good manners.

c. Relaxation. Relaxation after work or study puts you in a healthy frame of mind. Usually a weary mind is not a healthy mind. Activities that are relaxing include hobbies, sports, reading, radio, TV, and others of your choice.

d. Solving Your Personal Problems. Like most young people, you face similar problems at home, in school, and among friends. Many of these problems arise when you fail to do something, or when you cannot do what you want when you want to do it.

Two things you can do to help solve your personal problems are:

(1) Understanding the nature of the problem and its possible cause.

(2) Consulting your parents or seeking professional help to solve the problem.

Two ways that people unsuccessfully solve their problems are:

(1) Completely ignoring the problem. This is done by putting off action from day to day, feigning (pretending) physical illness so as not to undertake solving the problem, or pretending that there is no problem.

(2) Stubbornly resisting the solution of the problem and not seeking help.

The best way to solve a personal problem is to compromise and reach a reasonable solution. Often, consulting a professional can help.

3. IMPROVING YOUR APPEARANCE

It is normal for people to be concerned about their appearance (the way they look to other people and to themselves). Your appearance is often a clue to your personality. For this reason, employers usually hire well-groomed people.

Proper clothes will greatly enhance your appearance. According to many people, clothes should be selected according to your coloring, body build, and social situation.

a. The Coloring of Your Skin, Hair, and Eyes. The colors of your clothes should complement or harmonize with your coloring.

(1) *For dark hair, dark eyes, and dark skin.* Avoid dark colors. Soft, neutral colors are best for you.

(2) *For light hair, light eyes, and light skin.* Avoid light colors. Rich, deep colors should be your choice.

(3) *For red hair and light eyes.* Soft shades of gray or blue and dark colors are best for you.

b. Your Body Build. In addition to your coloring, you must also consider your body build in choosing the right clothes.

(1) *For thin persons.* Bright-colored clothing will make you appear heavier.

(2) *For heavy persons.* Dark or neutral-colored clothing will help make you appear taller and slimmer.

4. GOOD GROOMING HELPS YOUR APPEARANCE

Well-cared-for hair, teeth, and skin will add distinction to your general appearance.

a. Care of the Hair. Your hair may be kept short or long depending on your taste. The important thing to remember is that clean, well-cared-for hair indicates good general health as well as good personal habits. Hair that has not been brushed or washed recently may contain dirt particles. You should:

(1) Wash your hair and massage your scalp at least once a week.

(2) Brush your hair daily. Brushing cleans your hair and stimulates your scalp.

b. Care of the Teeth. For clean, healthy teeth, brush them after each meal, if possible, or at least twice a day. Visit your dentist at least twice a year.

c. Care of the Skin. For a clear, unblemished skin, wash your face daily with soap and water, using a washcloth. An oily skin may require more frequent washings. Following a rinsing with warm water, use cold water to close the pores (openings) of the skin. Bathe or shower daily.

Thorough, frequent washing of the skin removes dirt that has accumulated on the body. Washing also removes the wastes deposited on the skin by perspiration.

d. For Men Who Shave. Trimming a beard regularly or shaving daily shows that you care about your appearance.

5. SKIN CONDITIONS THAT MAR YOUR APPEARANCE

Some skin conditions that cause complexion problems are *blackheads, pimples,* and *acne.*

a. Blackheads. Found deep in the skin and around the root of each hair is an oil gland. These glands give off an oil that empties on the surface of the skin. Sometimes, when exposed to air, the oil forms a black plug, called a *blackhead,* around the bottom of a hair. This condition can be treated by regularly washing the skin with soap and warm water, rinsing with cold water, and massaging.

b. Pimples. Sometimes bacteria invade the hardened oil in an oil plug, or reach down around the base of a hair. The result may be a bacterial infection of the skin, called a *pimple.* It is marked by a red swelling, usually with a head. The pimple may disappear in a few days, or it may open and discharge pus. *Pus* is an accumulation of dead bacteria and white blood cells.

Never squeeze a pimple. Squeezing may push the bacteria into the tissue surrounding the pimple. This will spread the infection. Daily washing of the skin greatly reduces the possibility of pimples.

c. Acne. This skin condition is common in teenagers. In acne, groups of pimples appear on the face and sometimes on the back of the neck. Although acne usually disappears in time, you can care for the condition in the following ways:

(1) Wash the affected area frequently and thoroughly with soap and warm water, followed by cold-water rinses. At least twice a week, shampoo your hair to remove excess scalp oils. This is especially necessary if the hairstyle calls for hair touching the face or neck.

(2) Don't try to clear the condition by squeezing the pus out of an infected pimple. In addition to the possibility of spreading the infection, permanent scars may result.

(3) Avoid sweets and fatty foods if they seem to make the acne worse.

(4) Get plenty of rest and fresh air.

(5) If the condition is severe, consult your physician.

6. POSTURE

Good posture improves your appearance as well as your health. For proper posture, hold your head high, spine erect, shoulders back, chest out, abdomen in, and toes straight. Properly fitted shoes are also necessary for good posture.

Good posture enables the internal organs to perform their work efficiently. For example, when you slouch, your lungs become cramped and cannot take in as much air as they are capable of holding.

7. PREVENTING MENTAL ILLNESS

Mental illness is difficult to define and equally hard to recognize in an indvidual. A person who is sick, but has no sign of physical illness, may be mentally ill. That is, something troubling the individual makes him or her unable to carry on the usual daily activities. Mental illness may be avoided by:

— establishing good habits such as patience, industriousness, and regard for the rights of others.

— controlling your emotions.

— recognizing your abilities and developing them.

— not letting failure and mistakes discourage you.

— seeking help when you cannot solve your personal problems by yourself.

— learning how to use your leisure time.

— developing a sense of humor.

Newer techniques in medicine and in psychiatry make many mental illnesses subject to treatment and cure, just as physical illnesses are.

8. PHYSICAL HEALTH

Mental and physical health are closely related. It is often difficult to distinguish mental illness from physical illness because one affects the other. An example of a physical defect that affects the mind is the secretion of too little thyroxin by the thyroid gland. This condition can result in mental sluggishness and mental retardation. An example of a mental, or emotional, upset that affects the physical condition is continuing fear. In such cases, as we have noted before, the adrenal glands secrete extra adrenaline. This condition often leads to indigestion and exhaustion. It is a good health practice to seek professional help when poor health persists.

9. VISIT YOUR DOCTOR—TO BE SURE

You should visit your doctor not only when you feel ill, but also regularly for a checkup—about once a year. A thorough physical examination will give you peace of mind if your physical condition proves sound. On the other hand, if you have a defect or disease, immediate attention will increase your chances of recovery and speed up your return to good health.

10. THE MEDICAL EXAMINATION

A periodic checkup includes an examination of the following:

a. Heart. With a stethoscope, the doctor can hear the sounds of the heart in action. The sounds tell whether the heart is functioning properly. The number of heartbeats per minute are also an indication of proper functioning. By using a special cuff around the upper arm together with the stethoscope, the doctor can also measure blood pressure. Blood pressure is a very important indication of good health.

b. Lungs. Using a stethoscope, the doctor will listen to the lungs in action. What the doctor hears indicates whether a lung condition requiring attention is present.

c. Height and Weight. The doctor will also check your weight and height, and will suggest a diet if you are overweight or underweight.

d. Eyes, Ears, Nose, and Throat. These vital areas of your body will be thoroughly examined. Minor defects or infections will be corrected early, before becoming serious.

e. Abdominal Organs. Your doctor will also feel your abdomen to see if any organs are enlarged or abnormal in other respects.

f. Skin. Your skin will also be observed by the doctor. He or she will seek the cause of, and give treatment for, many common skin ailments.

g. Blood and Urine. By testing your blood and urine, the doctor can detect certain conditions early and help you remedy them. Among such conditions are anemia and diabetes.

Today, physicians use highly specialized equipment such as 3-dimensional X-rays, called CAT scan, to detect conditions that previously escaped detection. These advances of modern medicine go a long way toward insuring good health.

11. THE DENTAL EXAMINATION

Diseased teeth may affect your health and your appearance. Visit your dentist regularly and follow his or her suggestions for the cleaning and care of your teeth. You will thus reduce the chance of tooth decay and the formation of cavities.

12. SOME RULES FOR GOOD HEALTH

a. Eat a balanced diet, which includes the proper amount of all the nutrients, as explained on page 80, sections 5, 6.

b. Get plenty of rest and sleep.

c. Get plenty of fresh air and sunshine.

d. Get plenty of exercise.

e. Keep your body clean by taking a shower or bath daily.

f. Brush your teeth after each meal, but most thoroughly before going to bed.

g. See your doctor and dentist regularly.

13. WHAT IS FIRST AID?

During everyone's lifetime, accidents occur that demand prompt attention. At such times it is not always possible to obtain a doctor immediately. *First aid* is the prompt and temporary attention given a person until a doctor arrives at the scene. Very often proper first aid prevents permanent injury, or even saves a person's life. Another important reason for studying first aid is that, as one learns the causes of accidents, he or she is likely to become more careful and thus prevent accidents.

14. SOME BASIC RULES OF FIRST AID

 a. Until you have determined how serious the injury is, keep the person lying down.

 b. If the person appears to be seriously injured, call a doctor or hospital immediately.

 c. Conditions requiring immediate attention are excessive bleeding, stopping of breathing, internal poisoning.

 d. Do not move a seriously injured person unless absolutely necessary.

 e. Keep the person warm.

 f. Do not give any liquids to an unconscious person.

 g. Make the person as cheerful and comfortable as possible.

 h. Do not allow a crowd to gather around the person.

15. SOME COMMON EMERGENCIES

 a. Fainting. Conditions such as hunger, tiredness, and fear may cause a person to faint. When the brain does not receive a sufficient amount of blood, the face becomes very pale. Treatment involves placing the person on his or her back with the head lower than the rest of the body. Keep the person warm. If a place for lying down is not available, have the person place the head between his or her legs and take deep breaths. If the person does not recover right away, call a doctor or hospital.

 b. Excessive Bleeding. The spurting of blood from a wound indicates that an artery has been cut. To stop the bleeding, apply pressure between the wound and the heart. If a sterile pad is available, cover the wound with it and press firmly. If a sterile pad is not available, use a clean handkerchief. Keep up the firm pressure until medical help arrives. If bleeding persists, a tourniquet should be applied to that limb. (A *tourniquet* is a bandage twisted tight by a stick.) *Tourniquets may be harmful if applied for too long a time. They should be used only in situations which threaten the life of the victim.*

 c. Cuts or Lacerations. The main danger accompanying cuts or lacerations is infection. If the cut is large or deep, cover it with a sterile dressing until help arrives. Minor cuts and scratches may be washed with soap and water and then covered with a sterile bandage. A tourniquet should *never* be used to stop minor bleeding from a limb.

d. Bone Fractures. A fracture is a break in a bone. There are two main types of fractures. In a *simple fracture*, a broken bone has not pierced the skin. In a *compound fracture*, the broken bone has pierced the skin (Fig. 13-1).

A compound fracture is serious not only because of the broken bone itself, but also because the break in the skin provides a region where germs may enter the body and cause infection. A simple fracture must be handled carefully to prevent the broken bone from piercing the skin and thus causing a compound fracture.

First-aid treatment of fractures is difficult. Wait for the doctor. The most you can do is keep the affected part motionless. If the fracture is compound, cover the wound with a sterile dressing.

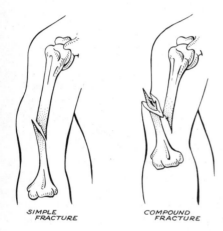

SIMPLE
FRACTURE

COMPOUND
FRACTURE

Fig. 13-1. Types of fractures

e. Burns. Burns may be serious. While the damaged tissues are slowly healing, the danger of infection is ever-present. A burn may be classified as a first-, second-, or third-degree burn.

In a *first-degree* burn, the skin is red, but not broken. Treat a burn with applications of cold water until the pain stops.

In a *second-degree* burn, blisters develop in the burned area. Do not break open the blisters. Cover them with a sterile dressing and send the victim for medical treatment.

In a *third-degree* burn, both the skin and tissue beneath have been burned. This is the most serious type. The possibility of infection is great. Cover the burned area with a thick, dry sterile dressing and seek medical attention immediately.

f. Asphyxiation. Asphyxiation is the stopping of breathing, as when suffocating or drowning. Normal breathing may be restored if *artificial respiration* is started immediately. Many people are saved from drowning and from smoke or gas poisoning by artificial respiration. (Read "First Aid for Choking" on next page.)

The *mouth-to-mouth* method of artificial respiration includes the following steps.

(1) Place the victim on his or her back. Remove any obstructions from the mouth and nose, and be sure that the tongue is flat.

(2) Keeping the victim's mouth open, grasp the victim's head with both hands in such a way as to pull the chin forward, and the back of the head downward.

(3) As you place your mouth over that of the victim, close the victim's nostrils with a thumb and forefinger.

(4) Exhale through your mouth as you blow into the victim's mouth.

(5) Stop, take a breath, and repeat, maintaining a rhythm of about 12 breaths per minute. Keep on until the victim breathes regularly or a doctor tells you to stop.

Note: If the victim is a small child, the first-aider's mouth should cover the nose and mouth of the child. Do not pinch the child's nostrils. The rhythm should be faster with less force.

FIRST AID FOR CHOKING

A person choking on an object, such as food, may be in serious danger. First aid for such a victim requires a special procedure called the *Heimlich Maneuver*. (See Fig. 13-2 on next page.) To carry out this procedure—

If the victim is standing or sitting:

1. Get behind the victim and wrap your arms around his or her waist, as in *A*.
2. Grab one of your fists with your other hand. Place the fist in the soft area just below the victim's chest, slightly above the waist and below the ribs, as in *B*.
3. Press your fist into this soft region with a *strong*, *quick*, *upward* thrust. Repeat a few times, if necessary.

If the victim is lying down:

1. Place the victim on his or her back.
2. Face and straddle the victim and place a knee on either side of his or her hips, as in *C*.
3. Place the heel of one of your hands on the victim's soft area just below the chest, slightly above the waist and below the ribs. Place your other hand over the fist.
4. Press into this soft region with a *strong*, *quick*, *upward* thrust. Repeat a few times, if necessary.

If the victim stops breathing after the air passage is clear, give artificial respiration.

If you are the victim and all alone:

Press into your abdomen yourself, in the area just below your ribs and slightly above your waist, *or:* Roll your abdomen against the edge of a sink or table.

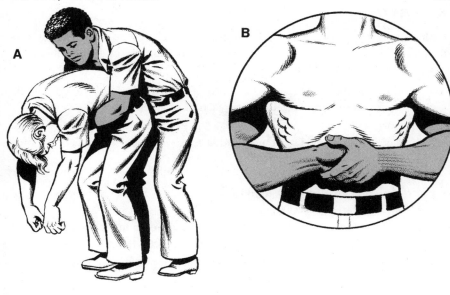

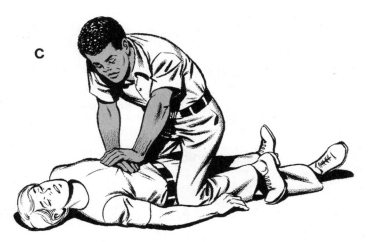

Fig. 13-2. The Heimlich Maneuver

16. SAFETY

More injuries occur at home than result from automobile accidents. Make your home a safe place to live in. Observe these simple precautions and you will remove the causes of countless accidents each year.

    a. Bottles of poisons should be stored in medicine cabinets. They should be clearly labeled and placed out of reach of small children.

    b. Stairways should be well lighted.

    c. Electrical appliances, switches, and wires should not be handled with wet hands, especially while bathing.

    d. Rugs should be put down so that they cannot skid.

    e. Toys and other objects should not be kept on floors or stairways where someone can trip over them.

    f. An automobile engine should not be kept running in a closed garage.

    g. Matches should be kept out of reach of small children.

    h. Oil-soaked rags should be stored in metal containers.

Some of the precautions you should observe on streets and highways are:

    a. Obey all traffic regulations.

    b. Cross only at designated areas.

    c. Look in both directions before crossing a street.

    d. Don't play in roadways.

    e. Where there are no sidewalks, walk on the left side of the road so that you can see the approaching traffic.

    f. When you ride a bicycle, follow the same traffic rules a motorist follows.

Multiple-Choice Questions

Write the number preceding the correct answer.

1. In listening to a person's heartbeat, a doctor uses a (1) microscope (2) periscope (3) stethoscope (4) telescope.
2. By taking the pulse rate, a doctor determines (1) the size of the arteries (2) the heartbeat (3) the condition of the blood (4) the functioning of the heart valves.
3. Many boards of health offer free skin tests in order to detect the presence of (1) cancer (2) heart disease (3) pneumonia (4) tuberculosis.

4. The best way to find out if a certain medicine will be of benefit to you is to (1) read the label on the container of the medicine (2) consult a doctor (3) read medical books (4) ask the advice of people who have tried the medicine.

5. It is wise to visit a dentist (1) only when you have a toothache (2) only when you detect a cavity (3) twice a year (4) only when your teeth need cleaning.

6. One basic rule of first aid is to (1) give an unconscious victim a drink (2) try to make an injured person sit up (3) describe the injury to the patient (4) never move a seriously injured person unless absolutely necessary.

7. If a person's face is white and he or she appears to be fainting, he or she should (1) be made to sit or lie down with the head lower than the rest of the body (2) be made to sit or lie down with the head higher than the rest of the body (3) have cold water thrown in his or her face (4) be made to walk rapidly until recovery.

8. When a person faints, he or she should be (1) given an alcoholic beverage (2) kept warm (3) shaken into consciousness (4) given artificial respiration.

9. When a bone is broken, the injury is called a (1) sprain (2) ligament (3) fracture (4) dislocation.

10. If a broken bone does not pierce the skin, the injury is called a (1) compound fracture (2) pulled tendon (3) simple fracture (4) dislocated vertebra.

11. A first-aid treatment for minor burns is to bandage the burn lightly and keep the bandage moist with (1) ammonia (2) cool water (3) iodine (4) vinegar.

12. A burn in which blisters develop is called a (1) singe (2) first-degree burn (3) second-degree burn (4) third-degree burn.

13. Artificial respiration is employed in cases of (1) drowning (2) lacerations (3) indigestion (4) burns.

14. The reason for covering deep cuts with a sterile dressing is to (1) prevent infection (2) keep the wound warm (3) make a tourniquet (4) make the victim feel better.

15. If blood flows out of a cut in spurts, it indicates the cutting of (1) a nerve (2) a capillary (3) a vein (4) an artery.

16. According to the National Safety Council, most accidents to people occur (1) in factories (2) in the home (3) on the streets and highways (4) while hunting and fishing.

17. All bottles in the medicine cabinet should be (1) clearly labeled (2) brown in color (3) shaken well before being used (4) washed after being used.

18. A thin child will appear stouter if he wears (1) bright colors (2) dark colors (3) neutral colors (4) vertical stripes.

19. For healthy hair it is recommended that, in addition to frequent washings, the hair be (1) cut weekly (2) given a permanent (3) brushed daily (4) shampooed daily.

20. Minute openings in the skin are known as (1) cells (2) pores (3) hairs (4) scales.

21. The clogging of some of the openings in the skin may result in (1) pores (2) pimples (3) a good complexion (4) dandruff.

22. Mental health refers to (1) high intelligence (2) a brain free of bacteria (3) a healthy mind (4) a healthy mind and a healthy body.
23. An example of an emotion is (1) hunger (2) thirst (3) joy (4) a hearty appetite.
24. Eating when angry (1) interferes with digestion (2) promotes digestion (3) releases the emotions (4) is good when you are on a special diet.

Completion Questions

Write the word or expression that correctly completes the statement.

1. In addition to listening to a person's heart with a stethoscope, a doctor can also listen to the action of the _____ with the same instrument.
2. If you are overweight, a doctor may put you on a (an) _____.
3. Acne is a common disease of the _____.
4. One way to keep your teeth healthy is to visit your _____ regularly.
5. Treatment rendered to a victim of an accident before a doctor arrives is called _____.
6. A principle of first aid is never to give _____ to an unconscious person.
7. An inadequate supply of blood to the brain may cause a person to _____.
8. Careless handling of a simple bone fracture may cause it to become a (an) _____ fracture.
9. A victim has a _____ degree burn when the skin and flesh have been destroyed.
10. Normal breathing may be restored in an asphyxiated person by applying _____.

Thought Questions

Give a reason for each of the following.

1. Describe how to carry out the Heimlich Maneuver for a standing person who is choking on a piece of meat.
2. Everyone should study first aid.
3. Treatment of fainting is begun by lowering the patient's head between his or her knees.
4. A basic rule of first aid is to keep the patient warm.
5. Compound fractures are usually more serious than simple fractures.
6. Third-degree burns are more serious than first-degree burns.
7. It is good to be in the company of friendly, happy people during meals.
8. An automobile engine should not be kept running in a closed garage.
9. Oil-soaked rags should be stored in metal containers.
10. People whose behavior is not normal may be mentally ill.

Chapter 14. Tobacco and Drugs

1. ADDICTIVE SUBSTANCES

Excessive use of *tobacco* and *alcohol* may impair one's health. The repeated use of these substances, as well as *narcotics* and other drugs, without the advice of a physician, usually leads to a craving for them. That is, they become habit-forming, or *addictive*. Teenagers, whose bodies are still developing, are particularly susceptible to the habit-forming and injurious qualities of these substances. Because narcotic drugs are so harmful, laws have been passed imposing severe penalties for the possession and sale of these drugs.

2. TOBACCO

Obtained from the leaf of the tobacco plant, tobacco contains a powerful poison, *nicotine*. In addition to nicotine, the smoke of burning tobacco contains tars, acids, and other irritating substances. Smoke, when inhaled, may:

a. irritate the lining of the nose, throat, and lungs.
b. affect the heart by increasing the rate of the heartbeat.
c. affect the blood vessels by causing them to become narrower (constricted).
d. raise the blood pressure.
e. interfere with digestion.

Nonsmokers inhaling the smoke produced by smokers may be subject to the same harmful effects.

Considerable research has been done indicating: (*a*) There is a link between excessive cigarette smoking and lung diseases such as emphysema and cancer. (*b*) Excessive cigarette smoking will shorten the lives of people having diseases of the circulatory system.

To protect the public's health, Congress passed laws prohibiting cigarette advertising on radio and television, and requiring that cigarette packages bear some message regarding the harm that smoking can do. One example is:

SURGEON GENERAL'S WARNING

Quitting Smoking Now Greatly Reduces
Serious Risks to Your Health.

---

3. ALCOHOL

All alcoholic beverages contain ethyl alcohol. When applied to the skin, ethyl alcohol is valuable as an antiseptic. Inside the body, however, it may be harmful. Since alcohol does not have to be digested, after being swallowed, it is absorbed into the bloodstream within a few minutes. Upon reaching the brain, alcohol acts on the nervous system, decreasing the control of the brain over the rest of the body. *Lesson 12th Answer #12*

For a short time after it has been swallowed, alcohol seems to act as a *stimulant*; that is, it seems to speed up body functions. After a while, though, it acts as a *depressant*; that is, it decreases the rate of activity of body functions. Excessive use of alcohol may have many harmful effects. Use of lesser amounts of alcohol and certain other drugs at the same time can likewise be very serious.

a. Effects on the Body. Alcohol irritates the lining of the stomach and intestine. It may cause cancer in these organs. Heavy drinkers may develop a disease of the liver in which the liver hardens and shrinks. Since alcoholics consume very little food, they usually suffer from malnutrition.

b. Effects on Behavior. Because excessive alcohol is a depressant, it affects behavior. The heavy drinker may become sluggish, see poorly, and lose body balance. His or her muscular coordination may also be impaired. For this reason, persons driving an automobile under the influence of alcohol are a menace to pedestrians and other motorists, as well as to themselves.

Driving under the influence of alcohol, called *DUI* (driving under the influence) or *DWI* (driving while intoxicated) is illegal and may result in fines or suspension of the driver's license.

Once a person becomes so given over to the use of alcoholic beverages, he or she depends on it and craves it. The addict may, depending on the amount used, become afflicted with the disease called *alcoholism*. The treatment of alcoholic addicts is long, difficult, and without any assurance of recovery. In some cases, cutting off the supply of alcohol to an addict causes a painful, violent nervous reaction of the body that can cause death.

4. NARCOTIC DRUGS

Narcotic drugs are chemicals that act on the nervous system and temporarily affect the activities of the body. Although some of these drugs have great value medicinally and are used to relieve pain, they should not be used, except when prescribed by a physician. All narcotics are habit-forming and dangerous, and therefore cannot be obtained legally except by order of a physician.

Narcotics addiction often leads to early death. As with addiction to alcohol, addiction to narcotic drugs is difficult to overcome. Even a temporary lack of a drug causes an addict to have very painful, uncontrollable cravings, and violent body reactions. Overdose of narcotic drugs is often fatal. The withdrawal of a drug (called "cold turkey") causes the addict to suffer acutely.

Newborn babies whose mothers are addicted to narcotics may be born addicted too.

Some narcotic drugs are:

a. Opium. This drug is obtained from the sap of the unripe fruits of the Oriental poppy. Although not employed much in the United States, it is still used in some Oriental countries, where it may be eaten or smoked. When smoked, it causes the person to go into a deep, dreamy stupor and sometimes unconsciousness.

b. Morphine. Derived from opium, morphine is used by doctors to relieve pain. Addicts may take morphine by mouth or by injection.

c. Heroin. Also obtained from opium, heroin is the most habit-forming of all the drugs. Its use in any form is outlawed in the United States. Users take it either by mouth, sniffing, or injection.

d. Methadone. This is a synthetic (manufactured) drug similar to heroin. Methadone, itself an addicting drug, appears to be helpful in treating heroin addicts who place themselves under medical care.

5. OTHER DRUGS

a. Barbiturates. These are sometimes prescribed by physicians to help people relax and sleep. Barbiturates are synthetic drugs. In large doses, barbiturates, called "downers," depress the brain. An overdose may cause death by affecting the breathing center of the brain. Like narcotics, the repeated use of barbiturates leads to addiction. Withdrawal symptoms for the user of barbiturates, however, are very serious, often causing convulsions and sometimes death.

b. Amphetamines. These drugs (called "pep pills," "uppers," or "speed") temporarily stimulate the body and enable a person to remain awake. They depress appetite and cause high blood pressure as well as a state of physical and mental excitement. When the drug wears off, its user often becomes severely depressed.

c. LSD. This drug, *lysergic acid diethylamide*, commonly called "acid," causes hallucinations. A person who takes LSD sees things that do not exist. This can occur even months after taking a dose of the drug. Some hallucinations brought on by LSD can be so frightening that users have been known to commit suicide.

BEWARE! A CONTAMINATED NEEDLE IS A DEADLY PIECE OF STEEL!

People who inject themselves with any drug, even for the first time, run a double risk—that of addiction to the drug and of contracting AIDS which, to date, is an incurable and fatal disease. The reason for the risk is simple to understand.

Addicts often pass used, unsterilized hypodermic needles from one addict to another. Should the needle be contaminated with the AIDS virus (Table 12-4, page 114), the needle can transmit the disease to everyone who uses that needle.

How can the risks be avoided?

SAY NO TO DRUGS.

---

d. Cocaine. Known as "coke" or "snow," this drug is obtained from the leaves of the coca bush. Physicians and dentists employ cocaine and related substances, such as novocain, as local anesthetics, which temporarily render a small area of the body insensitive to pain. Cocaine addicts may take the drug by mouth, sniffing, or injection.

"Crack," another form of cocaine, is smoked. It is stronger and more addictive than ordinary coke.

e. Marijuana. Marijuana is obtained from the flowers and leaves of the Indian hemp plant. Marijuana, also called "grass," is usually rolled and used in the form of crude cigarettes, called "reefers" or "joints." Smokers of marijuana obtain a feeling of exhilaration, but may lose their sense of reality and self-control. Hashish ("hash"), much stronger than "grass," is obtained from the sap of the hemp plant.

f. PCP. This drug, *phencyclidine*, is commonly called "angel dust" or "peace." It is taken either by mouth, sniffing, or injection. It can cause hallucination, loss of memory, and possibly, insanity.

Multiple-Choice Questions

Write the number preceding the correct answer.

1. The harmful substance found in tobacco is (1) smoke (2) nicotine (3) opium (4) marijuana.
2. A substance that speeds up certain body activities is known as (1) a depressant (2) an enzyme (3) a stimulant (4) a narcotic.
3. An organ that is likely to become diseased as the result of continued heavy drinking of alcoholic beverages is the (1) stomach (2) small intestine (3) heart (4) liver.
4. Heavy drinking is a major cause of traffic accidents because alcohol (1) is a stimulant (2) speeds up reaction time (3) makes an individual think better (4) decreases muscle coordination.
5. Drugs which slow the activity of the nervous system are called (1) stimulants (2) amphetamines (3) enzymes (4) depressants.
6. The most habit-forming drug obtained from opium is (1) heroin (2) morphine (3) marijuana (4) cocaine.
7. The narcotic "crack" is more dangerous than ordinary cocaine because the habit of smoking crack is harder to overcome than (1) smoking opium (2) sniffing "coke" (3) giving up tobacco (4) all of the preceding.

Completion Questions

Write the word or expression that correctly completes the statement.

1. Excessive smoking causes _____ (*an increase, a decrease*) in the rate of digestion.
2. The chemical substance found in all alcoholic beverages is _____.
3. Substances which decrease the rate at which certain body activities are performed are known as _____.
4. Narcotic drugs should be prescribed only by a (an) _____.
5. The drug _____ is obtained from the Oriental poppy.
6. _____ is used by doctors and dentists as a local anesthetic.
7. PCP, which can cause memory loss and even insanity, is another name for _____.

Matching Questions

Match the items in column A with those in column B.

Column A	*Column B*
1. reefers	*a.* tobacco
2. local anesthetic	*b.* drug related to cocaine
3. nicotine	*c.* marijuana
4. related to opium	*d.* lung cancer
5. excessive cigarette smoking	*e.* morphine
6. used in treating heroin addicts	*f.* methadone
7. causes hallucinations	*g.* painful withdrawal
8. leads to mental excitement which can be harmful	symptoms
9. a nonnarcotic that can stop your breathing	*h.* amphetamine
10. "cold turkey"	*i.* LSD
	j. barbiturate

Thought Question

Why is there a double risk when a person borrows a hypodermic needle to inject himself or herself with a drug?

REVIEW OF UNIT II

1. Give the function of the following cell structures: *(a)* nucleus, *(b)* cell membrane, *(c)* cytoplasm.
2. What is the relationship among tissues, cells, systems, and organs?
3. How does the shoulder joint differ in function from that of the knee joint?
4. Explain how tendons differ from ligaments.
5. Give the function of the following parts of the brain: *(a)* cerebrum, *(b)* cerebellum, *(c)* medulla.
6. *a.* What is a hormone?
   b. What is the function of thyroxin?
   c. What is the function of insulin?
7. Below are some false statements. Explain why each is false.
   a. Candy is a perfect food.
   b. Cigarettes are harmless.
   c. When used for testing foods, iodine turns proteins blue-black.
   d. Lean meat is a good source of carbohydrates.
   e. A carrot is rich in protein.
   f. Cod-liver oil is a good source of vitamin C.
   g. A food rich in carbohydrates is chicken.
8. Give one reason why you should:
   a. Wash your hands before eating.
   b. Keep flies away from food.
   c. Cover your mouth when sneezing.
   d. Have your dog inoculated against rabies.
9. Tell what happens in each of the following tests.
   a. Nitric acid is added to a test tube in which there is a piece of egg white. Heat is gently applied and then ammonium hydroxide is applied.
   b. A piece of apple placed in a test tube is covered with Fehling's (Benedict's) solution and heated.
   c. A drop of iodine is placed on a piece of bread and another drop on a piece of cheese.
10. Explain the meaning of each of the terms listed below.
    a. blood plasma   *d.* enzyme   *g.* digestion
    b. white corpuscle   *e.* gastric juice   *h.* absorption
    c. enamel   *f.* villus   *i.* ventricle
11. Explain why each of the following statements is false.
    a. A function of white corpuscles is to carry oxygen to the cells of the body.
    b. Oxygen is absorbed into the blood in the heart.
    c. Blood vessels that carry blood from the heart are known as veins.
    d. When food leaves the human stomach, it passes into the pancreas.
    e. Digestion of starch begins in the stomach.
    f. The skin is the only organ of excretion.

12. Listed below are the health and training rules set up by the coach for all members of the track team. Explain why each rule is important.
    a. Do not smoke.
    b. Do not drink alcoholic beverages.
    c. Get at least 8 hours of sleep daily.
    d. Eat a well-balanced diet.
    e. Report for every practice period.
    f. Take a shower after every practice period.
13. Tell what safety measures should be taken in each of the following situations.
    a. You are walking along a highway on which automobiles are speeding.
    b. The cellar steps are dark and there is no way to increase the light.
    c. Matches must be kept in a room where your young brothers and sisters play.
    d. There is a steep stairway leading from the porch on which your baby brother is to play.
    e. You have fallen and skinned your knee.
    f. You have just stepped on a rusty nail.
    g. Your route to school must cross a busy street where there is a stop light.
14. Describe a first-aid treatment you would use in the following situations.
    a. In opening a cardboard box with a sharp knife, a man cut his arm, causing the blood to flow in spurts.
    b. At the scene of an accident, a bystander slumped to the ground. He lost consciousness and his face turned pale.
    c. A victim is suspected of having a simple fracture.
    d. In a closed garage, a man is found slumped in his seat while the engine of his car is running.
    e. You touched a hot stove, causing your skin to become red but not broken.
15. A large number of serious automobile accidents are caused by drunken drivers. This is because alcohol affects the human body in several ways that make driving dangerous. Give two ways alcohol affects the body and tell why these effects are dangerous to drivers.
16. Tell why each of the following drugs is dangerous: *(a)* heroin, *(b)* LSD, *(c)* morphine, *(d)* "speed."
17. *a.* Give two examples of contagious diseases.
    b. Describe two ways in which contagious diseases may spread from one person to another.
    c. Give two methods used to prevent the spread of contagious diseases.
18. The skin helps prevent disease germs from entering the body.
    a. Give the conditions under which the germs of each of the following get through the skin: (1) hydrophobia (rabies), (2) lockjaw, (3) malaria, (4) yellow fever, (5) sleeping sickness.
    b. What should you do if you were to step on a rusty nail?

19. Explain the following health rules.
    a. People with colds should not go to school, to the movies, or to other public places.
    b. All milk should be pasteurized.
    c. Unsafe drinking water can be made safe to drink by boiling it.
    d. Pork should not be eaten raw.
    e. Flies should be kept out of our homes.
    f. All people should receive the Salk vaccine.
20. Give a reason for each of the following.
    a. A soiled handkerchief should not be used as a dressing on a cut.
    b. It may be dangerous to drink clear, cold water from a brook.
    c. Cuts in the skin should be treated immediately.
    d. Everyone should be vaccinated before going to camp.
    e. A boy vaccinated for smallpox may still contract scarlet fever.
    f. White blood cells are important in fighting disease.

Unit III.
The Survival of Living Things

Chapter 15. Life of a Green Plant

1. GREEN PLANTS

You will recall that animals depend on plants, protists, or other animals for food. Plants and protists that contain chlorophyll, the green chemical present in certain of their cells, can manufacture their own food. In some organisms, the green color of chlorophyll is masked by some other color. Such masking occurs in the maple variety called "*Crimson* King" and the protists known as *red* algae. Some organisms, such as the mold that produces penicillin, are also green. However, since their green coloring is not that of chlorophyll, they cannot manufacture their own food. They must obtain food in some other way.

In this chapter, we will concentrate only on green plants and how they live.

2. THE PARTS OF A GREEN PLANT

All the green plants with which you are familiar have *roots*, *stems*, and *leaves*. These are special structures that enable the plants to obtain the raw materials they need for food-making.

3. THE ROOT

The root grows deep into the soil and branches outward in all directions. The root has the following functions:

a. Roots anchor the plant in the soil.

b. In many plants, roots store the food that has been manufactured in the leaves but is not immediately needed.

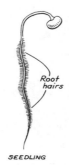

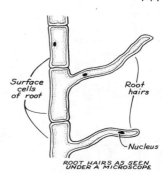

Fig. 15-1. Root hairs on a seedling. The many fine root hairs provide a large surface in the soil through which a plant can absorb soil water containing dissolved minerals.

c. Through their *root hairs*, roots absorb large quantities of soil water containing dissolved minerals. The water and minerals are essential to the plant for growth and food-making. The root hairs are tubular, hairlike structures that grow out of surface cells of the root (Fig. 15-1). Each of the surface cells passes water inward to other cells that, in turn, pass the water to special conducting tubes located near the center of the root. These tubes pass water upward to similar tubes in the stem with which they connect.

4. THE STEM

The stem usually grows upward and is usually above the soil. The stem has the following functions:

a. The stem holds the plant erect, thus allowing the leaves to obtain the maximum amount of sunlight.

b. The stem contains specialized cells that develop into two separate sets of tubes. Water and minerals essential to food-making are conducted upward to the leaves through one set of tubes. Through the other, the foods made in the leaves are carried downward either to supply the needs of all the cells of the plant or to be stored elsewhere.

5. THE LEAF

Food-making goes on in any green part of a plant (stem or leaf) that is exposed to light. However, practically all the food-making in a plant occurs in the leaf (Fig. 15-2 on next page). The upper side of the leaf, called the *upper epidermis*, consists of a single layer of cells. The lower side, called the *lower epidermis*, likewise consists of a single layer. These epidermal layers protect the inner layers of cells that contain chlorophyll.

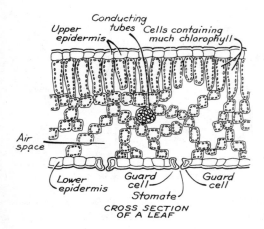

Fig. 15-2. Portion of a leaf, as seen under a microscope.

Found in the lower epidermis are minute openings called *stomates*. Each stomate is surrounded by two cells, called *guard cells*. Each pair of guard cells regulates the size of a stomate. In the light, guard cells enlarge the stomate; in the dark, or when water is scarce, they partly close it.

In the light, carbon dioxide passes through a stomate into air spaces in the leaf while oxygen passes out. In darkness, the opposite occurs. Water may pass out of a stomate at any time.

Directly beneath the upper epidermis are cells that contain a large amount of chlorophyll. These cells carry on the food-making process.

6. USING LIGHT ENERGY TO MAKE FOOD

The life of a green plant depends on either sunlight or artificial light. If a green plant is kept in a dark closet for a period of time, the leaves lose their color, wither, and soon die. This is because green plants require the energy of sunlight to make their food. In this process, a plant converts the energy of the sun into chemical energy, and stores the energy in the form of manufactured food. Food that is not immediately needed for the plant's life activities is stored in some part of the plant. It is this stored food that is the basic source of food for most other organisms. At the same time that they make food, the plants remove carbon dioxide from the air and release oxygen to it. Consequently, all other organisms are truly dependent upon green plants. As we see from the above, without the energy of sunlight, all life would soon disappear from the earth.

7. PHOTOSYNTHESIS—HOW GREEN PLANTS MAKE FOOD

The process by which green plants make food is called *photosynthesis*. This is a complex chemical process that occurs in the leaves and other green parts of plants, as described in the following Table.

Photosynthesis

Raw materials required	1. *Carbon dioxide*—obtained from the air entering the leaves through the stomates. 2. *Water*—absorbed from the soil through the root hairs.
Role of chlorophyll	Chlorophyll—green-colored material present mainly in the leaves; chlorophyll has the ability to bring about the food-making process. Chlorophyll uses light energy to chemically combine carbon dioxide with water and form simple sugars such as glucose. Oxygen is given off as a waste product.
Source of energy	The energy of light is necessary for the reaction to take place. Thus, photosynthesis occurs only during the daytime or whenever a plant receives light.
The chemistry of the process	carbon dioxide + water → sugars + oxygen

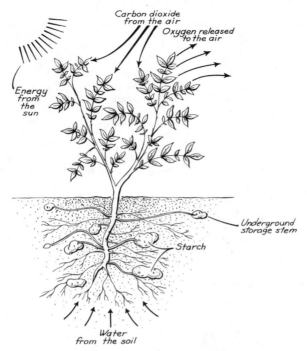

Fig. 15-3. A green plant stores the sun's energy. By carrying on photosynthesis, green plants store energy in the foods they make. The potato plant stores the food underground in the form of starch.

For its own life activities, the plant uses some of the sugar it has made. Excess sugar is changed by the plant into starch, which is stored in the roots or stem until needed (Fig. 15-3).

As a result of photosynthesis, a green plant manufactures sugars and starch, both of which are carbohydrates. After making these carbohydrates, the plant changes some of them into fats. It combines other carbohydrates with the minerals it has taken in from the soil and produces proteins and vitamins.

8. EXPERIMENTS TO SHOW CONDITIONS NECESSARY FOR PHOTOSYNTHESIS

a. The Need for Sunlight. To show that sunlight is necessary for photosynthesis, we use a geranium plant. Part of a leaf is covered on both top and bottom surfaces with pieces of cork pinned to the leaf (Fig. 15-4a). The cork keeps the sunlight from reaching the covered areas. The plant is kept in strong sunlight or artificial light for a day. After removing the cork, the leaf is then removed from the plant and tested for the presence of starch in the covered and uncovered portions.

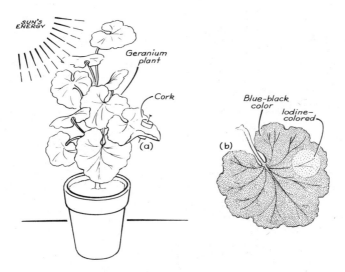

Fig. 15-4. Showing that plants need sunlight for photosynthesis.

The test for starch proceeds as follows: the chlorophyll is removed from the leaf. This is done by boiling the leaf first in water and then in alcohol (careful!) until the leaf becomes colorless. The leaf is then placed in a dish and completely covered with an iodine solution. The uncovered part of the leaf turns blue-black in color, indicating the presence of starch. The part of the leaf that was covered by the cork remains iodine-colored, indicating the absence of starch (Fig. 15-4b). The absence of starch in the covered area shows that photosynthesis takes place only in the presence of sunlight.

b. The Need for Chlorophyll. To show that chlorophyll is necessary for photosynthesis, we use a silver-leaf geranium plant whose leaves are partly white and partly green. This type of plant has no chlorophyll in the white part of its leaf. The plant is kept in strong sunlight or artificial light for a day. A leaf is then removed and tested for starch as in the preceding experiment. The blue-black color indicates that starch is present only in the green part of the leaf. The white part of the leaf remains iodine-colored. The absence of starch in the white part of the leaf shows that photosynthesis does not occur without chlorophyll (Fig. 15-5b.)

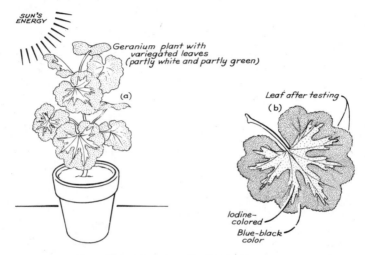

**Fig. 15-5. Showing that plants
need chlorophyll for photosynthesis.**

9. THE OXYGEN-CARBON DIOXIDE CYCLE

Green plants, as a result of photosynthesis, provide animals not only with food but also with a continuous supply of oxygen, which animals need for respiration. At the same time, as a result of their respiration, animals (as well as fires) provide plants with the carbon dioxide they need for photosynthesis. Thus, oxygen and carbon dioxide move round-and-round between organisms and the environment in what is known as the *oxygen-carbon dioxide cycle.*

A balanced aquarium containing fish and green plants illustrates the oxygen-carbon dioxide cycle in a water environment. The fish eat some of the plants, take in oxygen that is dissolved in the water, and give off carbon dioxide. The green plants use the carbon dioxide in photosynthesis and liberate oxygen.

10. PLANTS AND THE WATER CYCLE

We have seen that the roots of plants absorb large quantities of water from the soil. Part of this water is used in photosynthesis, but a great deal is released through the stomates (openings) in the leaf. The process of giving off water vapor by plants is called *transpiration*. The amount of water that plants give off daily by transpiration is very great. A corn plant, for example, may give off about three gallons of water daily, while an apple tree may release about 10 gallons of water daily.

Water vapor released by plant transpiration (and by ordinary evaporation) becomes part of the air. The water is returned to the soil (and bodies of water) by rain and snow. Thus, water released during transpiration moves round-and-round between plants and other organisms and the environment in what is called the *water cycle* (Fig. 15-6).

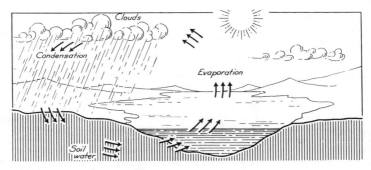

Fig. 15-6. The water cycle. The amount of water on the earth is kept constant by the water cycle. The water that enters the atmosphere as a vapor is returned to the earth as a liquid or solid.

Multiple-Choice Questions

Write the number preceding the correct answer.

1. For photosynthesis, a plant must have (1) bark (2) flowers (3) chlorophyll (4) woody support.
2. Plants absorb soil water containing dissolved minerals through their (1) guard cells (2) stems (3) root hairs (4) leaves.
3. One function of the stem of a plant is to (1) anchor the plant (2) conduct liquids (3) absorb soil water (4) store minerals.
4. The leaves of a green plant (1) absorb water (2) give off nitrogen (3) make food (4) protect the branches.

5. Gases enter and leave the leaf of a plant through tiny openings called (1) root hairs (2) guard cells (3) stomates (4) epidermis.

6. The food-making process in green plants is called (1) respiration (2) conduction (3) photosynthesis (4) absorption.

7. Plants that produce their own food with the help of light (1) must also have a supply of carbon dioxide and water (2) always have flowers (3) always live in open fields (4) always live two or more years.

8. In the process of manufacturing food, a green plant gives off (1) carbon dioxide (2) nitrogen (3) oxygen (4) ultraviolet rays.

9. A green plant stores its excess food in the form of (1) sugar (2) water (3) vitamins (4) starch.

10. Photosynthesis is a process that (1) makes leaves red in the fall (2) makes photographs on film (3) releases atomic energy (4) stores energy in plants.

11. To carry on the food-making process, a green plant must always have (1) nitrogen (2) sunlight (3) oxygen (4) warmth.

12. The materials needed to show that photosynthesis has taken place are a green leaf, a Bunsen burner, tincture of iodine, and (1) alcohol (2) ammonia (3) hydrochloric acid (4) table salt.

13. In a balanced aquarium, plants supply the fish with food and (1) water (2) carbon dioxide (3) oxygen (4) shelter.

14. A balanced aquarium illustrates a relationship between plants and animals known as (1) the nitrogen cycle (2) photosynthesis (3) the oxygen-carbon dioxide cycle (4) energy conversion.

15. The process by which plants release water vapor to the air is (1) photosynthesis (2) perspiration (3) carbohydrate synthesis (4) transpiration.

Completion Questions

Write the word or expression that correctly completes the statement.

1. A plant that contains _____ is called a green plant.
2. The part of the plant that anchors it in the soil is the _____.
3. The structure of the plant that supports the leaves and enables them to obtain sunlight is the _____.
4. The covering that protects the inner parts of a leaf is called the _____.
5. The two _____ cells regulate the size of the opening of a stomate.
6. Waste gases leave a plant through the _____.
7. To carry on photosynthesis, a plant must have carbon dioxide, water, _____, and _____.
8. Green plants help maintain a balanced composition of the air by giving off _____.
9. The source of all food on the earth depends on the _____ of the sun.
10. In a balanced aquarium, the fish use the gas _____ and release the gas _____.

Chapter 16. From Generation to Generation

1. HOW LIFE ARISES

In the distant past, people mistakenly believed that living things were produced from nonliving matter. For example, it was thought that a piece of decayed meat would give rise to maggots (wormlike stage of flies) or that horsehairs in water would develop into snakes. Many experiments were performed by scientists to disprove this belief. We now know that all living things arise from other living things of the same kind by the process of *reproduction*.

2. TYPES OF REPRODUCTION

All living things must reproduce more of their own kind. Otherwise, all life on earth would come to an end in a short time. There are two types of reproduction, *asexual* and *sexual*.

In *asexual* reproduction, one parent can produce another generation of organisms of the same kind. In *sexual* reproduction, two parents are necessary to start a new generation.

As we learned earlier, all living things are made up of one or more cells (page 63). Scientists have found that understanding what happens during reproduction depends upon knowing the part that cells play in this process. In both types of reproduction, cells divide, thus giving rise to more cells. At the time the division occurs, the most active part of a cell can be seen to be the *nucleus*.

3. THE CELL NUCLEUS

Careful studies of the nucleus have revealed that it is bounded by a membrane, called the *nuclear membrane*. Inside this membrane are the threadlike chromosomes. Chemical analysis of the chromosomes shows that they contain a chemical called deoxyribonucleic acid, or *DNA*, for short. Certain portions of the DNA make up the *genes*. It is the genes that govern, or direct, all the activities of a cell. They also determine the traits, or characteristics, that the next generation inherits from its parental generation.

4. WHEN CELLS DIVIDE

Upon growing to a certain size, a one-celled organism divides into two, forming two new identical, but smaller, one-celled organisms. In this case, cell division is the same as reproduction—asexual reproduction.

Every many-celled organism began life as a single cell—one that was formed by the union of a sex cell, an *egg cell*, from the mother with another, a *sperm cell*, from the father. This case involves sexual reproduction. The resulting single cell divides at first into two cells that stick together. These cells divide many times, forming others that continue to stay together. Before long a many-celled young organism, an *embryo*, is produced. As the embryo grows, tissues, organs, and systems form as the body takes shape. Here, cell division is not reproduction because reproduction refers only to the formation of a whole new organism.

5. THE PROCESS OF CELL DIVISION

When any cell divides, the DNA in its chromosomes becomes active—it duplicates, or copies, itself and moves around. It is the only chemical known that can duplicate. In other words, it is the only chemical that can reproduce.

By the time a cell divides, the DNA in its nucleus has already been duplicated. This is the same as saying that the chromosomes and genes within the cell have been duplicated too. The essential steps in the process of cell division are shown in Fig. 16-1.

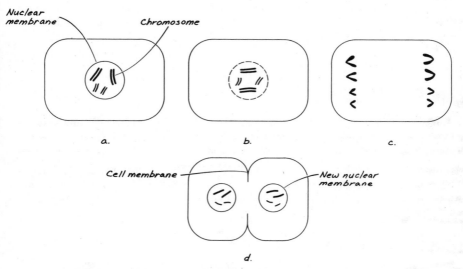

Fig. 16-1. Cell Division.
a. Cell before dividing; chromosomes have copied themselves.
b. Nuclear membrane disappearing.
c. Chromosomes move apart.
d. Cell membrane pinching in, forming two cells.

6. CHROMOSOMES IN SEX CELLS

We have already noted that, as a result of the union of an egg cell and a sperm cell, a many-celled organism begins its life. Egg cells are formed in the *ovaries* of females; sperm cells are formed in the *testes* of males. Before sex cells leave the body of a parent, they undergo changes in size, form, and the number of chromosomes in each of their nuclei. As a result, a mature egg cell and a mature sperm cell come to have half the usual number of chromosomes present in the parents' cells (Fig. 16-2).

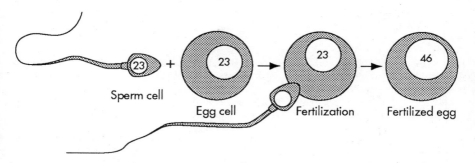

Fig. 16-2. Change in chromosome number as a result of fertilization.

When an egg cell unites with a sperm cell, the cell that is formed is called a *fertilized egg cell*. This cell then has the same number of chromosomes as do all other cells of the parent generation. For example, except for mature sex cells, the cells of humans normally have 46 chromosomes. Each mature sex cell has 23 chromosomes. When a sperm cell and egg cell unite, the fertilized egg has 46 chromosomes—the same number as in each parental cell.

7. GENES AND HEREDITY

Unlike the offspring produced in asexual reproduction, those produced in sexual reproduction are rarely exactly like either parent. For example, you may resemble your mother more than you do your father in some respects and be more like your father than your mother in other respects. This is because you inherited a pair of genes for each trait, one gene from one parent and the other gene from the other parent. For some traits, the two genes may have been the same and, for other traits, they may have been different. What a person looks like depends on the combination of the particular kinds of genes that the person inherited.

8. GENE COMBINATIONS

In any pair of genes for a trait, one gene may be *dominant* and one *recessive*. A dominant gene overshadows, or hides, the recessive gene. The trait determined by the dominant gene is the one that usually appears. For a recessive trait to appear, the individual must inherit a recessive gene from both parents. There are cases in which neither one of a pair of genes is completely dominant or recessive. In these cases, the trait that appears is a blend of the two opposite traits.

Some Inherited Traits in Humans

Trait	Type of Inheritance
Eye color	Dark eyes dominant over light.
Hair color	Dark hair dominant over light.
Earlobes	Unattached lobes dominant over attached.
Color vision	Normal color vision dominant over colorblindness.
Skin color	Normal color dominant over albino (lacks coloring).
Number of fingers and toes	Extra finger or toe dominant over normal five.

Some traits are determined by more than one pair of genes. Following the inheritance pattern of such traits is quite difficult because it is thought that humans have more than 50,000 genes in every cell nucleus.

How heredity operates is most easily understood by following what happens to a pair of genes for a trait as the genes pass from parent to offspring. Let us consider, for example, what happens in the case of the inheritance of hair form—wavy hair or straight hair.

> Let: W represent the gene for waviness, which is dominant, and let w represent the gene for straightness, which is recessive.

Suppose we diagram what happens when a wavy-haired mother mates with a wavy-haired father. (The horizontal lines in the Table below represent matings. The vertical lines lead to the next generation.) In *a*, the mother, like the father, has two genes for waviness, designated as WW. Each egg cell of the mother and each sperm cell of the father has only one gene for waviness, designated as W. As a result of fertilization, each child inherits two genes, WW, one W gene from each parent. This means that all children of these parents will have wavy hair.

a. Inheritance of Dominant Genes Only.

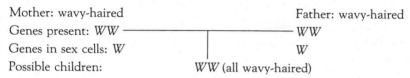

Mother: wavy-haired   Father: wavy-haired
Genes present: *WW* ————————————— *WW*
Genes in sex cells: *W*   *W*
Possible children: *WW* (all wavy-haired)

Diagram *b* shows what happens when the parents have only recessive genes.

b. Inheritance of Recessive Genes Only.

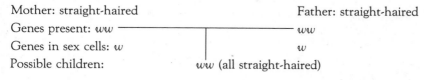

Mother: straight-haired   Father: straight-haired
Genes present: *ww* ————————————— *ww*
Genes in sex cells: *w*   *w*
Possible children: *ww* (all straight-haired)

Diagram *c* shows the inheritance of different combinations of dominant and recessive genes.

c. Inheritance of a Dominant and a Recessive Gene.

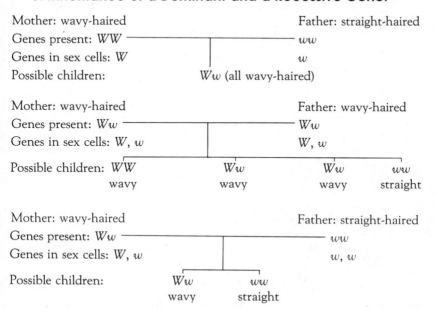

Mother: wavy-haired   Father: straight-haired
Genes present: *WW* ————————————— *ww*
Genes in sex cells: *W*   *w*
Possible children: *Ww* (all wavy-haired)

Mother: wavy-haired   Father: wavy-haired
Genes present: *Ww* ————————————— *Ww*
Genes in sex cells: *W, w*   *W, w*
Possible children: *WW*   *Ww*   *Ww*   *ww*
                   wavy   wavy   wavy   straight

Mother: wavy-haired   Father: straight-haired
Genes present: *Ww* ————————————— *ww*
Genes in sex cells: *W, w*   *w, w*
Possible children: *Ww*   *ww*
                        wavy   straight

TWINS, TRIPLETS—AND MORE!

In many kinds of animals, more than one offspring are born at the same time. In humans, the usual situation is for one baby to be born at a time. Occasionally, a mother gives birth to two or three babies at a time; more are rare. In these cases, more than one egg cell may be fertilized, or one fertilized egg may divide into separate embryos.

Twins that develop separately from two fertilized egg cells may be of the same or opposite sex. They are called *fraternal twins* (Fig. 16-3). Such twins resemble each other as do any brothers or sisters born at separate times. This is because each has inherited a different combination of genes.

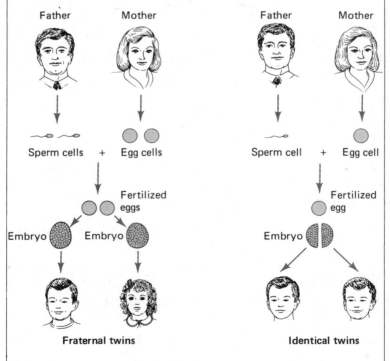

Figure 16-3. Development of identical and fraternal twins.

Twins that develop from one fertilized egg cell that split into two are called *identical twins*. These twins are always of the same sex and are so much alike that it is difficult to tell them apart. This happens because both children have inherited the same genes.

Triplets, quadruplets, and so on, may be born from separate fertilized egg cells, from one that has split into two or more parts, or a combination of both separate fertilizations and splittings. Triplets are much rarer than twins. The greater the number of children born at one time, the rarer is the event.

9. CHANGES IN GENES

Genes do change from time to time. Such changes are called *mutations*. If a mutation occurs in a gene of a sex cell, that gene will pass to an offspring that arises from it. An example of a mutation in humans and animals in one that changes the gene for the color of skin and hair. Instead of having normal coloring, the organism becomes an *albino*, one whose skin and hair color are white. Mutations can occur naturally or artificially.

a. Natural Mutations. Natural mutations are produced by natural radiation, which reaches us from outer space or from underground radioactive minerals, such as uranium oxide.

b. Artificial Mutations. Certain chemicals taken into the body can cause genes to change. LSD may be one of these chemicals. Mutations may also be caused by excessive exposure to X-rays or to the radiation released by the explosion of nuclear bombs. Accidents at nuclear energy plants may also cause mutations.

10. HEREDITY IN PLANT AND ANIMAL IMPROVEMENT

Knowledge of how heredity operates has enabled breeders of domesticated plants and animals to improve both the quality and quantity of the plants and animals that we use for food and other purposes. The methods breeders use are *selection*, *inbreeding*, *crossbreeding*, and *finding useful mutations*.

a. Selection. In this method, breeders choose for mating only those organisms that show the desired traits. A food plant that has been developed by this method is the type of wheat that not only resists disease but also has a high yield.

b. Inbreeding. This is the method by which only closely related individuals having a particular desirable trait are allowed to mate. For example, cows that produce large quantities of milk are allowed to mate only with bulls of the same breed.

c. Crossbreeding. This method involves combining the desirable traits of individuals from different breeds. Thus, the size and intelligence of horses have been combined with the strength and surefootedness of donkeys in *mules*.

d. Finding and Using Useful Mutations. Breeders are always on the lookout for mutations that may occur in their plants and animals. When a beneficial mutation is found, the organism showing it may be crossbred with one of the usual breed. Then later, by selection and inbreeding, a new valuable variety may be established. Thus, hornlessness in cattle, which arose as a mutation, was bred into other cattle breeds that normally had horns.

GENETIC ENGINEERING

Genetic engineering is a new branch of the science of heredity. It refers to the splicing, or joining, of a piece of DNA from one organism to the DNA of another organism. By such means, some special trait from one organism may be transferred into another that lacks the trait or has it in an abnormal form.

In some cases, this procedure has been successfully tried by injecting DNA from a rat into the nucleus of an egg cell of a mouse. The animal that developed was twice the size of an ordinary mouse.

In other cases, as in certain bacteria, the gene for manufacturing human insulin has been spliced from a human cell into the bacteria. This gene was carried into the DNA of the bacteria by a certain virus. Now, diabetes patients (those who lack insulin) can obtain human insulin from these bacteria instead of from the pancreas of slaughterhouse animals.

Some diseases, such as sickle-cell anemia and hemophilia (bleeder's disease) are due to the inheritance of defective genes. As more research is done in genetic engineering, the hope is, someday, to be able to transfer normal genes early enough in the development of such individuals to prevent the disease.

It is also possible that genetic engineering can be used to improve our food organisms to the extent that we can wipe out hunger in many parts of the world.

Multiple-Choice Questions

Write the number preceding the correct answer.

1. Reproduction involving only one parent is called (1) sexual (2) embryonic (3) asexual (4) fertilization.
2. During cell division, the most active cell structure is the (1) cell membrane (2) nucleus (3) cell wall (4) nerve tissue.
3. In a cell, the chemical DNA can be found in (1) cell membranes (2) chromosomes (3) cytoplasm (4) cell walls.
4. Every many-celled organism alive today began its life as (1) one cell (2) two cells (3) three cells (4) no cells.
5. Sexual reproduction involves both an egg cell and (1) a dividing cell (2) an embryo cell (3) a sperm cell (4) a muscle cell.
6. The only chemical known that can make an exact copy of itself is (1) an enzyme (2) a carbohydrate (3) a protein (4) DNA.
7. The number of sets of chromosomes that can be seen during cell division is (1) 0 (2) 2 (3) 3 (4) 4.
8. The number of cells produced by one cell division is (1) 1 (2) 2 (3) 3 (4) 4.
9. If the number of chromosomes in a mature egg cell is 4, the usual number of chromosomes in the other cells of that organism is (1) 2 (2) 4 (3) 6 (4) 8.
10. A fertilized egg cell is formed by the union of an egg cell with (1) a sperm cell (2) a nerve cell (3) another egg cell (4) a muscle cell.
11. The number of fertilized egg cells from which fraternal twins develop is (1) 1 (2) 3 (3) 0 (4) 2.
12. A change in a gene is called a(n) (1) dominant (2) recessive (3) mutation (4) identical twin.
13. When taken into the body, a substance that can cause body genes to change is (1) LSD (2) morphine (3) aspirin (4) glucose.

Completion Questions

Write the word or expression that correctly completes the statement.

1. Parents give rise to offspring by the process called _____ .
2. In _____ reproduction, two parents are needed to start a new generation.
3. Inherited traits are controlled by the _____ in chromosomes.
4. When a one-celled organism _____ , the process is the same as asexual reproduction.
5. Daughter cells that result from cell division are smaller than the parent cell but have the same _____ .

6. Egg cells are formed in the _____ of females.
7. _____ cells are formed in the testes of males.
8. The normal number of chromosomes in humans is _____ .
9. The normal number of chromosomes is restored by the process of _____ .
10. A gene that overshadows a recessive gene is called _____ .
11. Natural mutations may be caused by radiation that reaches the earth's surface from _____ or from outer space.
12. Genetic engineering is used to join _____ from one kind of organism to another.

Thought Questions

1. If two parents have straight hair, could their children have wavy hair? Explain your answer.
2. If the mother has the gene combination *WW* for wavy hair and the father has the gene combination *ww* for straight hair, all their children will have wavy hair. Explain why this is so.
3. Why are identical twins always of the same sex?
4. How does inbreeding differ from crossbreeding?

Chapter 17. Reproduction and Life Cycle of Animals

1. LIFE CYCLE

The stages that an organism passes through from birth to adulthood and then takes part in reproduction is called its *life cycle*. Upon reaching adulthood, some organisms may complete their life cycle by asexual reproduction at times, and sexual reproduction at other times.

2. ASEXUAL REPRODUCTION

As we learned earlier, asexual reproduction requires only one parent. There are two main types of asexual reproduction: *binary fission* and *budding*.

a. Binary Fission. In this process, the *ameba*, a one-celled animallike protist, reproduces asexually. The parent cell divides, forming two new, smaller amebas (Fig. 17-1).

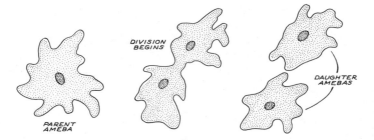

Fig. 17-1. The ameba reproducing by binary fission. By dividing in half, the parent ameba becomes two daughter amebas. Each new ameba grows to full size.

b. Budding. In this type of asexual reproduction, a small swelling, a *bud*, branches out of the main body of an organism and grows to resemble the parent. When mature, the bud separates from the parent and lives independently. Budding occurs in the simple animal, the *hydra* (Fig. 17-2 on next page). At times, the hydra can also reproduce sexually.

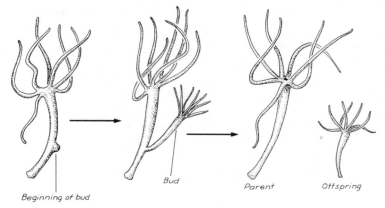

Beginning of bud

Bud *Parent* *Offspring*

Fig. 17-2. Budding in the hydra. An adult hydra forms a bud that grows and becomes another hydra. The offspring then lives independently and grows.

3. SEXUAL REPRODUCTION

The animals with which we are more familiar, such as insects, frogs, birds, and mammals, reproduce sexually. Recall that sexual reproduction requires a male and a female parent. The process involves the fertilizing of the female egg cell by the male sperm cell.

In some animals, the egg cell is fertilized after the female has laid the egg cell outside her body. In other animals, the egg cell is fertilized inside the female's body. The eggs of fish are laid in the water where they are fertilized and where the young develop. The fertilized eggs of mammals develop within the female's body, and when the young have sufficiently developed, they are born alive.

We will consider the life cycle of a few types of animals.

4. LIFE CYCLE OF A FISH

A female fish lays many unfertilized eggs at one time. The male sprays the eggs with sperm cells which swim to the eggs and fertilize them. Each egg contains stored food called *yolk*. The developing young feed on the yolk and hatch into tiny fishes. When a young fish uses up the yolk, it finds its own food. Upon reaching adulthood, the fish finds a mate and reproduces (Fig. 17-3 on next page).

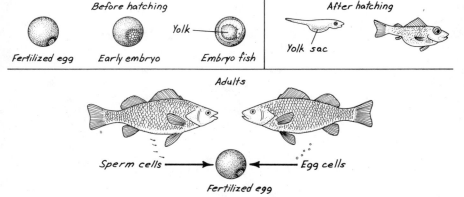

Fig. 17-3. Life cycle of a fish.

5. LIFE CYCLE OF AMPHIBIANS—FROG AND TOAD

Animals such as the frog and toad spend part of their lives in water and part on land. You will remember that they are called *amphibians.*

In the spring, the female frog deposits a mass of tiny eggs in the shallow water of a pond (Fig. 17-4). Sperm cells, released into the water by the male frog, swim to the eggs, and fertilize them. Then a layer of jelly swells up around each egg. A fertilized egg, after being warmed by the sun, develops into an embryo that is nourished by yolk. Before long, the embryo hatches into a *tadpole.* The tadpole is a fishlike animal, having gills suited to underwater breathing and a tail suited to swimming. After a while, hind legs appear. They are soon followed by forelegs. By that time, the gills disappear and are replaced by lungs. By the time that the tail is absorbed, the animal has become an adult frog that can hop out on land and can spend its life both on land and in water. When mature, frogs return to the water for mating and reproduction.

The toad develops in a similar manner. However, it spends its entire adult life on land, returning to the water only for reproduction.

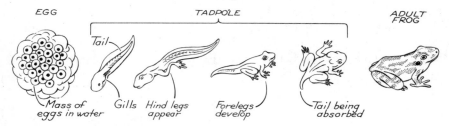

Fig. 17-4. Development of the frog. A tadpole, a gill-breathing water animal, develops into a frog, a lung-breathing land animal.

6. LIFE CYCLE OF A BIRD

Birds are hatched from eggs that have been fertilized in the body of the female. An egg (Fig. 17-5) is covered by a protective shell and contains a food supply that nourishes the embryo. The food consists of yolk (the yellow) and albumen (the white). The egg is *incubated* (kept warm) by the mother bird as she sits on it. In some species, the male sits on the egg while the female searches for food. In a few weeks, when the young bird is completely formed, it breaks out of its shell. After reaching adulthood, the bird finds a mate and reproduces.

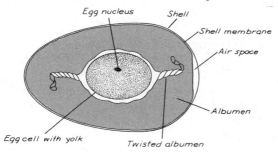

Fig. 17-5. A bird's egg. The yolk and albumen nourish the embryo. Oxygen for respiration enters through pores in the shell.

7. LIFE CYCLE OF MAMMALS

The highest type of animal is the *mammal*. Recall that a mammal is an animal that (*a*) is warm-blooded; (*b*) has hair or fur covering all or part of its body; (*c*) bears live young; and (*d*) has special structures, called *mammary glands*, which produce milk to feed its young. In addition to the human, some other mammals are the horse, cow, dog, bat, and monkey.

When mammals reproduce, the eggs are fertilized in the body of the female. A fertilized egg develops into an embryo inside the womb, or *uterus* (Fig. 17-6 on next page). As an embryo develops and grows, it receives food and oxygen from the mother's bloodstream. At the same time, the bloodstream picks up and removes carbon dioxide and other wastes from the embryo. After a period of time, which varies in different species, the animal is born. At that time, the muscles of the walls of the uterus automatically contract and push the baby mammal out of the mother's body. The newly born animal, usually helpless, feeds on milk furnished by the mother until old enough to take other food. Upon reaching adulthood, the mammal can mate.

8. LIFE CYCLE OF INSECTS

Of all the animals inhabiting the earth, the most numerous are the insects. Humans are constantly at war with them. Termites destroy wooden homes, moths

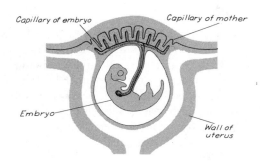

Fig. 17-6. Embryo of a mammal. Food and oxygen from the mother's capillaries are exchanged for wastes from the embryo's capillaries.

feed on clothing, grasshoppers attack food crops, the fly and the mosquito spread disease. Many insects, on the other hand, are useful to us. One type of insect, the lac, furnishes us with shellac. The silkworm moth provides us with silk, and the honeybee, with honey. Bees, butterflies, and certain moths transfer pollen from flower to flower and, in doing so, help plants to reproduce. Understanding the life cycle of various insects has enabled scientists to devise ways to control those insects that are harmful and to aid those that are helpful.

All insects reproduce sexually. Fertilization takes place in the body of the female. Usually, many egg cells are fertilized at one time. The female deposits the fertilized eggs near or on the type of food that the newly hatched young insects will feed upon.

a. Life Cycle of the Moth. A moth develops in four stages: *egg, larva, pupa,* and *adult* (Fig. 17-7). Depending on the species of moth, the female deposits her fertilized eggs on the leaves or other parts of a plant. After a while, usually in a

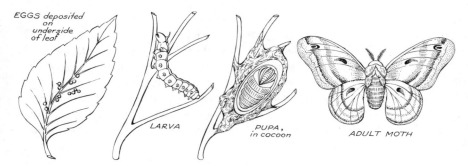

Fig. 17-7. Development of the moth. Note how the appearance changes in each stage of the development of the moth.

few days, an egg hatches into a larva. This is a wormlike form of the insect, called a *caterpillar*. In the larva stage, the insect is very destructive because it is doing its greatest amount of feeding. When fully grown, the caterpillar spins around itself a silky protective case, called a *cocoon*, and enters the pupa stage. During the cold months, the pupa rests in the cocoon. It is during this period that the pupa is transformed into the adult moth. In the spring, the cocoon breaks open and the adult moth comes out, ready to reproduce and repeat the life cycle.

Butterflies, bees, ants, mosquitoes, and houseflies also pass through four stages of development. However, their resting stage is not spent in a cocoon, but in a hard covering. In butterflies this stage is known as the *chrysalis*.

b. Life Cycle of the Grasshopper. The grasshopper develops in three stages: *egg, nymph,* and *adult* (Fig. 17-8). In the early fall, the female grasshopper digs holes in the ground and in them lays her fertilized eggs. In the spring, an egg hatches into a *nymph*, which is a young grasshopper. The nymph resembles the adult in form, except that the nymph is smaller, has a large head, and does not have wings.

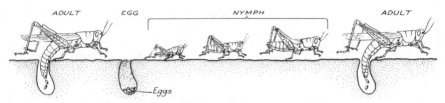

Fig. 17-8. Development of the grasshopper. Note the similarity in form between the nymph and adult grasshopper.

As the nymph feeds on plants, its body grows, but its skin does not grow. The insect simply sheds its outer covering and grows a new, larger covering. After several such sheddings, called *molts*, the young grasshopper develops wings and is now an adult and ready to find a mate.

Crickets, dragonflies, and walking sticks develop similarly.

9. HOW ANIMALS CARE FOR THEIR YOUNG

Insects generally deposit their eggs where conditions will be favorable for the newly hatched insects. For example, insects lay their eggs in places where a supply of food is readily available, such as on the leaves of trees. However, after the eggs are deposited, the female leaves the scene and does not return. Certain insects, such as bees and ants, establish colonies where the young are fed and protected until they are capable of reproducing and establishing new colonies.

Most fish and frogs lay great numbers of eggs protected by a jelly-like covering, but then offer no further care or protection. Reptiles, such as snakes and turtles, lay their eggs (covered with a leathery substance) in a nest on the ground. The eggs are incubated by the heat of the sun.

Although some birds build very simple nests, other birds build very complicated nests lined with feathers or hair. The fertilized eggs are laid in the nest, and then the female parent, or both parents, keep the eggs warm until they hatch. After the young hatch, the parents continue to feed and care for the young. Some birds even teach their young to fly.

In the highest types of animals, the mammals, we find the greatest amount of parental care. Young mammals have a longer period of infancy than do other animals. Their parents spend a great deal of time protecting and teaching them how to face the problems of living. Elephants, for example, watch over their young for several years. The highest degree of parental care is given by humans. Since the period of protection, teaching, and training is longest in the human, the chances for the young to reach adulthood are greatest.

Multiple-Choice Questions

Write the number preceding the correct answer.

1. The type of reproduction in which a swelling branches out of a parent's body and grows to resemble the parent is called (1) binary fission (2) germination (3) fertilization (4) budding.
2. The process in which an ameba divides in half to form two daughter amebas is known as (1) budding (2) sexual reproduction (3) binary fission (4) the life cycle.
3. The stored food in a bird's egg is composed of (1) albumen and jelly (2) albumen and yolk (3) yolk and shell (4) albumen and oxygen.
4. The group of living things having the largest number of members is the (1) whales (2) human beings (3) dogs (4) insects.
5. The type of reproduction used by all insects is known as (1) asexual (2) germination (3) metamorphosis (4) sexual.
6. A moth lays eggs during the stage known as (1) adult (2) caterpillar (3) cocoon (4) pupa.
7. The stage in its life history when an insect appears wormlike is (1) adult (2) egg (3) larva (4) pupa.
8. Moths are most destructive to clothing in the (1) adult (2) egg (3) larva (4) pupa stage.
9. Most moths survive through the winter in the (1) egg (2) larva (3) pupa (4) adult stage.
10. When butterfly eggs hatch, the young are (1) little butterflies (2) big butterflies (3) worms (4) caterpillars.
11. The hard case in which a butterfly spends its resting stage is the (1) cocoon (2) larva (3) egg (4) chrysalis.

12. An insect that does not have four stages in its life cycle is the (1) butterfly (2) moth (3) grasshopper (4) bee.
13. A newly hatched grasshopper is called (1) an egg (2) an adult (3) a nymph (4) a pupa.
14. The shedding of the skin by an insect is called (1) reproduction (2) germination (3) metamorphosis (4) molting.
15. An animal that sheds its outer skin several times during its lifetime is the (1) cow (2) dog (3) robin (4) grasshopper.
16. An animal that begins its life in water and spends the rest of its life on land is the (1) codling moth (2) duck (3) fish (4) toad.
17. Frogs and toads lay their eggs (1) in trees (2) under stones (3) at the roots of plants (4) in ponds.
18. A pupil sees tadpoles swimming in a lake. He should conclude that eggs have been deposited in the lake by (1) fish or crayfish (2) frogs or toads (3) snakes or eels (4) turtles or lizards.
19. When frog eggs hatch, the young look almost like (1) insects (2) fish (3) adult frogs (4) snakes.
20. Before a fertilized egg of a bird can hatch, it must be (1) germinated (2) molted (3) incubated (4) absorbed.
21. The embryo of a bird obtains its food (1) from the mother bird (2) by scratching for it (3) from food stored in the egg (4) by living on plants.
22. The fertilized eggs of mammals (1) must be incubated (2) develop outside the mother's body (3) develop inside the mother's body (4) have a hard covering surrounding them.
23. Which one of the following animals gives birth to a living offspring? (1) trout (2) robin (3) frog (4) rabbit.
24. An animal that provides milk for its young is the (1) mouse (2) turtle (3) snake (4) ostrich.
25. An insect that establishes colonies for feeding and protecting the young is the (1) grasshopper (2) bee (3) moth (4) housefly.

Completion Questions

Write the word or expression that correctly completes the statement.

1. In sexual reproduction, an egg cell must be _____ by a sperm cell.
2. New insects develop _____ (*inside, outside*) the body of the female.
3. The caterpillar is actually the _____ stage in the development of a moth.
4. An insect in its developing, resting stage is known as a (an) _____.
5. The silky case that protects a moth pupa is called a (an) _____.
6. A nymph and an adult grasshopper are _____ (*similar, dissimilar*) in form.
7. The structures that produce milk in certain animals are called _____.
8. Animals which feed their young with milk are known as _____.
9. An insect that provides its offspring with a degree of care is the _____.
10. The greatest amount of parental care is given offspring by _____.

Chapter 18. Reproduction and Life Cycle of Plants

1. LIFE CYCLE

In Chapter 17, we noted that a life cycle refers to stages in the life of an organism from the time it is born until it matures and gives rise to others like itself. Plants and plantlike protists have a life cycle much the same as animals have. Their life cycle may include stages of asexual reproduction or sexual reproduction or both.

2. ASEXUAL REPRODUCTION IN PLANTLIKE PROTISTS

As animallike protists and some animals do, plantlike protists reproduce by *binary fission* and *budding*. In addition, some plantlike protists reproduce by *sporing*.

a. Binary Fission. Recall that in this process, a parent organism divides in half and forms two new organisms. Bacteria and one-celled algae reproduce in this way.

b. Budding. Recall, also, that in budding a small swelling pushes out from the parent and eventually the swelling of the bud breaks off and develops into a new individual. This type of asexual reproduction occurs in yeast (Fig. 18-1).

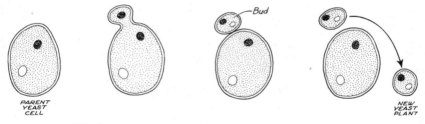

Fig. 18-1. Budding in yeast. The small outgrowth, the bud, develops on the parent yeast cell. The bud breaks off from the parent and becomes a new yeast plant.

c. Sporing. Sporing is like binary fission except that many small cells of equal size are formed instead of only two cells. The small cells, called *spores*, can resist unfavorable conditions. When conditions become favorable, the spores grow into new individuals. Sporing may occur in yeasts, molds, and mushrooms (Fig. 18-2 on next page).

168

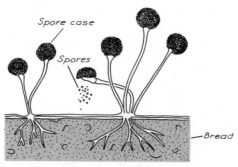

Fig. 18-2. Sporing in bread mold. Cells in the spore case divide into numerous cells of equal size, each becoming a spore.

3. ASEXUAL REPRODUCTION IN PLANTS

In general, plants reproduce sexually, as we shall shortly see. Some plants do pass through an asexual stage during their life cycle. These stages occur naturally in such familiar plants as tulips, potatoes, and carrots. Plant growers often take advantage of this characteristic by causing the plants to reproduce artificially by a process called *vegetative propagation*, or *vegetative reproduction*. Whether vegetative propagation takes place naturally or artificially, it involves reproducing an entire plant from a part that normally makes, carries, or stores food.

a. Natural Vegetative Propagation

(1) Bulbs are really buds that develop underground and enlarge as their thick leaves become full of stored food. Plants that form bulbs are tulips, onions, and garlic.

(2) Tubers are thickened underground stems that are full of stored food. A plant that produces tubers is the white potato.

(3) Fleshy roots are roots that have become very thick as a result of storing food. Plants having such roots are the carrot, beet, and sweet potato.

b. Artificial Vegetative Propagation

Among methods used in artificially propagating plants are *cutting* and *grafting*.

(1) Cutting. A part of a stem containing a few leaves is cut from a plant such as the geranium and placed in moist soil. The cutting develops into a new geranium plant, complete with roots and leaves. Other plants that can be reproduced in this manner are the ivy, rose, and begonia.

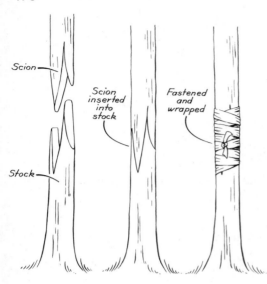

Scion

Scion
inserted
into
stock

Fastened
and
wrapped

Stock

Fig. 18-3. How a graft is made. The scion and stock are cut in such a way that the scion can be snugly inserted into the stock. After insertion, the scion is securely tied to the stock and waxed. After a while, the scion becomes a permanent branch of the stock.

(2) Grafting. A branch, called a *scion*, is cut from a plant. The scion is then inserted into the cut surface of a rooted plant, called the *stock.* The combination is then bandaged and waxed (Fig. 18-3). The cut surfaces heal, and the scion continues to grow, obtaining the necessary minerals and water from the stock to which it is attached.

Grafting may be used to increase the yield of a desired type of fruit. There are plants that bear good fruit that never ripens because the roots of such plants die as a result of a soil disease. Related plants may bear poor fruit but have roots that resist the soil disease. By grafting scions of the first plant onto rooted stocks of the second, good fruit can be grown until ripe and then be harvested. Such grafting has been done with grapes.

Grafting is also used to continue seedless fruits that have no other way of re-producing the species. The seedless navel orange is propagated in this way.

4. SEXUAL REPRODUCTION IN PLANTS

In plants, as in animals, sexual reproduction requires one parent that produces sperm cells and the other, egg cells. Recall that the union of these sex cells produces fertilized eggs. Since the process of fertilization is not readily seen in plants, we will discuss how the process of sexual reproduction is carried out in the plants that are most familiar to us—the *flowering* plants.

5. FLOWERING PLANTS

In one stage of their life cycle, flowering plants produce *seeds*. Every seed contains a plant embryo—the beginning of a new generation. To raise a new crop, or generation, of corn, wheat, tomatoes, zinnias, or marigolds, you would plant seeds which would soon develop into new plants of the same species. In turn, these plants would grow and form flowers that, in their turn, would produce seeds, thus completing the life cycle.

6. THE FLOWER AND ITS PARTS

A flower is the structure that bears the sex organs of a plant and in which sexual reproduction takes place.

An examination of a flower, like a gladiolus or a cherry, reveals the following parts (Fig. 18-4).

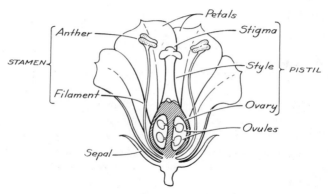

Fig. 18-4. Parts of a flower.

a. The Sepals. At the base of the flower are green leaflike parts called *sepals*. Sepals surround the other flower parts and protect them while in the bud stage. Sepals are arranged in a circle known as the *calyx*.

b. The Petals. Within the calyx is another circle of parts called the *corolla*. The corolla is composed of *petals*. Since the petals are usually colored or scented, they attract insects to the flower.

The sepals and the petals do not take part in the seed-producing process of the flower.

c. The Stamens. Located inside the corolla are the *stamens*. They are considered to be the male reproductive organs because they are responsible, eventually, for giving rise to sperm cells. A stamen consists of the *anther* and the *filament*.

(1) The *anther*, the enlarged boxlike structure at the top of the stamen, produces the pollen (pollen grains).

(2) The *filament* is a long slender stalk that supports the anther.

d. The Pistil. The *pistil* is considered to be the female reproductive organ because it produces egg cells. The pistil is usually found in the center of the flower. Some flowers, such as the one shown (Fig. 18-4), contain only one pistil; others have many pistils. A pistil consists of three parts: the *stigma*, *style*, and *ovary*.

(1) The *stigma* is the knoblike tip of the pistil. Being sticky, it is able to catch and hold the pollen grains that come in contact with it.

(2) The *style*, a slender cylindrical structure, supports the stigma and connects the stigma with the ovary.

(3) The *ovary* is the swollen base of the pistil. It contains several small bodies, the ovules in which egg cells are formed. After fertilization, ovules become seeds.

Since both the pistil and the stamen are required for seed-formation, they are called the *essential* parts of a flower.

In the lily, the rose, and the cherry, both the pistil and the stamen are in the same flower. However, not all plants have flowers with both the male and female parts in the same flower. Some plants, such as the corn, the pussy willow, and the palm tree, have two different kinds of flowers. One type of flower has only stamens, which produce the pollen, while another type of flower has only pistils, which contain the ovules.

7. POLLINATION

Before a seed can be produced, pollination must take place. *Pollination* is the transfer of pollen from the anther to the stigma. There are two types of pollination (Fig. 18-5 on next page).

a. Self-pollination. The transfer of pollen from the anther of a flower to the stigma of the same flower is called *self-pollination*. Self-pollination may also take place between flowers on the same plant.

b. Cross-pollination. The transfer of pollen from the anther of one flower to the stigma of a flower on another plant of the same species is known as *cross-pollination*.

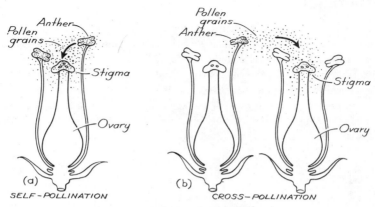

Fig. 18-5. Types of pollination

8. HOW POLLINATION TAKES PLACE

Flowers are naturally pollinated mainly by the wind, insects, or birds. Flowers may be artificially pollinated by humans.

a. Wind Pollination. Gusts of wind pick up dry pollen grains, transport them, and deposit them on the stigma of a flower. Some wind-pollinated plants are corn, oats, ragweed, grass, and maple trees.

b. Insect and Bird Pollination. Certain flowers produce a sugary substance called *nectar*. Insects, such as bees, visit flowers to obtain the nectar which they use as food. As it gathers the nectar, a bee brushes against the stamens and picks up moist, sticky pollen grains on its hairy body. When the bee visits another flower, some pollen from the bee's hairs may brush against and stick to the stigma of this flower.

Birds, particularly hummingbirds, also visit flowers to obtain nectar. Pollen, which they pick up on their feathers, is thereby transferred from one flower to another.

c. Artificial Pollination. To produce new breeds of plants, breeders may employ artificial self- or cross-pollination. In this process, a ripe anther may be removed from a flower and touched to, or shaken over, a stigma of the same or other flower. A valuable plant that originated by artificial cross-pollination is modern corn.

9. FERTILIZATION

When a pollen grain falls on the stigma of a flower, the pollen grain begins to grow and produces a threadlike *pollen tube* that grows downward through the stigma and style into the ovary. The male sex cell, the sperm cell, develops within the pollen tube (Fig. 18-6). In the ovary, the ovule contains the female sex cell, the egg cell. When the pollen tube reaches an ovule, the sperm cell passes from the tube into the ovule, where it unites with the egg cell. In time, the fertilized egg cell and the rest of the ovule develop into a seed. At the same time, the ovary enlarges and ripens as the seed grows larger.

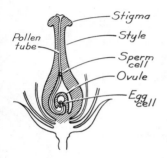

Fig. 18-6. Growth of a pollen tube. The sperm cell of the pollen tube enters the ovule and fertilizes the egg cell.

10. THE SEED

A *seed* (Fig. 18-7) consists of (*a*) a tiny new plant, the embryo, (*b*) sufficient stored food material that sustains the young plant until it can make its own food, and (*c*) a tough outer covering which protects the embryo and its food supply. Seeds produce new plants, which, in turn, will complete the life cycle by producing their own seeds.

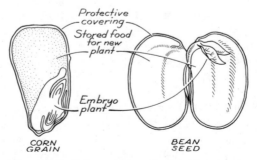

Fig. 18-7. Two common types of seeds

11. THE FRUIT

The *fruit* of a plant is a ripened ovary containing one or more seeds. Thus, an apple or a pear is a swollen ovary in which the seeds are found. Some fruits, such as the peach and cherry, contain a single seed. Other fruits, such as the apple and tomato, contain many seeds. Fruits protect seeds and help scatter them.

12. SEED DISPERSAL

The ripe seeds of many kinds of plants require a period of rest. After that, they are ready to develop into new plants as soon as they reach a suitable place to live and grow, such as a moist, rich soil. The new plants will develop and grow better if they are a great distance from the parent plant. If the seeds fall close to the parent, most young plants will die while competing with one another and with the parent for light and other necessities.

The process of scattering seeds great distances from the plant that produced them is called *seed dispersal*. Seeds may be dispersed in several ways (Fig. 18-8).

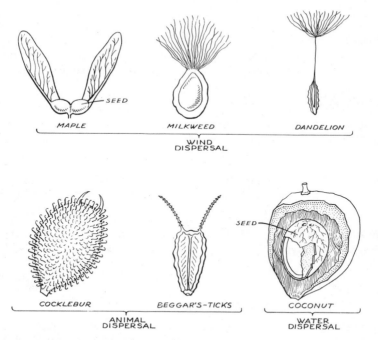

Fig. 18-8. Types of seed dispersal. Seeds have special structures that help in their dispersal by wind, water, or animals.

a. Dispersal by Wind. The seeds of the maple and ash trees are attached to winglike structures. When ripe, the seeds fall and spin in the air. Even a slight breeze carries them out and away from under the parent trees. The very light milkweed and dandelion seeds are attached to feathery tufts. These structures resemble parachutes and enable the seeds to float through air. The wind is thus able to carry these seeds a great distance from the parent plants.

b. Dispersal by Water. The seed of a coconut is enclosed in a waterproof fruit that can float. When dropped into a moving body of water, the seed is carried far from the parent plant. The floating seeds of certain weeds, such as the sedges, may be carried by water currents for great distances.

c. Dispersal by Animals. The seeds of the burdock, beggar's-ticks, and cocklebur have tiny stickers or hooks on them. By these means, the seeds become attached to the fur of animals, or to people's clothing and may be transported great distances before they drop off.

Some fruits, such as plums and cherries, have seeds with a hard coating. When eaten, these seeds cannot be digested. As a result, they may be dropped by the animal a distance away from the plants that produced them.

d. Dispersal by Mechanical Means. In fruits such as the touch-me-not and the pea pod, the walls of the fruit split apart suddenly when they are ripe and dry. The explosion causes the seeds to shoot away from the parent plant.

13. GERMINATION OF A SEED

In some species, seeds remain inactive (dormant) in the soil until the next growing season. Then, if conditions are favorable, the seeds begin to grow, or *sprout*, a process called *germination*. In order to germinate, a seed must be provided with:

a. Moisture. Water softens the seed coat, passes inward to the cells of the embryo, and revives them. The water enables the cells to enlarge and carry on their life activities.

b. Warmth. Most kinds of seeds, as do most living things, require warmth to carry on their life activities. Under natural conditions, warmth is supplied by the sun.

c. Oxygen. The embryo plants inside seeds that are germinating carry on rapid growth and require much oxygen for their life activities.

While the seed is sprouting, the embryo plant uses the food stored in the seed. As soon as the plant develops leaves, however, it begins to make its own food and continues to grow.

14. LIFE CYCLE OF A FLOWERING PLANT SUMMARIZED

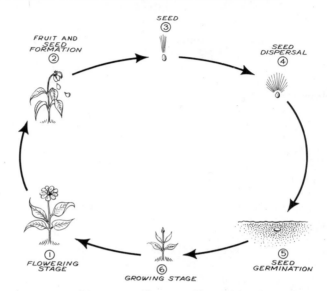

Fig. 18-9. Life cycle—from plant to seed to plant

A plant life cycle (Fig. 18-9) begins with a fertilized egg which develops into an embryo plant inside a seed. Under the proper conditions, the seed germinates into a young plant with roots, stem, and leaves. Upon receiving the proper amounts of sunlight, moisture, minerals, and carbon dioxide, the plant makes its own food and grows. It finally becomes an adult plant that produces flowers. The flowers produce pollen grains and ovules. Pollination takes place, followed by fertilization and the formation of seeds and fruits. After this, the flowers wither and die. The seeds are dispersed and some germinate, forming new plants.

Different types of plants require different lengths of time to complete their life cycle. Plants like the bean, pea, corn, and wheat, which complete their life cycle in one year (or one growing season) and then die, are called *annuals*. Their seeds remain on or in the soil over the winter. Plants like the beet and carrot, which require two growing seasons to complete their life cycle, are called *biennials*. They pass the winter in the soil as fleshy roots and produce flowers and seeds during the next growing season. Other plants, such as the oak tree, poplar tree, and willow tree, which live for periods longer than two years, are called *perennials*. After reaching maturity, perennials may produce flowers and seeds many times during their lifetime.

Multiple-Choice Questions

Write the number preceding the correct answer.

1. The stages in the life of a living thing from the time it is produced until it is able to reproduce are called (1) asexual reproduction (2) the spores (3) the life cycle (4) vegetative reproduction.
2. When a yeast cell reproduces, the small outgrowth that develops into the new organism is the (1) egg cell (2) stem (3) bud (4) nucleus.
3. Small cells that are asexually produced and that can withstand unfavorable conditions are called (1) buds (2) seeds (3) tubers (4) spores.
4. Sporing normally occurs in (1) amebas (2) roots (3) mushrooms (4) grafting.
5. The structure in which the reproductive parts of a seed-forming plant are found is the (1) seed (2) flower (3) root (4) stems.
6. The parts that enclose the flower and protect it while it is in bud are the (1) petals (2) sepals (3) anthers (4) stamens.
7. Pollen grains are produced by the (1) sepals (2) ovaries (3) pistils (4) stamens.
8. The ovary of a flower is part of the (1) calyx (2) anther (3) pistil (4) stigma.
9. The small structure in the ovary of a flower from which a seed is formed is the (1) style (2) ovule (3) stigma (4) pistil.
10. The essential structures of a flower are the pistils and the (1) leaves (2) petals (3) sepals (4) stamens.
11. A plant that produces tubers is the (1) carrot (2) beet (3) white potato (4) cherry.
12. When pollen is brought from the anther of a flower to the stigma of another flower on the same plant, the process is known as (1) fertilization (2) cross–pollination (3) self-pollination (4) germination.
13. Roses are often reproduced artificially by means of (1) seeds (2) cuttings (3) tubers (4) sporing.
14. A plant whose flower is usually pollinated by the wind is the (1) bean (2) clover (3) corn (4) tomato.
15. Bees visit flowers in order to (1) scatter seeds (2) eat the flowers (3) lay eggs (4) obtain food.
16. The uniting of a sperm and egg cell in a flowering plant takes place in the (1) filament (2) style (3) ovule (4) pollen grain.
17. The stalk that supports the anther of a flower is the (1) pistil (2) filament (3) style (4) stamen.
18. The structure that consists of the tiny new plant and stored food, both surrounded by a protective coat, is (1) a fruit (2) an anther (3) a seed (4) an ovary.
19. The structure in the seed that develops into the new plant is the (1) food (2) outer covering (3) embryo (4) ovary.

20. The part of a flower that becomes the fruit is the (1) calyx (2) ovule (3) ovary (4) stamen.
21. A fruit that contains more than one seed is the (1) peach (2) apricot (3) cherry (4) tomato.
22. For seed dispersal, the dandelion depends chiefly upon (1) the wind (2) water (3) animals (4) other plants.
23. A plant that depends upon animals to disperse its seeds is the (1) milkweed (2) ash tree (3) burdock (4) maple tree.
24. Two things necessary for the germination of seeds are air and (1) chlorophyll (2) moisture (3) soil (4) sunlight.
25. A garden plant that bears seeds during the first year of its growth is the (1) beet (2) willow (3) carrot (4) corn.
26. If you want to grow a geranium plant from a friend's geranium plant, you (1) obtain one of its seeds (2) obtain a cutting from the geranium (3) graft a piece of the geranium's stem (4) fertilize the geranium.

Completion Questions

Write the word or expression that correctly completes the statement.

1. The asexual process by which bread mold reproduces is _____.
2. The onion is an example of a plant that can be asexually reproduced from a(n) _____.
3. When a one-celled alga produces two new plants by dividing in half, the process is called _____.
4. Reproducing a plant from a part that normally makes or stores food is called _____ reproduction.
5. The process in which a scion and stock are joined is known as _____.
6. Because of their bright colors, the _____ of certain plants attract insects.
7. The part of the stamen in which the pollen grains are produced is the _____.
8. The flower structure to which pollen grains stick is the _____.
9. The transfer of pollen from the anther of a flower to the stigma of a flower on a different plant is called _____.
10. Some insects and birds visit flowers to obtain a sugary material known as _____.
11. The seeds of the maple tree are dispersed by the _____.
12. A type of plant which completes its life cycle in one year is known as a (an) _____.
13. Some plants, such as the beet, require two growing seasons to complete their life cycle and are therefore called _____.
14. The rooted tree onto which a graft is made is called _____.
15. Seedless fruits are continued by the process known as _____.

Matching Questions

Match the items in column A with those in column B.

Column A	Column B
1. process requiring egg and sperm	a. asexual reproduction
2. reproductive process in bacteria	b. calyx
3. arrangement of sepals	c. corolla
4. composed of petals	d. stamens
5. female reproductive structures	e. fruit
6. male reproductive structures	f. carrot
7. ripened ovary	g. dandelion
8. biennial	h. evergreen tree
9. seed dispersed by wind	i. pistils
10. perennial	j. sexual reproduction

Chapter 19. Changes in Living Things

1. SPECIES CONTINUE

A *species*, you will recall, refers to organisms of the same kind that can reproduce with one another. Also recall that when organisms reach adulthood, they reproduce; they become parents of a new generation of organisms of their own kind. Sooner or later, individual organisms die, but, as a result of reproduction, the species lives on. That is, under normal conditions, the species continues from generation to generation.

2. SPECIES CHANGE

Fossils are the naturally preserved remains of forms of life that, for some reason, no longer exist. Fossils of many different kinds of organisms—protists, plants, and animals—have been found that differ in many respects from modern, related living organisms. An example is the mammoth shown in Fig. 19-1.

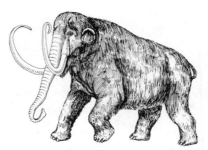

Fig. 19-1. Woolly Mammoth.
Which living animal is related to the mammoth?

Studies of fossils and rocks indicate that, as the earth slowly changed since the time it first formed, so did the living things that developed on it. The gradual changes in organisms, from the time they came into existence until the present, is known as *evolution*. Learning how fossils were formed, what the extinct organisms were like, and the kind of environment in which they lived will help you understand how evolution may have come about.

3. WAYS IN WHICH FOSSILS FORMED

Ordinarily, decay bacteria and exposure to air break down dead bodies until nothing visible remains of them. In places where fossils formed, the natural conditions prevented or slowed the breakdown processes. Examples follow.

a. Refrigeration. *Woolly mammoths* lived during the Ice Age about 25,000 years ago. Some of these animals became buried in wet soil that later froze, and some animals fell into cracks in glaciers where they remained until they were discovered in modern times.

b. Entrapment in Sticky Substances. Long ago, small animals such as insects became stuck in the resin of pine trees that no longer exist. Eventually, the resin covered the insects and preserved them in *amber*, the hardened resin of extinct pine trees.

Large animals, such as the *sabertooth* (Fig. 19-2), were engulfed by tar as they stepped into tar pools which had risen to the surface above petroleum deposits. Tar pools can be seen in the La Brea Tar Pits of Los Angeles, California.

Fig. 19-2. Sabertooth. With which family of modern animals would you place this animal?

c. Preservation in Sediments. Some ancient organisms became buried in sediments (small, solid particles) that were being deposited under water. In time, the sediments turned into sedimentary rock (pages 407–408, section 5-b). Under these conditions, the soft body parts of the organisms slowly decayed; their hard parts—bones or shells—did not. Now, all that is left in the rocks of the soft parts are hollow spaces, or *molds*. Filling a mold with plaster (making a cast) reveals the outward appearance of an organism. It is from such remains that we know what dinosaurs were like.

d. Other Examples. Impressions of dinosaur footprints have been found in rock that had once been mud. Similarly, imprints of leaves of extinct tree ferns have been found in coal.

Wood that *petrified*, or "turned into stone"—minerals replaced normal cells— can be seen in The Petrified Forest of Arizona.

4. AGE OF THE EARTH

How old is the earth? When did organisms first appear on the earth? When did modern plants and animals develop? Scientists have given us some answers to these questions.

a. Dating the Age of the Earth. Sediments that hardened under water at different times were deposited in layers, the lower layers being older than those above them. Thus, the sequence of layers provides a general idea of the earth's age (Fig. 19-3).

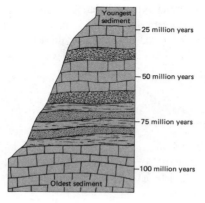

Fig. 19-3

Since the discovery of the radioactive decay of elements, such as uranium-238, scientists have made a more specific estimate of the age of the earth. (See page 274.) They estimate the age to be about 4.5 billion years.

b. Dating the Ages of Living Things. Fossils and nearby rock layers have been examined for the presence of radioactivity. Studies have led to the idea that the first, simplest forms of life may have arisen about 4 billion years ago. Since then, the earth has undergone many changes including cooling and the appearance of water and the atmosphere. And, as the environment changed, so did the early species of organisms gradually change into other species.

5. CHANGES IN LIVING THINGS THROUGH THE AGES

The record of living things in the rock layers indicates that small, simple forms of life came into being first.

a. Earliest Ages. The first organisms are thought to have arisen in a watery environment about 4 billion years ago. These organisms may have been protists similar to modern bacteria. They probably fed on chemicals present in the water. Some time later, simple algae possessing chlorophyll, or a similar chemical, developed. Such organisms made their own food by photosynthesis and, at the same time, released oxygen. The oxygen entered the water and atmosphere and enabled simple animallike protists and soft-bodied animals to develop. By the time these early ages were over, jellyfish, worms, shellfish, and other invertebrate water-dwellers were present.

b. Ages of Fishes and Amphibians. With the production of food and oxygen by organisms that carried on photosynthesis, large, more complex organisms developed. Fishes appeared about 500 million years ago. After 100 million years had passed, amphibians and insects had developed as had land plants.

c. Ages of Reptiles and Mammals. Small reptiles first appeared about 350 million years ago; giant reptiles, the dinosaurs, appeared later. Before the dinosaurs became extinct, about 135 million years ago, birds and mammals had already evolved from some types of reptiles.

d. Age of Humans. Humans, the most highly developed mammals, appeared about 100,000 years ago in the form of the *Neanderthal* people (Fig. 19-4a). About 30,000 years ago, the *Cro-Magnon* people developed (Fig. 19-4b). These people looked very much like today's people.

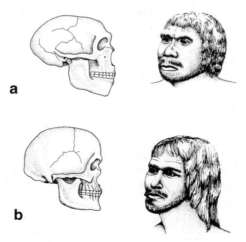

**Fig. 19-4. Two early types of humans:
(*a*) Neanderthal, (*b*) Cro-Magnon.**

6. EXPLAINING EVOLUTIONARY CHANGES

When the organisms in the fossil record are compared with modern organisms, it becomes clear that living things have changed throughout the earth's history. What is not clear, is how the changes came about. In the past, several explanations were proposed and then rejected by scientists for lack of evidence.

a. Darwin's Theory to Explain Evolution. In 1859, *Charles Darwin*, an English naturalist, offered an explanation generally accepted today by scientists, but with some modifications. Darwin's theory, called the "Origin of Species by Means of Natural Selection," has five main points.

(1) Overproduction. When organisms reproduce, more offspring are formed than can survive in the environment.

(2) Struggle for Existence. After being born, many offspring die because they are killed by natural enemies, unfavorable environmental conditions, or lack of food. Those who manage to survive do so only after struggling to exist.

(3) Variation. Organisms of a species differ from one another in size, strength, health, and other ways.

(4) Natural Selection, or Survival of the Fittest. Some individuals possess variations that fit, or adapt, them to their environment. Such favorable variations enable them to survive in the struggle for existence. Other individuals, not so well adapted, soon die. Those that survive the struggle are said to be *naturally selected*.

(5) Inheritance. The naturally selected survivors pass on their variations to their offspring who, in turn, are naturally selected to survive and reproduce. In time, as this process repeats itself in each succeeding generation, a new species having the favorable variations develops.

b. Modern Theory to Explain Evolution. When Darwin proposed his theory, the part played by genes, chromosomes, and mutations in inheritance had not yet been discovered. Present-day scientists have added the following to Darwin's ideas of variation and inheritance.

(1) During sexual reproduction, the inheritance of genes from two parents often results in variations that may be helpful, harmful, or neither. Offspring inheriting helpful variations have the best chance of surviving in the struggle for existence and of passing on the variations to their offspring.

(2) Mutations (page 156, section 9) are also responsible for variations. New traits that arise through mutations may better adapt offspring to a changing environment. Accordingly, such offspring pass on the mutation to following generations.

Thus, as the environment changes and variations in organisms continue to appear, new species evolve.

EVOLUTION IN RECENT TIMES

Evolutionary changes in organisms are still going on. Some recent evidences follow.

1. By selective breeding and crossbreeding (page 156, section 10), humans have domesticated many animals and plants that are markedly different from their wild ancestors. Examples are the various breeds of dogs which are descended from the wolf, and the several varieties of many-petaled roses which are descended from the wild five-petaled rose.

2. Penicillin was first used to fight disease in the 1940's. At that time, it worked well against many types of disease bacteria. Some years later, however, it was found that some types of bacteria became resistant to penicillin and passed on that trait to their offspring. Today, a type of bacterium has evolved that not only resists penicillin, but also requires it to stay alive. (This is one reason why a search for new antibiotics still goes on.)

3. When DDT was first used against flies and mosquitoes, it worked well. Now, DDT is no longer used not only because it harms birds and other animals, but also because the insects have developed forms that resist DDT.

Multiple-Choice Questions

Write the number preceding the correct answer.

1. The changes in species over time is known as (1) evolution (2) asexual reproduction (3) vegetative propagation (4) grafting.
2. The naturally preserved remains of organisms that are no longer present on earth are called (1) mutants (2) albinos (3) fossils (4) larvae.
3. The living animal that is most closely related to the extinct woolly mammoth is the (1) rhinoceros (2) hippopotamus (3) giraffe (4) elephant.
4. Some fossils have been preserved in (1) glaciers (2) lava (3) salty water (4) hot geysers.
5. Insect fossils are often seen embedded in (1) ice (2) amber (3) lava (4) pupae.
6. Scientists estimate the age of the earth to be closest to (1) 5,500 years (2) 2 million years (3) 4 billion years (4) 25 billion years.
7. In layers of sedimentary rock that have not been disturbed, the youngest layer is the one (1) at the bottom (2) next to the bottom (3) in the middle (4) at the top.
8. The earliest forms of life on earth are believed to have arisen in water about (1) 5,500 (2) 2 million (3) 4 billion (4) 10 billion   years ago.
9. Since the earth came into existence, its temperature has (1) increased (2) decreased (3) remained the same.
10. The earliest organisms that appeared on earth are likely to have resembled modern (1) mushrooms (2) bacteria (3) ferns (4) worms.
11. Before dinosaurs became extinct, some reptilelike animal became the ancestor of (1) mammals (2) amphibians (3) protists (4) insects.
12. Sabertooth fossils have been discovered in natural (1) ice (2) tar pools (3) amber (4) petrified wood.

Modified True-False Questions

If a statement is true, write the word true. *If a statement is false, write the word or expression that must be substituted for the italicized expression to make the statement true.*

1. The earliest humans are thought to have appeared about *3 million* years ago.
2. That organisms of the same species, such as cats, differ from one another in some respect is called *natural selection*.
3. Organisms that have *helpful mutations* have the best chance to survive in the struggle for existence.
4. Over long periods of time, new species tend to evolve as a result of *environmental changes* and inherited variations.
5. Under natural conditions in a community, more offspring tend to be produced than can survive. This tendency is known as *heredity*.

Thought Questions

1. Why is it impossible to burn petrified wood?
2. Why do scientists believe that the oxygen present in the modern atmosphere depended on the development of chlorophyll?
3. Fish skeletons have been found inside rocks that have been split apart. How could the skeletons have gotten into the rocks?

REVIEW OF UNIT III

1. Food is manufactured by green plants.
   a. In what part of the plant is most of the food made?
   b. What is the source of energy for the process?
   c. Name the two raw materials used by the plant in the process of food-making, and name the parts of the plant through which each material enters the plant.
2. Give one function or use of each of the following parts of a plant: (*a*) root, (*b*) stem, (*c*) leaf.
3. *a.* What is the function of genes?
   b. How are genes, chromosomes, and DNA related?
4. *a.* Outline the steps that occur during cell division.
   b. When cell division has been completed, how do the genes of the new cells compare with those of the parent cell?
5. Define: fertilization, dominant gene, mutation.
6. In humans, dark hair color is dominant over light hair color. If one parent has two dominant genes for hair color and the other parent has two recessive genes for hair color, what hair color should their children have?
7. Why are identical twins always of the same sex while fraternal twins may or may not be?
8. Explain the meaning of each of the following terms: sperm cell, embryo, cocoon, larva, pupa.
9. The illustrations below represent the life history of the housefly.

    1   2   3   4

   a. Give the name of each of the four stages: 1, 2, 3, and 4.
   b. During which stage does the most growth take place?
   c. Tell what happens when stage 3 changes into stage 4.

10. Give an example of each of the following
    a. an insect that winters in the pupa stage
    b. an animal that is adapted to live the first part of its life in the water and the last part of its life on land
11. Sketch in the missing part of the diagram of an adult insect, and name the missing part.

12. Even though an adult clothes moth does not eat, it should be destroyed. Explain.
13. The parts of a flower in the diagram below are numbered.

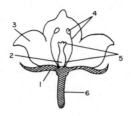

    a. From the following list of terms, choose the name for each part of the flower: petal, sepal, stamen, pistil, ovary.
    b. Choose the number of the part of the flower which correctly completes each of the following statements.
       (1) Seeds are formed in the_____.
       (2) Pollen is produced by the_____.
       (3) Bees are attracted by the color of the_____.
       (4) When the flower is in the bud stage, it is protected by the_____.
       (5) The part of the flower that forms the fruit is the_____.
14. Arrange the following events in the order in which they normally occur.
    a. fruiting   b. pollination
       flowering   seed formation

15. Give an example of each of the following.
    a. a plant whose seeds are distributed by clinging to the fur of animals
    b. a plant grown from cuttings
    c. a plant whose seeds are distributed by the wind
    d. a wind-pollinated plant
16. Give a reason for each of the following.
    a. Placing hives of bees in an apple orchard increases fruit production.
    b. Only one parent is required for reproduction of yeast plants.
    c. Pollination must precede fertilization.
17. Describe the process of fertilization in flowering plants.
18. a. Describe the makeup of a seed.
    b. What is seed dispersal?
    c. Briefly describe two methods of seed dispersal.
19. a. What is a fruit?
    b. State two functions of a fruit.
20. a. What is meant by germination of a seed?
    b. State three conditions necessary for seed germination.
21. a. How would you propagate a geranium asexually?
    b. Describe the process of grafting.
22. Define: (a) fossil, (b) evolution.
23. Arrange the following organisms in the order in which they probably evolved: reptiles, algae, humans, fish, bacteria, birds, frogs.
24. List the five main points in Darwin's theory of evolution.

Unit IV.
Chemicals in Our Lives

Chapter 20. What Is Matter?

1. MEASURING MATTER

a. Matter is anything—an object, a body, a substance—that takes up space. For example, air, water, and rocks are composed of matter. The amount of matter in a substance is called its *mass*. It can be determined by using a balance, or scale, which compares the unknown mass with a known mass (Fig. 20-1). The mass of any given body always remains the same.

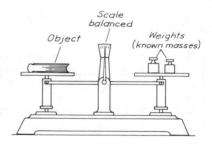

Fig. 20-1. Determining the mass of an object on an equal arm (platform) balance. The object is placed on one pan. Known masses are placed on the other pan. When the pointer stops swinging and is at the center of the scale, the sum of the known masses equals the mass of the object.

b. Weight depends on the mass of a body and the pull, or force, of gravity. As the mass of a body increases, the gravitational pull increases and the weight of the body increases. Since the pull of gravity on earth does not vary much, the mass and the weight of a given body on earth are the same. If two objects have the same weight at the same location on earth, the bodies have the same mass. However, as an astronaut moves away from the earth, the pull of gravity decreases and the weight of the astronaut decreases. In fact, the weight of an astronaut on the moon is about one-sixth of his (or her) weight on earth.

c. Volume is the amount of space a body occupies and does not depend on its location.

2. UNITS OF MEASUREMENT

A discussion of units of measurement appears on page 264. For our present needs, we will list some units of mass, weight, and volume in Table 20-1.

Table 20-1. Some Common Units

Mass	gram (g), kilogram (kg)
Weight	newton (N)
Volume	cubic centimeter (cm^3) milliliter (mL) liter (L)

A mass of 1 kilogram (kg) weighs 9.8 newtons (N) at earth's surface.
1,000 grams (g) equals 1 kilogram (kg).
1,000 cubic centimeters (cm^3) equals 1 liter (L). 1,000 milliliters (mL) equals
    1 liter (L).

3. FORMS OF MATTER

Matter may exist in three different forms, also called *phases* or *states*: gas, liquid, or solid.

a. Gas. A gas has no definite shape and no definite volume; a gas will fill any container in which it is placed. Some common gases are air, oxygen, hydrogen, carbon dioxide.

b. Liquid. A liquid has a definite volume; its shape is that of its container. Some common liquids are water, alcohol, kerosene.

c. Solid. A solid has a definite shape and a definite volume. Some common solids are salt, sugar, concrete.

All matter consists of tiny particles called *molecules*, which are in rapid motion. The arrangement and speed of these molecules determine the state of matter. In general, molecules move most rapidly in gases, less rapidly in liquids, and least rapidly in solids.

Changes in temperature may change the phase of matter from one form to another. In general, raising the temperature tends to change matter from the solid to liquid phase, and from the liquid to gaseous phase. For example, if a piece of ice is heated, it changes from a solid (ice) to a liquid (water). If water is heated sufficiently, it will change from a liquid to a gas (water vapor). On the other hand, lowering the temperature tends to have the opposite effect; that is, lowering the temperature changes a gas to a liquid, and a liquid to a solid.

The change from a solid to a liquid (or a liquid to a solid) takes place at the *melting point* of the solid or the *freezing point* of the liquid. Thus, ice melts at 0° (zero degrees) Celsius, and water freezes at the same temperature. (See also page 229.)

At sea level, liquids boil at their *boiling points*. Thus, water boils at 100°C, at sea level.

4. COMPOSITION OF MATTER

There are three kinds of matter: *elements, compounds*, and *mixtures*.

a. Elements. An *element* is considered to be the simplest type of matter. It is made up of only one kind of material. Elements are the basic units from which all other matter is built. There are over one hundred known elements. Eighty-eight elements exist in nature, while the others are made in the laboratory. The smallest part of an element that still has the properties of the element is an *atom*.

Elements can be distinguished by their individual properties; that is, by their appearance and behavior. Elements may exist in any of the three phases of matter. Most elements are solids, some are gases, and a very few are liquids. (See Table 20-2.) Chemists use abbreviations, called *symbols*, to describe elements.

Table 20-2. Some Common Elements

State	Element	Chemical symbol	Properties
Solids	Carbon	C	Black substance
	Sulfur	S	Yellow solid
	Sodium	Na	Silvery metal
	Iron	Fe	Grayish metal
	Aluminum	Al	Silvery metal
	Radium	Ra	Radioactive metal
Gases	Oxygen	O	Colorless; odorless; supports combustion
	Hydrogen	H	Colorless; odorless; lightest gas
	Nitrogen	N	Colorless; odorless; does not support combustion
	Chlorine	Cl	Greenish; irritating odor
	Radon	Rn	Colorless; odorless; poisonous gas
Liquids	Mercury	Hg	Silvery metal
	Bromine	Br	Reddish; irritating odor

LESSON 2# ANSWER #

b. Compounds. When two or more elements combine chemically, a new type of matter, called a *compound*, is formed. The compound has new properties and does not resemble any of the elements that have combined to form the compound. For example, when the elements hydrogen and oxygen—both gases—combine chemically, they form the compound water, which is a liquid at room temperature.

The smallest part of a compound that retains the properties of the compound is a *molecule*. Water, as we have just seen, is a compound consisting of molecules made up of atoms of hydrogen and atoms of oxygen. Compounds have a definite composition. For example, every molecule of water always has two atoms of hydrogen and one atom of oxygen. Since all samples of a given compound have the same composition, compounds are said to be *homogeneous*.

Chemists use *formulas* to describe the composition of compounds. Table 20-3 lists some common compounds, their formulas, and properties.

LESSON 2# ANSWER #

Table 20-3. Some Common Compounds

Compound	Chemical Formula	Properties
Water	H_2O	Colorless; odorless liquid
Salt	NaCl	White solid
Carbon dioxide	CO_2	Colorless; odorless gas

c. Mixtures. When elements or compounds combine physically, another kind of matter, called a *mixture*, forms. The matter in the mixture remains unchanged and retains its original properties. Thus, a mixture of iron filings (black) and powdered sulfur (yellow) is magnetic because the iron is unchanged; the mixture is a shade of yellow because the sulfur is unchanged. However, when the mixture is heated, new matter—the compound iron sulfide—is formed. The compound is nonmagnetic and black, showing that it possesses new properties.

The composition of a mixture may vary. Thus, different quantities of iron filings and powdered sulfur can form a variety of mixtures. Recall that the composition of a compound does not vary and that the compound is referred to as homogeneous matter. This means that the composition of the compound is the same throughout the compound. On the other hand, the composition of a mixture may not be the same throughout the mixture—it may vary—and the mixture is referred to as *nonhomogeneous* matter.

Some mixtures, such as *solutions*, are homogeneous. For example, only a fixed amount of salt dissolves in a fixed amount of water (at a given temperature). Equal parts of the solution contain the same quantity of salt. Solutions are presented in greater detail on page 230, sections 7, 8.

5. STRUCTURE OF AN ATOM

All matter is made up of elements which, in turn, are made of building blocks, called *atoms*. Atoms are composed of tiny particles most of which are electrical in nature.

The core of the atom, called the *nucleus*, is very dense. Found in the nucleus are *protons* and *neutrons*. Protons are positively charged particles, while neutrons have no electrical charge. Outside the nucleus there are *electrons*, which are negatively charged particles.

The location and arrangement of the electrons have been described by scientists, using mental images, or pictures. These mental images, called *models*, are based on the results of many experiments. Models continue to change as more information from these experiments becomes available. For example, during the early 20th century, an atom was pictured as a dense nucleus surrounded by shells of electrons lettered K, L, M, and so on, as we go further away from the nucleus (Fig. 20-2).

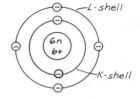

Fig. 20-2. The electron shell model. A carbon atom has 6 protons (+) and 6 neutrons (n) in the nucleus; and 6 electrons outside the nucleus, 2 in the K-shell and 4 in the L-shell.

Today, scientists no longer believe in this electron shell model. Instead, they believe that the electrons in atoms form a kind of *electron cloud* of varying density. The densest portion of the cloud shows the area in an atom where the electrons are most likely to be found (Fig. 20-3).

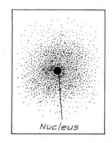

Fig. 20-3. The electron cloud model. In an atom of hydrogen, the single electron is most probably located outside the nucleus in the area that is most dense (has the most dots).

As you progress in your study of science, you will learn more about the electron cloud model. For the present, we will use the older electron shell model because it is simpler and can help you understand elementary chemical changes.

The properties of each atom depend upon the number and arrangement of its protons, neutrons, and electrons (Fig. 20-4).

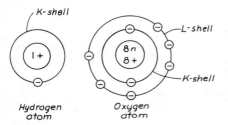

Fig. 20-4. Atomic structure of two common elements. The hydrogen atom has one proton (+) in the nucleus and one electron (−) outside the nucleus in the K-shell. The oxygen atom has 8 protons and 8 neutrons (n) in the nucleus; and 8 electrons outside the nucleus, 2 in the K-shell and 6 in the L-shell.

The numbers of atomic particles have been determined by chemists, and are expressed as follows:

atomic number—the number of protons *or* the number of electrons
atomic mass—the *sum* of the protons and neutrons in the nucleus

In any given atom, the number of electrons equals the number of protons; that is, an atom is said to be electrically neutral. For example, the atomic number of sodium is 11: there are 11 electrons and 11 protons. Since the atomic mass of sodium is 23, the nucleus of a sodium atom contains 11 protons and 12 neutrons (Fig. 20-5).

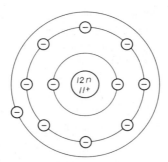

Fig. 20-5. A sodium atom.

Atoms, when they react to form molecules, complete their outer electron shells. The K-shell is complete with 2 electrons, the L-shell with 8, and the M-shell with 8. Atoms complete their outer shells by gaining or losing (transferring) electrons, or by sharing electrons (Figs. 20-6 and 20-7).

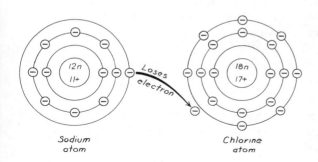

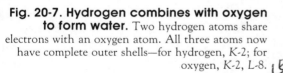

Sodium
atom

Chlorine
atom

Fig. 20-6. Sodium combines with chlorine to form sodium chloride. The sodium atom loses one electron from the outer shell, which is transferred to a chlorine atom in its outer shell. Both atoms now have complete outer shells—for sodium, K-2, L-8; for chlorine, K-2, L-8, M-8.

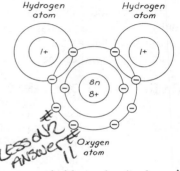

Hydrogen
atom

Hydrogen
atom

Oxygen
atom

Fig. 20-7. Hydrogen combines with oxygen to form water. Two hydrogen atoms share electrons with an oxygen atom. All three atoms now have complete outer shells—for hydrogen, K-2; for oxygen, K-2, L-8.

When atoms combine to form molecules, the atoms are held together by forces of attraction, called *chemical bonds*. Notice that when a sodium atom transfers an electron to a chlorine atom (Fig. 20-6), the sodium atom now has 11 protons and 10 electrons. Similarly, the chlorine atom has 17 protons and 18 electrons. The sodium atom now has one *less* electron and is said to have a charge of 1+. In the same way, the chlorine atom has one *more* electron and is said to have a charge of 1−. The oppositely charged particles, by attracting one another, form a chemical bond, or *bond*, for short.

Recently, scientists have been able to change one atom into a different atom by rearranging the atomic particles. For example, in an atom bomb, the nucleus of a uranium atom splits into atoms of barium and krypton. Some elements are able to change into other elements by throwing off atomic particles without outside help. Such elements are called *naturally radioactive*, and the change is said to be *spontaneous*. Two such radioactive elements are uranium and radium.

6. PHYSICAL AND CHEMICAL CHANGES

Matter may undergo change in two ways: *physical* and *chemical.*

a. Physical Changes. A *physical change* occurs when the size or shape of matter is altered. The matter remains unchanged; that is, it is not changed to different matter. Some examples of physical changes are (1) tearing, breaking, or grinding matter; (2) changing water into steam or into ice; (3) turning wood into sawdust; and (4) dissolving salt or sugar in water.

Notice that in each of these examples the same matter is present after change, although the form, shape, or size of the matter has been altered.

b. Chemical Changes. In Fig. 20-6, a sodium atom combines with a chlorine atom to form new matter, a crystal of sodium chloride (or table salt). In Fig. 20-7, two hydrogen atoms combine with one oxygen atom to form new matter, a molecule of water. When coal burns, carbon dioxide is formed. Carbon atoms in the coal have combined with oxygen atoms in air to form new matter, molecules of carbon dioxide. The formation of molecules of new matter having characteristics different from the original matter is called a *chemical change.* Some other examples of chemical changes are (1) rusting of iron; (2) souring of milk; and (3) decaying of food. In each of these examples, matter with new properties has been formed.

7. THE NATURE OF CHEMICAL CHANGES

Chemical changes may occur slowly or rapidly, depending on the substances involved. Energy in the form of heat is frequently required to start a chemical reaction. This energy is called *activation energy.* For example, when heated, the compound potassium chlorate gives off oxygen very rapidly. Adding another chemical, manganese dioxide, to the potassium chlorate speeds up the rate at which the oxygen is given off. **CAUTION: DO NOT PERFORM THESE EXPERIMENTS.** A substance such as manganese dioxide which can change the speed of a chemical reaction without being permanently changed itself is called a *catalyst.*

Most often, a catalyst is used to hasten a reaction, but in some instances a catalyst is employed to reduce the speed of the reaction. For example, a negative catalyst is used to slow down the decomposition of hydrogen peroxide, which changes to water upon standing.

Chemical changes involve energy changes. Every chemical reaction involves some form of energy, such as light, heat, or electrical energy. For example, when coal burns, stored chemical energy in the coal changes to light and heat energy.

Multiple-Choice Questions

Write the number preceding the correct answer.

1. To determine the amount of pull the earth exerts on an object, we find the object's (1) weight (2) volume (3) length (4) width.

2. Milliliters are used to express an object's (1) height (2) weight (3) width (4) volume.

3. The volume of an object can be expressed in (1) newtons (2) liters (3) grams (4) centimeters.

4. A form of matter that has a definite volume but no definite shape is a (1) gas (2) liquid (3) solid.

5. The state of matter depends on the arrangement and rate of movement of very small particles called (1) elements (2) compounds (3) mixtures (4) molecules.

6. The building blocks from which all elements are composed are known as (1) atoms (2) molecules (3) gases (4) liquids.

7. Found in the nucleus of an atom are (1) electrons and protons (2) electrons and neutrons (3) neutrons only (4) neutrons and protons.

8. Of the following, the one that is an element is (1) water (2) hydrogen (3) carbon dioxide (4) salt.

9. A metal that is liquid at room temperature is (1) copper (2) lead (3) mercury (4) zinc.

10. A compound results from the chemical union of (1) an electron and a proton (2) two or more elements (3) a neutron and an atom (4) a neutron and a proton.

11. An example of a compound is (1) nitrogen (2) oxygen (3) carbon dioxide (4) iodine.

12. The smallest part of a compound is (1) an atom (2) a molecule (3) an electron (4) a proton.

13. An element that is naturally radioactive is (1) radon (2) helium (3) magnesium (4) potassium.

14. When matter undergoes a change in size and appearance only, the change is called (1) chemical (2) physical (3) radioactive (4) fission.

15. When matter is changed into new matter having different properties, the type of change is (1) physical (2) chemical (3) electrical (4) atomic.

Modified True-False Questions

If a statement is true, write the word true. *If a statement is false, write the word or expression that must be substituted for the italicized expression to make the statement true.*

1. To determine how much matter there is in a substance, you must find the *volume* of the substance.
2. Mass may be expressed in units such as *cubic centimeters.*
3. A *gas* is a phase of matter which has both a definite shape and a definite volume.
4. Molecules move about most rapidly in *solids.*
5. The simplest type of matter is a *compound.*
6. Water is always composed of the elements hydrogen and *carbon.*
7. The composition of a *mixture* never changes.
8. The substances present in a mixture *retain* their original properties.
9. The dense part of an atom in which the protons are found is called the *neutron.*
10. The *proton* is the negatively charged particle found in every atom.
11. An uncharged particle found in an atom is the *electron.*
12. The burning of wood in air is an example of a *physical* change.
13. Chemical changes *always* take place rapidly.
14. A substance which changes the speed of a chemical reaction without itself being changed is called a *catalyst.*
15. Chemical reactions are accompanied by the release of some form of *energy.*
16. The parts of a given mixture have the *same* composition.

Completion Questions

Write the word or expression that correctly completes the statement.

1. The amount of matter in a body is called its _____ .
2. At extremely high temperatures, matter is usually in the _____ phase.
3. Most elements are in the _____ phase.
4. Water is an example of a compound because _____ .
5. A catalyst always _____ the speed of a chemical reaction.
6. When atoms unite to form molecules, _____ are transferred or shared.
7. Scientists use mental pictures called _____ .
8. An uncharged particle in the nucleus of an atom is the _____ .
9. In molecules, atoms are held together by chemical _____ .
10. When atoms gain or lose electrons, the atoms become _____ .

Matching Questions

Match the items in Column A with those in Column B.

Column A	Column B
1. unit of volume	*a.* newton
2. gaseous compound	*b.* liter
3. liquid element	*c.* chlorine
4. mixture	*d.* bromine
5. lightest element	*e.* chemical change
6. unit of force	*f.* carbon dioxide
7. naturally radioactive	*g.* physical change
8. burning	*h.* hydrogen
9. melting ice	*i.* uranium
10. greenish gas	*j.* air

Chapter 21. How We Can Safely Produce Some Chemical Changes

1. SYMBOLS, FORMULAS, AND EQUATIONS

We have already indicated that chemists use symbols and formulas to describe the composition of elements and compounds. But symbols and formulas tell us even more.

a. Two-element Compounds. Recall that atomic number was defined as the number of protons or electrons present in an atom. Atomic mass was defined as the sum of the protons and neutrons in the nucleus of an atom. The actual mass of the proton is a very, very small number. Rather than work with these tiny numbers, chemists invented a unit called an *atomic mass unit, amu* for short, and assigned to the proton an atomic mass unit of 1. The electron—an even lighter unit than a proton—was found to have about 1/1837th the mass of a proton. The neutron was found to have about the same mass as a proton and is also assigned 1 amu. Table 21-1 lists the atomic numbers and atomic masses of some common elements.

Table 21-1. Atomic Numbers and Atomic Masses

Element	Symbol	Atomic Number	Atomic Mass
Hydrogen	H	1	1
Carbon	C	6	12
Nitrogen	N	7	14
Oxygen	O	8	16
Neon	Ne	10	20
Sodium	Na	11	23
Sulfur	S	16	32
Chlorine	Cl	17	35
Calcium	Ca	20	40

Let us return to symbols and formulas. The symbol H, for hydrogen, stands for 1 atomic mass of hydrogen. In the formula for water, H_2O, we find 2 atomic masses of hydrogen and 1 atomic mass of oxygen. The proportions of elements in compounds are determined when the atoms in the elements gain, lose, or share electrons to complete their outer electron shells (see Figs. 20-6, 20-7 on page 197).

202

Formulas of compounds, therefore, tell us the relative atomic masses of the components that make up the compound. For example, the formula CO_2, for carbon dioxide, shows 1 atomic mass of carbon and 2 atomic masses of oxygen. From the table of atomic masses on the previous page, we see that in the formula CO_2, there are 12 parts of carbon (1 atomic mass) to 32 parts of oxygen (2 atomic masses). A formula therefore describes the composition of a compound. Such information is very useful to industrial chemists, many of whom are engaged in manufacturing chemicals.

Up to this point, you will note that our discussion of formulas has been limited to compounds that contain only two different elements, such as carbon dioxide, CO_2, or sodium chloride, NaCl. Compounds that are made up of two different elements are called *binary* compounds.

b. Three-element Compounds. Compounds may contain three different elements, called *ternary* compounds. For example, in calcium carbonate, the elements calcium, carbon, and oxygen have combined to form $CaCO_3$. One carbon atom and three oxygen atoms behave as a unit, called a *radical*, written CO_3. Table 21-2 lists some common compounds that contain radicals.

Table 21-2. Compounds and Radicals

Compound	Name	Radical
Na_2SO_4	sodium sulfate	sulfate (SO_4)
KNO_3	potassium nitrate	nitrate (NO_3)
$Ca(OH)_2$	calcium hydroxide	hydroxide (OH)

Recall that formulas show the relative atomic masses in a compound. Thus, in Na_2SO_4, there are 2 atomic masses of sodium, 1 atomic mass of sulfur, and 4 atomic masses of oxygen. These numbers are called *subscripts*.

c. Using Equations. Chemical changes may also be described by using symbols and formulas. For example, when hydrogen combines with oxygen to form water, we can write

$$hydrogen + oxygen \rightarrow water$$

The arrow $\rightarrow$ means "forms" or "yields." Suppose we now substitute symbols for the elements and a formula for the compound.

$$H + O \rightarrow H_2O$$

Notice that we have 1 atomic mass of hydrogen (H) on the left side of the arrow and 2 atomic masses of hydrogen in H_2O on the right side. Scientists have shown that mass cannot be created nor destroyed but, instead, is conserved. (See also page 271, section 1.) Therefore, we must write

$$2H + O \rightarrow H_2O$$

This statement, called an *equation*, now reads as follows:

2 atomic masses of hydrogen + 1 atomic mass of oxygen yields
2 atomic masses of hydrogen + 1 atomic mass of oxygen in one molecule of H_2O.

Going one step further and consulting the table of atomic masses, we find that 2 atomic mass units of hydrogen in 2 H + 16 atomic mass units of oxygen in 1 O form 18 atomic mass units of hydrogen and oxygen in water. Note that mass has been conserved.

Chemists found that elemental gases, like hydrogen and oxygen, are usually written as H_2 and O_2. The equation for the formation of water can be rewritten as

$$2H_2 + O_2 \rightarrow 2H_2O$$

The numbers in front of the formulas are called *coefficients*. Notice that coefficients are used to conserve mass, and we call this procedure *balancing the equation*. Also note that the prefix "equa" in the word "equation" suggests an equality. The masses on both sides of a balanced equation are equal. Some sample equations are:

$$2Na + Cl_2 \rightarrow 2NaCl$$
$$46 + 71 \quad 117$$
$$2H_2O_2 \rightarrow 2H_2O + O_2$$
$$68 \quad 36 + 32$$
$$CaCO_3 + 2HCl \rightarrow CaCl_2 + H_2O + CO_2$$
$$100 + 73 \quad 111 + 18 + 44$$
$$C + O_2 \rightarrow CO_2$$
$$12 + 32 \quad 44$$

2. PRECAUTIONS WHEN PERFORMING CHEMICAL EXPERIMENTS

You can learn a great deal about chemicals and chemical changes by *experimenting*. However, it is not wise to work with chemicals without knowing the dangers involved. Some substances, if improperly handled, may injure you. It is important, therefore, that before handling chemicals or performing experiments, you carefully follow these precautions:

a. Learn as much as you can about the experiment before you perform the experiment. Always perform an experiment in the presence of an authority.

b. After cutting glass tubing, fire-polish the cut ends to eliminate sharp edges. This is done by slowly rotating the cut ends in a Bunsen flame. Remember to allow all heated glass to cool.

c. Wet or lubricate glass tubing before attempting to insert or remove the tubing from rubber stoppers. Seek assistance if in doubt.

d. Always dilute acids by slowly adding the acid to water, while stirring the mixture constantly.

e. Where heat is required, use heat-resistant glassware so that the danger of cracking is lessened.

f. Do not taste any chemicals. Many are poisonous.

g. Always wear safety goggles in the laboratory.

3. SOME TYPICAL CHEMICAL CHANGES: OXYGEN

When mercuric oxide is heated, mercury and oxygen are formed (Fig. 21-1). This is a chemical change because new matter has been produced. The equation for this change can be written as follows:

$$2HgO \rightarrow 2Hg + O_2$$

mercuric mercury oxygen
oxide

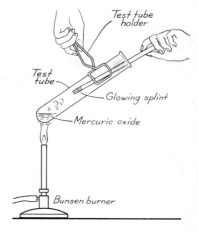

Fig. 21-1. Preparing oxygen. The test tube containing red mercuric oxide is heated for about two minutes. Heating causes the mercuric oxide to decompose (break down) into mercury and oxygen. The mercury appears as a silvery deposit on the upper, cooler portion of the test tube. We test for the presence of oxygen in the tube by inserting a glowing splint. If the splint bursts into flame, oxygen is present. This is the test for oxygen.

Oxygen can also be made by carefully heating dilute (3%) hydrogen peroxide in the presence of manganese dioxide.

Most living things need oxygen to maintain their life functions. Burning also requires the presence of oxygen.

4. CARBON DIOXIDE

Carbon dioxide can be prepared and collected by the reaction between an acid, such as hydrochloric acid, HCl, and marble chips, $CaCO_3$. The equation for this change is

$$2HCl + CaCO_3 \rightarrow CaCl_2 + H_2O + CO_2$$

| | marble | calcium chloride | | carbon dioxide |

Since carbon dioxide does not dissolve very readily in water, the gas is collected by the displacement of water (Fig. 21-2). This means that the carbon dioxide takes the space occupied by the water and pushes the water out of the collecting bottle into the trough.

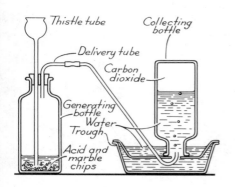

Fig. 21-2. Preparing and collecting carbon dioxide. The hydrochloric acid is added to the marble by pouring the acid through the thistle tube. The bubbles of gas which result from the reaction enter the collecting bottle. Because the bubbles of gas do not dissolve readily in water, they displace the water.

A burning splint inserted into a bottle of carbon dioxide is extinguished. This happens because carbon dioxide does not support (permit) combustion. Bubbling carbon dioxide through limewater causes the limewater to turn milky. This is the test for carbon dioxide.

Carbon dioxide can also be prepared by (1) adding water to baking powder, or (2) by adding vinegar (acetic acid) or sour milk (lactic acid) to baking soda (bicarbonate of soda).

Carbon dioxide is used to make dry ice (solid carbon dioxide) and also carbonated beverages. Fizzing is the release of dissolved carbon dioxide from the beverage.

Carbon dioxide, on a large scale, results from the burning of coal. Carbon dioxide blankets the atmosphere and is partly responsible for warming the earth. Read the *greenhouse effect* on page 364.

5. HYDROGEN

The lightest of all gases, hydrogen is prepared in the laboratory by the reaction of certain metals and certain acids. For example, when zinc is added to hydrochloric acid, bubbles of hydrogen are given off. Since hydrogen, like carbon dioxide, does not dissolve readily in water, it may also be collected by water displacement. The equation for this change is

$$Zn + 2HCl \rightarrow ZnCl_2 + H_2$$

zinc   hydro-   zinc   hydrogen
       chloric chloride
       acid

When hydrogen burns, it combines with oxygen to form water. Hydrogen is an important part of many fuels. A mixture of hydrogen and oxygen (or air) will explode when ignited. Therefore, great care should be exercised when working with hydrogen.

6. CHEMICAL CHANGES PRODUCED BY ELECTRICITY

The passage of electricity through certain solutions results in the formation of new substances and is therefore a chemical change. In this manner, water can be decomposed into two gases, hydrogen and oxygen. By means of an electric current, metals can be plated on objects (Fig. 21-3).

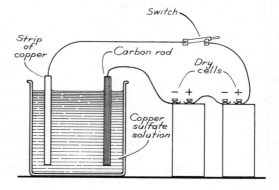

Fig. 21-3. Electroplating copper. The carbon rod is connected to one of the negative (−) terminals of the dry cells. The strip of copper is connected to one of the positive (+) terminals. Both the carbon rod and the copper strip are suspended in the copper sulfate solution. After the switch is closed for a few minutes, the carbon rod becomes plated with pure copper.

7. ACIDS AND BASES

It is frequently necessary to know if matter is acidic or basic (alkaline). To find out, a chemist uses an indicator, a substance which changes color when placed in an acid or base. One common indicator is a plant extract called *litmus*. A piece of blue litmus paper will turn pink or red when placed in an acid; a piece of red litmus paper will turn blue when placed in a base (Fig. 21-4).

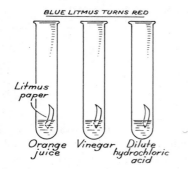
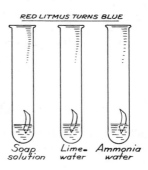

Fig. 21-4. Testing for acids and bases. By placing a strip of blue litmus paper into each of the first three test tubes, we can determine that each of the substances is an acid. Inserting red litmus paper into the other tubes shows that each of those substances is a base.

Acids and bases are chemical opposites. If the proper quantity of acid is mixed with a base, the resulting solution will be neither acidic nor basic. Such a solution is said to be *neutral*.

A physician frequently tests blood and urine to determine the presence of acid or base. Blood is normally slightly basic; urine is acidic.

Acids and bases should be handled with great care. Some of these substances can produce serious burns if brought into contact with the body. The best immediate first-aid treatment is to wash the affected part of the body with water. If an eye is affected, wash with water and seek medical help immediately. Some common acidic and basic substances are:

ACIDIC	BASIC
Vinegar	Bicarbonate of soda
Lemon juice	Washing soda
Sour milk	Household ammonia
Carbonated soda	Milk
Hydrochloric acid	Lye

8. THE SCIENTIFIC METHOD

Scientists are men and women who try to follow a series of logical steps in solving a problem. They first try to understand all the aspects of the problem being studied. They then perform various experiments, recording faithfully all results and observations. When sufficient observations have been made, they try to state the law of nature controlling these happenings. This law is sometimes called a *regularity* of nature. They accept this law or principle until it is disproved by other findings. This type of procedure for solving problems is called the *scientific method*. It includes the following main steps:

a. A clear statement of the problem to be solved.

b. Suggestions for conducting the experiment.

c. Performing the experiment.

d. Gathering and recording the observations and results.

e. Tentatively trying to explain the results.

f. Stating the law, principle, or regularity that has been discovered.

Whether or not you enter scientific work in later life, applying the logical thinking of the scientific method may help you solve many problems of daily living.

9. USING SCIENTIFIC MODELS

Suppose you want to explain why gases exert pressure against the walls of a container. Since you cannot see what a gas is made of, it might be useful to compare the enclosed gas with the behavior of something related to this gas; for example, billiard balls contained on a billiard table. The billiard balls would serve as a *model*, or mental picture of the particles in the gas. Scientists know what happens when one of these billiard balls strikes a bunch of billiard balls. All the balls fly out in special ways in different directions. Some of the balls may hit the sides of the table and rebound. From this model, you can reason that the tiny particles in a gas, like billiard balls, strike one another and, in turn, strike the walls of the container, thus producing pressure. Models help scientists resolve certain problems.

Multiple-Choice Questions

Write the number preceding the correct answer.

1. Before glass tubing is inserted into a rubber stopper, the tubing should be (1) sharpened (2) cooled (3) dipped into water (4) heated.
2. The gas produced when mercuric oxide is heated is (1) carbon dioxide (2) mercury (3) hydrogen (4) oxygen.
3. A girl thrusts a glowing splint into a bottle containing a gas. If the splint bursts into flame, the gas is (1) steam (2) oxygen (3) carbon dioxide (4) nitrogen.
4. Baking soda produces carbon dioxide when mixed with (1) water (2) sweet milk (3) sour milk (4) flour.
5. If a burning match is held over a mixture of baking powder and water (1) an explosion will occur (2) the match will be extinguished (3) the match will burn more brightly (4) the match will burn normally.
6. The bubbling in soft drinks or sodas is due to (1) air dissolved in the liquid (2) carbon dioxide dissolved in the liquid (3) alcohol in the liquid (4) sugar in the liquid.
7. A gas that is much lighter than air is (1) hydrogen (2) nitrogen (3) carbon dioxide (4) oxygen.
8. When hydrogen is burned (1) carbon dioxide is formed (2) oxygen is formed (3) water is formed (4) a physical change takes place.
9. A spoon can be silverplated by (1) immersing the spoon in a silvery substance (2) using an electric current (3) wiping on liquid silver (4) rubbing the spoon against a pure silver spoon.
10. A substance that causes blue litmus paper to turn red is (1) alcohol (2) an acid (3) a base (4) a salt.
11. If a strong acid spills on your hand, you should (1) rub your hand with a clean handkerchief (2) run water on the hand (3) pour a different acid on the hand (4) throw salt on the hand.
12. A common substance containing acid is (1) baking soda (2) flour (3) soap flakes (4) vinegar.
13. A substance containing enough acid to be tasted is (1) lemonade (2) fresh milk (3) cocoa (4) maple sugar.
14. Scientists find the answers to many problems by (1) guesswork only (2) using the scientific method (3) listening to hearsay (4) jumping at conclusions.
15. In solving a problem, a scientist (1) uses a model (2) records only certain findings (3) never changes his conclusions (4) does not listen to other scientists.
16. The symbol for sodium is (1) S (2) So (3) N (4) Na.
17. A neutron has an atomic mass unit of (1) 1 (2) 1/1837 (3) 3 (4) 16.

18. In the formula H_2O_2, the atomic mass of oxygen is (1) 1 (2) 2 (3) 16 (4) 32.
19. To balance the equation $H_2 + O_2 \rightarrow H_2O$, the proper coefficient for H_2O is (1) 1 (2) 2 (3) 16 (4) 18.
20. The atomic mass of sodium is (1) 11 (2) 12 (3) 23 (4) 34.

Completion Questions

Write the word or expression that correctly completes the statement.

1. Acids are diluted by adding the _____ to _____.
2. _____ is a type of glassware that can be heated to high temperatures without cracking.
3. Heating mercuric oxide produces oxygen and _____.
4. The gas that causes limewater to turn milky is _____.
5. Carbon dioxide may be prepared in the laboratory by reacting _____ with an acid.
6. The gas from which dry ice is manufactured is _____.
7. Baking powder is used in cake-making because the baking powder serves as a source of _____.
8. A burning splint when placed in a bottle containing carbon dioxide will _____.
9. If a substance causes red litmus paper to turn blue, the substance must be a (an) _____.
10. Ammonia water used for household cleaning is a (an) _____ (acid, base).

Reasoning Questions

Give a reason for each of the following.

1. Before inserting or removing glass tubing from rubber stoppers, it is necessary to wet the glass tubing.
2. Mercuric oxide is an example of a compound.
3. A burning splint inserted into a bottle of carbon dioxide is quickly extinguished.
4. Care should be exercised when working with hydrogen in the laboratory.
5. The object that is to be electroplated is connected to the negative terminal of the battery.
6. An acid is the chemical opposite of a base.
7. Many problems can be solved by applying the scientific method.
8. Scientific models change from time to time.
9. The sum of all the atomic masses on the left side of a balanced equation equals the sum of the atomic masses on the right side.
10. Atoms cannot be weighed on ordinary balances.

Chapter 22. What Happens When Substances Burn?

1. FUELS AND ENERGY

LESSON 2# ANSWER 3#

A *fuel* is any substance that is combustible (can burn), producing heat energy. A fuel may be a solid, liquid, or gas. The efficiency of a fuel depends both on (*a*) the amount of heat a given quantity of fuel releases when burned, and (*b*) its cost. Coal, oil (petroleum), and natural gas, called *fossil fuels*, are the most widely used fuels. Nuclear fuels (Fig. 28-2, page 272) are also important sources of energy. A substance that does not burn, such as sand or asbestos, is called a *noncombustible*.

2. TOXIC PRODUCTS OF COMBUSTION

Because so much fuel is being consumed, we must be concerned with the products of combustion, other than heat energy. Some of these products are poisonous, or *toxic*, and the great increase in the quantities entering the atmosphere may threaten the existence of all living things.

For example, when coal burns, it releases toxic sulfur and nitrogen compounds. These substances are gases and contribute to the formation of smoke and fog, called *smog*. This is a dense, clinging vapor that can create serious health problems, especially in breathing. Further, the sulfur and nitrogen compounds are washed into the soil by rain, forming *acid rain*. This can be damaging to plant life. The acid rain problem is especially severe in the Northeast because the prevailing winds blow the toxic gases in this direction. Burning coal also forms very large amounts of carbon dioxide, a gas that blankets the earth. Carbon dioxide is chiefly responsible for the *greenhouse effect* (page 364).

Both the gasoline and diesel engines also produce very harmful gases that can reach very dangerous levels in the atmosphere.

FUELS AND OUR WORLD

The increase in the world's population has made enormous demands on our energy resources. Coal, oil, and natural gas, also called *fossil fuels*, are the major sources of fuels. It has been estimated that there are about 7 trillion (7,000,000,000,000) tons of coal within the earth as well as about 1 trillion barrels of oil. Yet the coal supply is not expected to last more than four or five hundred years. Further, the world burns more than 4 million barrels of oil every hour. Spills are also depleting our oil supplies. Since natural gas is related to oil production, the supply of natural gas is also limited.

Steps are being taken to lessen the effects of this energy crisis. Conservation practices are helping somewhat. Improvements in our technology are permitting the development of new sources of fuels. The extraction of coal and oil from the ground are becoming more efficient, and fuel losses are becoming smaller. The future of our energy sources is expected to be related to the development of nuclear fuels. This source, however, has many problems that have yet to be solved.

The use of fuels to meet our energy needs is the concern of all peoples on this planet. This is our first and most important priority, if we are to survive.

3. TYPES OF FUELS

There are four common groups of fuels.

a. Forms of carbon, such as coke, charcoal, and coal.

Some Common Fuels

State	Fuels	Source	Uses
Solids	Coke	Soft coal	Fuel; aids in extracting iron from iron ores
	Charcoal	Wood	Fuel
	Coal	Nature	Fuel; source of chemicals used to make dyes and drugs
Liquids	Petroleum	Nature	Fuel; source of hydrocarbons
	Gasoline	Petroleum	Fuel in gasoline engine
	Kerosene	Petroleum	Household fuel; provides lighting; fuel in rocket engines
Gases	Natural gas	Nature	Household and commercial fuel
	Acetylene	Reacting calcium carbide with water	Torches to cut metal
	Hydrogen	Water	Torches to cut metal

b. Mixtures of hydrocarbons, such as petroleum. Petroleum can be broken down into simpler hydrocarbon mixtures, like gasoline and kerosene. Paraffin, or wax, is a mixture of solid hydrocarbons also derived from petroleum.

c. Hydrocarbons, which are compounds of hydrogen and carbon. Natural gas, also called methane, is a hydrocarbon.

d. Fissionable elements, such as plutonium. These elements are used as "fuels" in nuclear reactors, which are important power sources. (See page 272, section 2.)

4. SOURCES OF FUELS

Some fuels are obtained from nature; other fuels are manufactured.

a. From Nature. Fossil fuels, such as coal, petroleum, and natural gas, are produced in the earth by the decay of dead organisms, or organic matter. The sun is responsible for the growth of the organic matter from which the fuel was formed. The sun therefore is the source of most of the energy on the earth.

b. By Artificial Means. Manufactured fuels are used for special purposes. The process of *destructive distillation* produces two forms of carbon used as fuels: charcoal and coke. Charcoal is produced by the destructive distillation of wood; coke is produced by the destructive distillation of soft coal. Destructive distillation is the heating of a substance in the absence of air (Fig. 22-1).

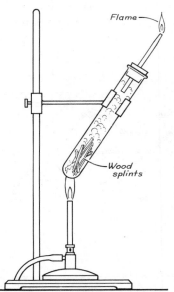

Fig. 22-1. Destructive distillation. Heating wood in the airtight test tube drives off many substances. The solid residue left in the test tube is charcoal. The liquid residue is wood tar, and the gas that burns is a mixture of hydrocarbons.

Acetylene and hydrogen are produced by other special processes.

(*1*) The addition of water to calcium carbide produces acetylene.

$$CaC_2 + 2H_2O \rightarrow C_2H_2 + Ca(OH)_2$$

calcium   acetylene calcium
carbide   hydroxide

(*2*) The electrolysis of water produces hydrogen.

$$2H_2O \xrightarrow{\text{electrolysis}} 2H_2 + O_2$$

5. CONDITIONS NECESSARY FOR BURNING

In order for burning to take place, three conditions must be met:

a. A *fuel* must be present.

b. The fuel must be brought to its *kindling temperature*. Kindling temperature is the lowest temperature at which a substance catches fire and continues to burn.

Different fuels have different kindling temperatures (Fig. 22-2). A fuel is raised to its kindling temperature by applying the proper amount of heat. Paper catches fire easily because it has a low kindling temperature. Coal, because of its high kindling temperature, requires much heat before it will begin to burn. This is why burning paper and then wood are required to start a coal fire. Matches are tipped with phosphorus, or some other low kindling material, to permit the small amount of heat produced by friction to ignite the phosphorus on the head of the match.

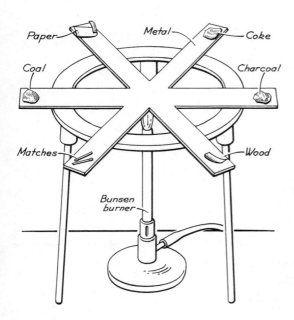

Fig. 22-2. Kindling temperatures. A metal cross containing six sections rests on an iron ring held directly above the burner. A different material is placed on the tip of each section. Since different amounts of heat are required, each material bursts into flame at a different time.

Fig. 22-3. Burning requires oxygen. After the candle burns in the glass tumbler for about a minute, the tumbler is covered with a glass plate. The flame soon goes out, showing that burning requires a continuous supply of oxygen.

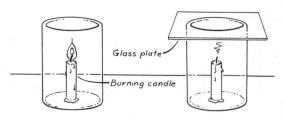

Glass plate

Burning candle

c. A supply of *oxygen* (or air) must be present (Fig. 22-3). The greater the amount of oxygen available, the more rapidly a fuel will burn.

6. PRODUCTS OF COMBUSTION

Various substances result from burning, or combustion. When a hydrocarbon burns, different products are formed, depending upon the amount of oxygen present.

   a. When a sufficient supply of oxygen is present, *complete combustion* takes place, yielding water and carbon dioxide.
   b. When an insufficient supply of oxygen is present, *incomplete combustion* occurs, forming water and carbon (Fig. 22-4).

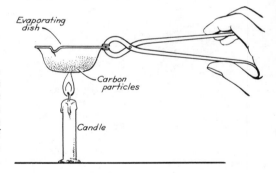

Evaporating dish

Carbon particles

Candle

Fig. 22-4. The candle flame. A black deposit appears on the cold, white dish held above the flame. The yellow hydrocarbon flame from the burning candle contains heated particles of carbon. These particles, when cooled, deposit on the dish.

   c. Under certain conditions, incomplete combustion of a hydrocarbon produces water and carbon monoxide. This gas is colorless, odorless, and poisonous. This is why the engine of an automobile must not be left running in a closed garage. The formation of carbon monoxide can be deadly.

7. THE BUNSEN BURNER

The *Bunsen burner* (Fig. 22-5), which uses a gaseous fuel, is a convenient heating device used in the laboratory. By controlling the amount of air entering the burner, it is possible to control the temperature of the flame. The Tirrill and Meker burners are also used in the laboratory to provide hotter flames.

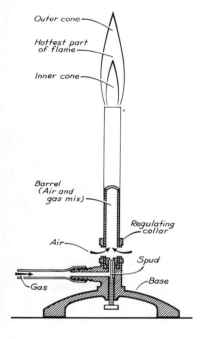

Fig. 22-5. How a Bunsen burner works.
The mixture of air and gas is ignited and burns as it leaves the top of the barrel. A proper mixture of air and gas results in a colorless, hot flame. A mixture containing too little air burns with a yellow flame. Such a flame will deposit carbon particles on cool surfaces, as the candle flame did in the previous figure.

Complete combustion takes place in the outer cone, incomplete combustion in the inner cone.

8. KINDS OF OXIDATION

Oxidation is the combining of a substance with oxygen to form oxides. There are two kinds of oxidation: *rapid* and *slow*.

a. Rapid Oxidation. In *rapid oxidation*, oxygen combines quickly with a substance, giving off noticeable heat and light. When magnesium burns, magnesium oxide is formed.

$$2Mg + O_2 \rightarrow 2MgO$$
$$\text{magnesium}$$
$$\text{oxide}$$

Ordinary burning, also called *combustion*, is an example of rapid oxidation.

b. Slow Oxidation. In *slow oxidation*, oxygen combines so slowly with a substance that no noticeable heat or light is produced. The rusting of iron is an example of slow oxidation (Fig. 22-6). Thus, when iron rusts, iron oxide is formed.

$$2Fe + O_2 \rightarrow 2FeO$$
iron   iron oxide

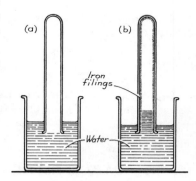

Fig. 22-6. The rusting of iron. One tube (*b*) has moist iron filings sprinkled inside of it, while the other (*a*) does not. Both test tubes have been allowed to stand in water, mouth-down, overnight. In rusting, the iron filings combine slowly with the oxygen of the air. A volume of water rises in the test tube equal approximately to the volume of oxygen used up in the rusting. To check the results of the experiment, the other tube (*a*) is used as a *control*. A control experiment is a parallel experiment in which one of the conditions has been removed. In the control (*a*), where iron filings were not present, water did not rise in the rube.

9. HOW TO PREVENT RUSTING

Rusting is slowed down considerably when the oxygen of the air is prevented from coming in contact with the iron. This is done by covering the surface of the iron with a film of paint or oil. Rusting may also be prevented by coating the iron with another metal like tin or zinc which forms protective oxide coverings.

10. SPONTANEOUS COMBUSTION

Fires often seem to start without outside help. The bursting into flame of a substance which has not intentionally been raised to its kindling temperature is called *spontaneous combustion*. Spontaneous combustion occurs when the heat resulting from slow oxidation accumulates until the kindling temperature of the combustible substance is reached.

Thus, if oily rags are kept in a poorly ventilated place, such as a closet, the oil will oxidize slowly. Heat will accumulate until the kindling temperature of the oil is reached. In storing an object that oxidizes slowly, the safest procedure is to enclose it in a covered metal container. If this cannot be done, make sure there is an adequate circulation of air to permit the heat to escape rapidly. For example, oily rags should be spread out and hung up in the open.

11. HOW DO WE PUT OUT FIRES?

Burning requires that (a) a fuel be present, (b) the fuel be raised to its kindling temperature, and (c) oxygen be available. To extinguish a fire, we must remove at least one of these conditions.

a. Remove or Scatter the Fuel. For example, spreading the burning embers of a small fire will cause the fire to go out.

b. Lower the Temperature of the Burning Material Below Its Kindling Point. Using certain fire extinguishers or pouring water on a piece of burning wood lowers the temperature of the wood below its kindling point and puts the fire out.

c. Cut Off the Supply of Oxygen. Wrapping a blanket around a person whose clothes are on fire smothers the fire by removing the supply of oxygen. Some types of fire extinguishers release a heavy noncombustible gas that sinks over the fire, thus keeping oxygen away. Water poured on a fire may also smother the fire.

12. THE SODA-ACID FIRE EXTINGUISHER

The *soda-acid fire extinguisher* is still the most commonly used extinguisher. This type of extinguisher, holding about 9 liters of liquid, consists of a brass or copper tank containing bicarbonate of soda ($NaHCO_3$) dissolved in water. Suspended from the top of the tank is a loosely-stoppered bottle containing sulfuric acid, H_2SO_4 (Fig. 22-7).

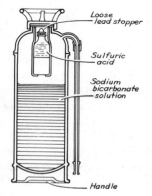

Loose lead stopper

Sulfuric acid

Sodium bicarbonate solution

Handle

Fig. 22-7. Soda-acid fire extinguisher. When the extinguisher is turned upside down, the sulfuric acid spills out of the bottle and reacts with the bicarbonate of soda. The reaction produces water and carbon dioxide.

Since the carbon dioxide is generated in a closed container, it builds up sufficient pressure to force out a stream of water and carbon dioxide through the nozzle of the hose. The fire is extinguished because (a) the water cools the burning fuel below its kindling temperature, and (b) the carbon dioxide cuts off the supply of oxygen.

The soda-acid fire extinguisher is useful on small fires but cannot be used on the following kinds of fires:

a. Electrical Fires. The liquid issuing from the extinguisher is a good conductor of electricity. Electrical fires may therefore spread if soda-acid fire extinguishers are used.

b. Oil Fires. Since oil floats on water, the effect of spraying water on such a fire will be to spread the fire.

13. OTHER TYPES OF FIRE EXTINGUISHERS

a. Foam. This type releases a heavy foam which puts out an oil fire by cutting off the supply of oxygen.

b. Carbon Dioxide. This type contains liquid carbon dioxide under pressure. Opening the valve causes the carbon dioxide to vaporize and shoot out in the form of a "snow" which blankets the fire. Carbon dioxide fire extinguishers may be used on electrical and oil fires.

c. Dry Chemicals. This type releases a powder consisting of either sodium bicarbonate, potassium bicarbonate, or ammonium phosphate. When sodium bicarbonate or potassium bicarbonate becomes hot, carbon dioxide is released. When ammonium phosphate becomes hot, it melts and forms a sticky layer on the burning material. Thus, dry-powder extinguishers release substances that cut off the oxygen from a fire and may therefore be used on electrical and oil fires.

14. HOW CAN FIRES BE PREVENTED?

Good common sense and a little knowledge can prevent most fires, or at least minimize damage and injury—if a fire has started. The following simple rules should be observed:

a. Matches should be completely extinguished before being thrown away. If used out of doors, they should be broken into smaller bits after being extinguished.
b. Keep combustible materials in closed metal containers. The storing of excessive quantities of flammable materials in attics and basements is a fire hazard.
c. Repair all faulty electrical wiring. Don't overload a circuit; that is, don't use too many appliances on a single outlet. When a circuit breaker flips, do not restore the circuit until the cause of the flip is corrected.

d. The first thing to do to extinguish an electrical fire is to shut off the current. Electric appliances, such as irons or toasters, should be disconnected when not in use. Electric cords should be kept away from radiators and steam pipes. Worn or frayed cords should be replaced.

e. Know where the nearest fire extinguisher is and how to use it. Always keep the extinguisher where it is easily accessible, and never keep it locked.

f. Become fire-conscious. Remember: "The best time to fight fires is BEFORE they start."

Multiple-Choice Questions

Write the number preceding the correct answer.

1. An element present in all common fuels is (1) carbon (2) nitrogen (3) phosphorus (4) sulfur.
2. The source of all our energy is (1) coal (2) hydroelectric plants (3) petroleum (4) the sun.
3. The destructive distillation of wood produces (1) soft coal (2) coke (3) charcoal (4) fires.
4. The part of a match that ignites at the lowest temperature is (1) the part containing phosphorus (2) the part containing sulfur (3) the part containing paraffin (4) the wood.
5. Asbestos does not burn because it (1) does not combine readily with oxygen (2) is a mineral (3) is chemically treated (4) is easily separated into fibers.
6. In order to burn, a substance must unite with (1) carbon dioxide (2) oxygen (3) nitrogen (4) water vapor.
7. Two products formed when a candle burns are carbon dioxide and (1) nitrogen (2) oxygen (3) sodium bicarbonate (4) water.
8. When a candle flame is held under a cold dish, a black spot often forms on the dish. This black spot is caused by (1) the scorching of the dish (2) ashes from the burned part of the dish (3) condensed water vapor (4) carbon from the paraffin of the candle.
9. The poisonous and odorless gas given off during the operation of an automobile engine is (1) carbon dioxide (2) carbon monoxide (3) nitrogen (4) mustard gas.
10. A kerosene stove, not connected to a chimney, burns in a small room. The air in the room now contains more (1) carbon dioxide (2) hydrogen (3) nitrogen (4) oxygen.
11. Oxidation in which noticeable heat and light are given off is called (1) combustion (2) decay (3) rusting (4) tarnishing.
12. Oxidation takes place during the process of (1) burning (2) melting (3) absorption (4) evaporation.

13. Oil or grease prevents steel from rusting because it (1) keeps the air away from the metal (2) keeps the light away from the metal (3) keeps the metal warm (4) makes the metal slippery.

14. Oily rags should not be left in closets where there is poor circulation of air because (1) fumes of the oil may be poisonous (2) oil in rags will stain the woodwork (3) slow oxidation of the oil may cause the rags to burn (4) rags serve as a breeding place for mice.

15. It is dangerous to heat cooking oils to very high temperatures because (1) food fried in oil loses its vitamins (2) food fried in oil may become charred (3) the oil may cause a food to become poisonous (4) the oil may burst into flame.

16. A gas commonly used to put out small fires is (1) nitrogen (2) helium (3) carbon dioxide (4) oxygen.

17. Burning oil is best extinguished by (1) pouring water on it (2) blowing out the flame (3) smothering the fire with something that will not burn (4) covering the fire with oxygen.

18. The dry-chemical fire extinguisher puts out fires by (1) blowing out the fire (2) combining with the oxygen and removing it from the air (3) forming a heavy layer that shuts off the air (4) scattering the fuel.

19. The most common cause of forest fires is (1) dry weather (2) human carelessness (3) railroads (4) spontaneous combustion.

20. A fire hazard is created when a person uses gasoline to clean materials indoors because the gasoline vapors (1) have a bad odor (2) affect paint (3) produce a combustible mixture with the air (4) escape easily.

Completion Questions

Write the word or expression that correctly completes the statement.

1. A combustible material that can be burned to release heat energy is called a (an) _____ .

2. Compounds containing hydrogen and carbon only are known as _____ .

3. Suspicious fires may be the result of _____ combustion.

4. Before any substance can burn, heat must be applied to bring the substance to its _____ temperature.

5. If carbon dioxide is produced when a fuel burns, the fuel must contain the element _____ .

6. When a substance combines with oxygen but no visible light or heat is produced, the process is called _____ .

7. Rusting is the combining of _____ with oxygen.

8. When a substance bursts into flame by itself, we say that the process of _____ has occurred.

9. When a fire has been put out by water, the firefighters watch to see that the material does not again reach its _____ .

10. You would not use the _____ fire extinguisher to put out an oil fire.

Modified True-False Questions

If a statement is true, write the word true. *If a statement is false, write the word or expression that must be substituted for the italicized expression to make the statement true.*

1. Coal, *acetylene*, and natural gas are fossil fuels.
2. When coal burns, it releases toxic *sulfur* and nitrogen compounds.
3. *Carbon dioxide* plays an important part in the greenhouse effect.
4. Our supplies of naturally occurring fuels are *unlimited*.
5. Destructive distillation is the heating of a substance in the *absence* of air.

Reasoning Questions

Give a reason for each of the following.

1. Nuclear fuels may take the place of fossil fuels in the future.
2. All fuels do not have the same kindling temperature.
3. A soda-acid fire extinguisher should not be used on electrical fires.
4. Metal surfaces should be thoroughly clean before they are painted.
5. The best time to fight fires is before they start.

Chapter 23. How Does Water Affect Our Lives?

1. IMPORTANCE OF WATER

Water is the most abundant compound on the earth. Water covers about three-fourths of the surface of the earth. Water is present in our oceans, rivers, lakes, soil, and in the atmosphere. The temperature of the earth, unlike that of other planets, is such that it permits water to be present in all three phases of matter; that is, as *gas* (water vapor), *liquid* (water), and *solid* (ice).

Depending on the temperature, water may evaporate to form water vapor, or it may freeze to form ice or snow. Upon warming, water returns to its liquid form. The series of changes from gas to liquid to solid is called the *water cycle* (Fig. 23-1). It is responsible for the movement of water from the atmosphere to oceans and rivers and back to the atmosphere.

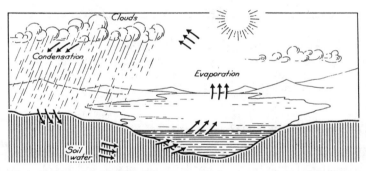

Fig. 23-1. The water cycle. The amount of water on the earth is kept constant by the water cycle. The water that enters the atmosphere as a vapor is returned to the earth as a liquid or solid.

All living things require water. Humans require fresh water, which is only a very small percentage of the total water on our planet.

Many common substances can be dissolved in water. Valuable elements, like magnesium and bromine, are recovered from their compounds in ocean water. Other elements such as silver, gold, and uranium are also present in sea water but in quantities that are too small to be recovered cheaply.

225

The following table shows the approximate percentage of water in different kinds of matter.

Human body 65%
Milk 90%
Bread......................35%
Meats ....50 to 70%

Figure 23-2 demonstrates a method of testing substances for the presence of water.

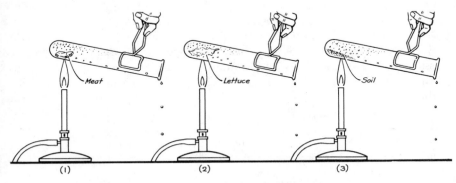

Fig. 23-2. Testing for the presence of water. The test tubes containing meat (1), lettuce (2), and soil (3) are heated slowly. Drops of water collect on the upper, cooler portions of the tubes and drip down, showing the presence of water in each of the substances.

2. WHY IS WATER PURIFIED?

Water found in nature is never pure. It contains dissolved substances as well as suspended matter, such as bacteria, small particles of soil, and bits of decaying plant and animal matter.

Water is purified for two reasons:

a. To make it *potable*, that is, fit for drinking. Potable water is free of disease-causing bacteria and impurities that give water an undesirable taste, color, or odor. Not all the impurities found in water make it unfit for human use. Many harmless minerals dissolved in water actually improve its taste. Some minerals, such as fluorides, are added to water supplies to strengthen teeth and make them less susceptible to the formation of cavities.

b. To make water chemically pure for use in drugs and industry. Chemically pure water is free of minerals and all other matter.

3. PURIFYING DRINKING WATER

Drinking water is purified in the following ways:

a. Settling. Water is allowed to stand in large basins, or *reservoirs*. As undissolved solids sink to the bottom, the clear water is pumped off.

b. Filtration. Water is allowed to pass through layers of sand and gravel. As the water seeps through these materials, suspended particles are filtered out. Bacteria and dissolved substances, however, cannot be removed by this process.

c. Coagulation. The settling of very small suspended particles can be speeded up by adding a *coagulant*, such as alum, to water. Alum, a sulfate compound of potassium and aluminum, produces a jellylike substance in the water, which traps and then drags down the suspended materials. The jellylike substance also holds together the finer particles which might otherwise pass through sand filters.

d. Chlorination. Chlorine is added to water in small, controlled amounts to destroy bacteria. The addition of chlorine is a cheap and effective means of water purification on a large scale, such as for a city.

e. Aeration. Water is sprayed into the air. Aeration allows the oxygen in the air to destroy bacteria and to remove bad odors and tastes. In addition, some of the air dissolves in the water and gives it a pleasant taste.

f. Boiling. Boiling water destroys many kinds of bacteria present in the water. Because of the cost involved, boiling is usually limited to small-scale water purification.

g. Desalinization (desalting). Under certain conditions and in certain places such as ocean liners, drinking water may be obtained from sea water by special chemical processes, called *ion-exchange*, or by distillation.

4. DISTILLATION OF WATER

Chemically pure water is made by *distillation*, a process that removes all dissolved minerals from water. Distilled water is not usually used for drinking because the removal of minerals and air makes the water taste flat. Minerals, however, may be added to restore the taste and make the water potable. Distilled water finds use in the preparation of medicines and in storage batteries.

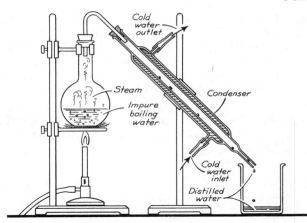

Fig. 23-3. Distilling water. Heating water in the flask causes the water to boil and change to steam. The steam is cooled as it passes through the cool inner tube of the condenser. The cooling process causes the steam to condense, forming pure (distilled) water.

LESSON 2# Answer 6

The distillation of water (Fig. 23-3) involves two steps: *boiling* and *condensing* (turning into a liquid). The impure water is boiled, forming steam. Upon cooling, the steam condenses to form liquid water. Since the mineral impurities do not vaporize easily (are nonvolatile), they remain behind in the distilling vessel. The condensed steam is chemically pure water. Rain water closely resembles distilled water because rain water results from the condensation of water vapor in the air.

Distillation may be used to recover a substance which has been dissolved in a liquid. For example, table salt can be recovered from the water in which it is dissolved. When the solution is heated, the nonvolatile salt remains behind in the distilling flask. Since the water vaporizes easily (is volatile), it boils and forms steam, which then condenses in the receiving vessel, where it is collected.

5. COMPOSITION OF WATER

Water, as we have learned, is a compound made up of two volumes of hydrogen and one volume of oxygen. Water can be broken down into these gases by passing an electric current through the water (Fig. 23-4 on next page). Two volumes of hydrogen and one volume of oxygen are obtained. This method of decomposing a compound into its elements is called *electrolysis*.

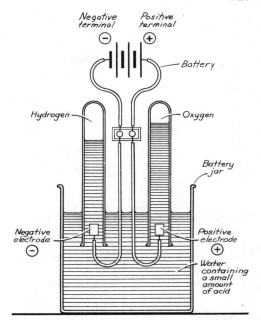

Fig. 23-4. Decomposing water by electrolysis. An electric current, from a battery, is passed through water. The water is acidified slightly, to make it a better conductor of electricity. The hydrogen obtained occupies twice the volume of the oxygen. This suggests that water consists of two parts of hydrogen to one part of oxygen by volume.

6. PROPERTIES OF WATER

Water may exist as a solid, liquid, or gas. At sea level, water boils at 212° Fahrenheit or 100° Celsius (centigrade); it freezes at 32°F or 0°C.

Most substances contract when cooled, but water expands when cooled below 4°C. This unusual property of water has a number of important consequences:

    a. Ice is lighter (less dense) than water and will float on water. Large bodies of water will therefore freeze along the top surface only, permitting aquatic life to exist below the surface.

    b. In freezing temperatures, water expands, and may burst pipes. Therefore, owners of summer residences drain water from the pipes before closing their homes for the winter.

    c. In cold weather, alcohol or some other antifreeze, such as ethylene glycol (Prestone), is added to the water in an automobile radiator to lower the freezing point of the liquid.

7. WATER AS A SOLVENT

Water is called the *universal solvent* because it can dissolve so many common substances. A *solvent* is a substance, usually a liquid, that can dissolve another substance. The *solute* is the substance dissolved. The combination of a solvent and a solute forms a *solution*.

For example, in a sugar solution, water is the solvent and sugar is the solute. If we were to study samples taken from different but equal parts of the solution, we would find that the sugar is distributed evenly (uniformly) throughout the water. A solution, therefore, is a uniform mixture of a solute and a solvent. This also means that a solution is *homogeneous*; that is, equal parts of a solution contain the same quantity of solute.

8. INCREASING THE SOLUBILITY OF SUBSTANCES IN WATER

There are a number of ways by which we can speed up dissolving various solutes in water. The method to be used depends on the phase of the solute.

a. Solid Solutes. Grinding (pulverizing or powdering) the particles of solids hastens the rate of solution. Heating and stirring the solution also speeds up dissolving the solute.

b. Liquid Solutes. Stirring, or shaking, hastens the rate of solution.

c. Gaseous Solutes. Cooling the water and increasing the pressure of a gas speed up dissolving the gas in water. Carbonated beverages, on standing, will taste flat because, as the beverage becomes warmer and the gas pressure decreases, bubbles of carbon dioxide leave the solution. Drinking water also tastes flat on standing because bubbles of dissolved air leave the water.

9. CRYSTALS AND CRYSTALLIZATION

If a solution containing a solid solute is allowed to evaporate slowly, or is allowed to stand, some of the solute will settle out. This process is called *crystallization*. Examining the solid that remains (the residue) reveals that it consists of many small solids, each having a definite geometric shape. These solids are called *crystals*. Rock candy, for example, is a mass of large sugar crystals.

10. CLEANSING ACTION OF SOAP AND DETERGENTS

a. Soap is made by boiling fat or oil with an alkali (base), such as lye (sodium hydroxide).

$$fat + lye \rightarrow soap + glycerine$$

Note that glycerine is an important by-product (additional product) in the manufacture of soap. Glycerine is used in drugs and in making certain explosives. When soap dissolves in water, it produces a solution which will form suds (lather).

b. Detergents are soap-like materials made without using fats. The lather of soap or detergents can break grease into tiny droplets, while water alone cannot. Grease is therefore washed away by soap and water or by detergents and water.

Certain detergents, especially phosphates, promote the growth of microorganisms, such as algae, which use up the available oxygen in water. This means that fish and other sea life cannot receive enough oxygen to survive. Pollution of natural waters from the use of these phosphates must be carefully controlled if aquatic life is to be maintained.

11. HARD WATER

Because water is an excellent solvent, it dissolves out many minerals from rocks and soil as it flows over them. Some of these minerals are compounds of calcium and magnesium. Water containing such dissolved minerals is called *hard water.* Hard water is undesirable for washing purposes because the dissolved calcium and magnesium compounds prevent the formation of soapsuds. Water which permits the easy formation of lather is called *soft water.* Rainwater and most kinds of drinking water are examples of soft water.

Hard waters present four problems:

a. The *taste* of hard water is unpleasant.

b. Hard water *wastes soap.*

c. Hard waters, especially those containing iron compounds, *stain laundry.*

d. Hard water *deposits minerals* in boilers and pipes, a condition called *boiler scale.* As minerals accumulate in a pipe, the inner diameter becomes narrower. As the pipe becomes clogged, the passage of water from the boiler slows down. Boiler explosions sometimes occur in this way.

12. SOFTENING HARD WATER

Hard water can be softened in several ways, depending on the kind of mineral present in the water.

a. By Boiling. Upon boiling, some of the minerals settle out. Then they can be removed by filtration. This type of hard water is called *temporary hard water*. Temporary hard water contains dissolved bicarbonates of calcium and magnesium. These minerals were dissolved out of limestone rock by running water containing carbon dioxide.

b. By Treatment with Water Softeners. Hard water that cannot be softened by boiling is called *permanent hard water*. Permanent hard water contains dissolved sulfates of magnesium, calcium, or iron. Water softeners, such as washing soda or borax, remove these minerals from solution.

Large-scale water softening is carried out by passing water through columns of certain silicate compounds, called *zeolites*, or by using special chemicals called *ion-exchange resins*. In these processes, both temporary and permanent hard waters in a water supply can be softened at the same time.

13. SOME SPECIAL USES OF WATER

a. Hardening of Plaster of Paris. When water is added to plaster of Paris, a sulfate of calcium, a thick paste, is formed. As the paste dries, it hardens into solid plaster. Plaster of Paris is used for making casts and impressions.

b. Setting of Concrete. Concrete consists of a mixture of cement, gravel, and sand to which water has been added. Cement is made from clay and limestone. Upon standing, even under water, concrete will harden. Concrete is used extensively in buildings and roads, for it is durable and fireproof.

WATER, WATER, EVERYWHERE

Oceans, rivers, and lakes have supplied us with water for many centuries. Wells, dug deep into the earth, have also been a source of water. From time to time, rainfall has replenished our water supply. It is almost reasonable to expect that we will never run out of water. But is this so?

All over the world, about 2 trillion gallons of fresh water are needed to meet human needs every day. In the United States alone, some 350 billion gallons of fresh water are used daily. If all the water in rainfall—or even a significant portion—could be regained, the supply of water would be adequate to meet our needs. Unfortunately, much of the water in rainfall cannot be recovered—at least not inexpensively. To make matters worse, tremendous quantities of water are being wasted by pollution and by carelessness.

The problem of an adequate water supply is becoming more serious as the population of the world continues to increase at an alarming rate. At present, about 5 billion people inhabit the earth, with an additional 75 million persons each year. Should this increase continue at the same rate, the world population is expected to double every 35 to 40 years. Are our water sources sufficient to meet the needs of this increasing population?

We are faced with a most important problem. It is serious enough or will soon become serious enough to threaten the survival of all living things including humans. What to do?

Some countries like China—population about 1 billion—are introducing population-control measures. Such programs appear to have halted the population explosion, but it is uncertain that the decrease will continue. Legislation designed to lessen pollution and waste are beginning to have an effect.

Newer methods of waste disposal may diminish the pollution of natural waters. More efficient recovery of water from rainfall shows promise. Redistribution of populations from large urban areas to smaller rural areas may also improve the water supply.

What lessons do we learn from all these facts and figures? The supply of water is not unlimited. Indeed, it is very limited. Only care, thoughtfulness, and ingenuity may enable us to survive.

Multiple-Choice Questions

Write the number preceding the correct answer.

1. Of the following, the metal obtained in large quantities from ocean water is (1) copper (2) iron (3) magnesium (4) zinc.
2. The salt in the ocean comes from (1) constant evaporation of the ocean water (2) decaying plants (3) minerals dissolved from the soil (4) rain.
3. Alum is used in the process of water purification called (1) boiling (2) distillation (3) coagulation (4) aeration.
4. Chlorine is often used in water purification to (1) clear muddy water (2) kill some harmful bacteria (3) serve as a substitute for soap (4) soften hard water.
5. The process used to improve the taste of water is (1) distillation (2) fluoridation (3) aeration (4) chlorination.
6. The process of distillation is used to produce water that (1) is soft (2) is chemically pure (3) contains many minerals (4) is hard.
7. One way to determine whether water has minerals dissolved in it is to (1) boil off the water to see if there is a residue (2) filter the water to see whether anything filters out (3) pour sugar into the water to see if the sugar will dissolve (4) smell the water to see if it has a mineral odor.
8. Water that has just been boiled will taste flat because (1) dissolved air has escaped from the water (2) it has been exposed to the light (3) the water has absorbed more air (4) the water has partially evaporated.
9. When salt water is boiled in an open pan (1) only the salt evaporates (2) only the water evaporates (3) both the salt and the water evaporate (4) neither the salt nor the water evaporate.
10. Water is composed of the elements (1) carbon and oxygen (2) carbon, hydrogen, and oxygen (3) hydrogen and oxygen (4) nitrogen and oxygen.

11. To separate water into its elements, it is necessary to (1) add salt and then boil the solution rapidly (2) add sulfuric acid to the water slowly (3) boil the water rapidly (4) pass an electric current through the water.
12. On earth, water may exist as a (1) solid or liquid only (2) gas or liquid only (3) liquid only (4) gas, liquid, or solid.
13. The boiling point of water on the Celsius scale is (1) 32° (2) 98° (3) 100° (4) 212°.
14. When sugar is dissolved in water, the water is called the (1) emulsion (2) precipitate (3) residue (4) solvent.
15. Solids dissolved in water (1) cannot color the water (2) can be removed by filtering (3) will leave no trace if the water is allowed to evaporate (4) will not settle out.
16. Salt that has been dissolved in water can be recovered by (1) evaporating the water (2) filtering the salt solution (3) pouring off the upper part of the solution (4) siphoning off the lower part of the solution.
17. Soap is made by boiling (1) fat and an alkali (2) fat and glycerine (3) fat and vegetable oils (4) fat and washing soda.
18. Hard water may be softened by (1) adding table salt (2) adding washing soda (3) filtering (4) freezing.
19. In a control experiment for testing the hardness of water, the water that should be used for comparison is (1) boiled water (2) distilled water (3) soda water (4) well water.
20. A substance that hardens when mixed with water is (1) baking soda (2) Epsom salts (3) plaster of Paris (4) table salt.
21. A substance not found in sea water is (1) fluorine (2) gold (3) silver (4) salt.
22. Ion-exchange resins are used to (1) flavor water (2) make soft water hard (3) make hard water soft (4) add oxygen to water.
23. Which of the following is *not* a method of purifying water? (1) coagulation (2) boiling (3) freezing (4) distillation.
24. Distillation involves boiling and (1) freezing (2) evaporation (3) filtration (4) condensation.
25. The proportion that represents the volume composition of water is hydrogen:oxygen as (1) 1:2 (2) 1:8 (3) 2:1 (4) 8:1.

Completion Questions

Write the word or expression that correctly completes the statement.

1. Water that can be used for human consumption is called _____ .
2. If you are on a hike, the surest way to make spring water safe for drinking is to _____ the water.
3. The process of _____ is used to remove bad tastes and odors from water.

4. In distilling water, first boil the water and then _____ the vapors.
5. When water freezes, it _____ (*expands, contracts*).
6. When salt dissolves in water, the salt is called the _____.
7. Solids that have a definite geometric shape are known as _____.
8. Soap forms abundant suds in _____ water.
9. Unlike soap, _____ is not required to make detergents.
10. Hard water can be softened by adding a water softener such as washing soda or _____.

Modified True-False Questions

If a statement is true, write the word true. *If a statement is false, write the word or expression that must be substituted for the italicized expression to make the statement true.*

1. Water is called the universal solvent because it *is so abundant*.
2. Nonvolatile solutes have *higher* boiling points than pure water.
3. Filtration cannot remove *bacteria*.
4. Boiling may be used for *large* scale water purification.
5. Distilled water is commonly used in *dry* cells.
6. Water is a (an) *mixture* of hydrogen and oxygen.
7. Ice floats on water because water is *denser* than ice.
8. When water dissolves in alcohol, the water is called the *solvent*.
9. Soaps are soluble in *soft* water.
10. *Temporary* hard water may be softened on a large scale by using chemical water softeners.

Reasoning Questions

Give a reason for each of the following.

1. Ice floats on water.
2. Dissolved solids cannot be separated from the solvent by filtration.
3. Rainfall restores only a small portion of our natural waters.
4. Only distilled water is useful in the manufacture of drugs.
5. If water did not expand on freezing, there would be no life on this planet.
6. Dissolved gases in water form volatile solutes.

Chapter 24. Chemistry and Your World

1. CHEMICAL BONDS

Recall, in Chapter 20, that when atoms combine to form molecules, attractive forces—called *bonds*—hold the atoms together. How do these bonds form? We will study two kinds of chemical bonds.

a. Ionic Bonds. Study Figure 20-6 on page 197 showing a sodium atom, atomic number 11; and a chlorine atom, atomic number 17. When these atoms combine, sodium loses its outermost electron and chlorine gains this electron. The sodium atom, having lost an electron, now has 10 electrons and still has 11 protons. The sodium atom has a charge of $1+$. The chlorine atom, having gained an electron, now has 18 electrons and still has 17 protons. The chlorine atom has a charge of $1-$. Charged atoms are called *ions*. The oppositely charged ions attract one another and form an *ionic bond*. Chemists sometimes use *electron-dot* formulas to show these changes.

In an electron-dot formula, dots are used together with the symbol of the element to indicate the electrons in the *outermost electron shell*. For example, Na represents a sodium atom, and Cl represents a chlorine atom. We can now show the transfer of one electron and the formation of the ionic bond, as follows:

$$\text{Na}^{\bullet} \xrightarrow{\text{ionic bond}} {\cdot}\ddot{\underset{\cdot\cdot}{\text{Cl}}}{:}$$

$$\text{Na}^{+} \left[{:}\ddot{\underset{\cdot\cdot}{\text{Cl}}}{:} \right]^{-}$$

Elements containing atoms that tend to lose electrons during chemical changes are called *metals*. When they lose electrons, metals form *positive ions*. Such elements are solids, have a shiny appearance, and conduct heat and electricity. Elements containing atoms that tend to gain electrons are called *nonmetals*. When they gain electrons, nonmetals form *negative ions*. Such elements may be solids or gases and are generally poor conductors of heat and electricity.

Table 24-1. Metals and Nonmetals

Metals	*Nonmetals*
Sodium	Chlorine
Potassium	Oxygen
Copper	Iodine
Silver	Nitrogen
Iron	Sulfur

b. Covalent Bonds. Recall again from Fig. 20-7 on page 197 that certain atoms may combine by sharing electrons. In this manner, each of the combining atoms attains a complete outermost electron shell. Using electron-dot formulas, note how two hydrogen atoms combine with one oxygen atom to form water.

$$H : \overset{..}{\underset{..}{O}} : H$$

In the electron structure for water, hydrogen has a complete outermost (K) shell with 2 electrons, and oxygen has a complete outermost (L) shell with 8 electrons. Bonds, or attractive forces, between the atoms that share electrons are called *covalent bonds*.

2. CHEMICAL CHANGES

Chemical changes, also called chemical reactions, were introduced in Chapter 21. Let us again examine the reaction between hydrochloric acid and calcium carbonate (marble chips). We can write the equation for this change as follows:

$$2HCl + CaCO_3 \rightarrow CaCl_2 + H_2O + CO_2$$

Note that the coefficient 2 in front of HCl enables us to balance all the atomic masses. In terms of chemical bonds, what is happening in this change? Notice that bonds are broken in HCl and $CaCO_3$. Recall that CO_3 is a radical—one carbon atom and three oxygen atoms behaving as a single unit. The four atoms are held together by covalent bonds. As bonds are broken on the left side of the equation, new bonds are formed on the right side. Thus, chemical changes are marked by bond-breaking and bond-making. When you continue your study of science, you will learn more about bonds, especially how bonds and energy are related.

For the present, as we continue our discussion of chemical changes, we will be interested in some important chemical reactions that shape our lives.

3. METALS AND ALLOYS

Metals find considerable use as structural materials and as conductors of heat and electricity. The properties of metals can be multiplied and improved by combination with other metals and nonmetals. Such improved metals are called *alloys*, and they play an important role in our daily lives. For example, steel, an alloy of iron and other metals and nonmetals, is the economic backbone of our world. Imagine where we would be without automobiles, railroads, bridges, and skyscrapers. And, add to these uses armaments, aircraft, and computers. In more recent times, aluminum alloys and magnesium alloys are also playing important roles in our technology.

Table 24-2 lists the composition and uses of some metals and their alloys.

Table 24-2. Metals and Alloys

Metal	Alloy	Composition	Uses
iron	steel	iron, carbon, manganese, molybdenum	structural steel, auto parts
	duriron	iron, carbon, silicon	acid-resistant materials
	stainless steel	iron, chromium, nickel	corrosion-resistant materials
aluminum	duralumin (dural)	aluminum, copper, magnesium, manganese, silicon	aircraft parts
magnesium	magnalium	magnesium, aluminum	household appliances, scientific instruments
nickel	nichrome	nickel, chromium	heating elements
lead	linotype metal	lead, antimony, tin	printing

4. INDUSTRIAL CHEMICALS

The chemical industry is one of the largest in the world. Manufactured chemicals are used directly or are converted into a variety of related compounds, called *derivatives*. Modern technology depends upon chemicals for growth and development. Chemists and chemical engineers are trained in our colleges and universities to meet these needs. Further study is helpful before seeking a job. If you have an inquisitive mind and enjoy science and mathematics, you might consider chemistry or chemical engineering as a career.

a. Sulfuric Acid. The world's most widely used single chemical is sulfuric acid. In the United States alone, many millions of tons of sulfuric acid are used annually in the production of steel, in the petroleum industry, and in the manufacture of fertilizers. There is probably no single chemical industry that does not use sulfuric acid at one stage or another.

The source of sulfuric acid is the element sulfur, which is extracted from underground mineral deposits by the *Frasch* process. Superheated steam (steam above 100°C) is pumped into the ground where it melts the sulfur. Compressed air then raises the melted sulfur to the ground.

In the manufacture of sulfuric acid, sulfur and sulfur-containing minerals are burned to form sulfur dioxide gas. The sulfur dioxide gas is converted to sulfur trioxide, using a catalyst at a temperature around 400°C. The sulfur trioxide, which is a white solid, is the source of sulfuric acid.

b. Sodium Hydroxide. Another important industrial chemical is sodium hydroxide, also called caustic soda. Recall the electrolysis of water on page 228, section 5. Sodium hydroxide is manufactured by the electrolysis of a concentrated solution of sodium chloride (salt). Sodium hydroxide is used in the petroleum and soap industries.

5. ORGANIC CHEMICALS

The substances we have discussed so far are of mineral origin and are called *inorganic* compounds. Another huge number of compounds of the element carbon are derived from living things and are called *organic* compounds. These substances of plant and animal origin, as well as many that have been made in the laboratory (synthesized), include foods, petroleum fuels, dyes, and drugs. Although fewer than a half-million inorganic compounds are known, more than two million organic materials are known. Why this tremendous difference?

We have discussed the formation of inorganic compounds, such as sodium chloride and calcium fluoride. These compounds were formed by electron transfer. Other inorganic compounds, especially those containing radicals—sulfates and nitrates—are formed by electron-sharing.

The element carbon, atomic number 6 and essential to all organic compounds, is most unusual. We can picture an atom of carbon as

$$\boxed{6+} \quad \overset{K}{\underset{\Big/}{\Big\backslash}} \, 2e^- \quad \overset{L}{\underset{\Big/}{\Big\backslash}} \, 4e^- \qquad \text{or} \qquad \cdot \overset{\cdot}{\underset{\cdot}{C}} \cdot$$

Carbon can complete its outermost electron shell most frequently by sharing electrons. Further, one carbon atom can share its *L*-electrons with other carbon atoms. For example:

$$\cdot \overset{\cdot}{C} \!:\! \overset{\cdot}{C} \cdot \quad \text{in the compound} \quad \overset{\text{H H}}{\underset{\text{H H}}{H \!:\! \overset{\cdot\cdot}{C} \!:\! \overset{\cdot\cdot}{C} \!:\! H}} \quad C_2H_6, \text{ called } \textit{ethane}$$

Carbon atoms may link together in endless chains, forming new substances with a variety of atoms, such as hydrogen, oxygen, or chlorine. In addition, carbon atoms may join together to form closed structures of varying shapes. Thus, the possibilities for compound formation are enormous and help to account for the large number of organic compounds. These substances are studied in a special branch of chemistry called *organic chemistry*, which you may want to pursue someday.

CHEMICAL INDUSTRIES AND THE ENVIRONMENT

The growth of chemical industries has improved our lives by creating more jobs and by raising the standard of living. At the same time, these industries have become among the chief polluters of our air and our water. For example, air is contaminated with the waste products of burning coal, which produces carbon dioxide, sulfur oxides, and nitrogen oxides. Carbon dioxide, especially, contributes to the *greenhouse effect*, described on page 364. Our protective *ozone layer* is threatened by the discharge of excessive quantities of freon into the atmosphere from coolants used in refrigeration and from pressurized containers. Discharge of metallic and plastic waste residues endangers our water supplies. Industries that allow millions of gallons of heated waste materials to flow into our lakes and rivers are causing *thermal pollution*. As these bodies of water become warmer, the amount of dissolved oxygen required to maintain aquatic life bubbles out of the water. Plant and animal life becomes threatened.

Environmental agencies at all levels are seeking a balance between the destructive, polluting forces and the forces that seek to improve our lives. Awareness of these problems and programs designed to alleviate them will go a long way toward effecting solutions.

Multiple-Choice Questions

Write the number preceding the correct answer.

1. The nucleus of an atom with atomic number 10 contains (1) 8 protons (2) 10 protons (3) 8 electrons (4) 10 electrons.
2. When an atom loses two electrons, it attains a charge of (1) 2+ (2) 2− (3) 1+ (4) 0.
3. Bonds between atoms formed by the transfer of electrons are called (1) covalent (2) atomic (3) ionic (4) molecular.
4. Elements containing atoms that tend to gain electrons are called (1) nonmetals (2) metals (3) monomers (4) polymers.
5. Electron sharing results in the formation of (1) ionic bonds (2) atoms (3) positive ions (4) radicals.
6. Alloys are most closely related to (1) metals (2) plastics (3) polymers (4) ions.
7. Stainless steel contains the elements iron, nickel, and (1) manganese (2) tin (3) chromium (4) copper.
8. The world's most widely used chemical is (1) sulfuric acid (2) sodium hydroxide (3) carbon dioxide (4) salt.
9. The element present in all organic compounds is (1) oxygen (2) hydrogen (3) sulfur (4) carbon.
10. Natural rubber is a (1) polymer (2) monomer (3) metal (4) alloy.

Completion Questions

Write the word or expression that correctly completes the statement.

1. The compound of carbon that is chiefly responsible for the greenhouse effect is _____.
2. A kind of pollution caused by dumping heated wastes into our natural water is called _____.
3. The electron-dot formula for hydrogen is _____.
4. Elements that are poor conductors of heat are _____ (*metals, nonmetals*).

Reasoning Questions

Give a reason for each of the following.

1. Atoms that gain electrons during chemical change form negative ions.
2. The atoms in a radical are held together by covalent bonds.
3. Metals tend to lose electrons during chemical changes.

4. Steel is a very important metal in our economy.
5. Chemistry and chemical engineering are rewarding professions.
6. The preparation of sulfur trioxide from sulfur dioxide requires the use of a catalyst.
7. Superheated steam is used in the Frasch process.
8. Organic compounds are more numerous than inorganic compounds.
9. The burning of large quantities of coal contributes to the greenhouse effect.

REVIEW OF UNIT IV

1. Explain the following.
   a. A glass tube should be dipped into water before it is inserted into a rubber stopper.
   b. When you blow through a straw into limewater, the limewater becomes milky (cloudy).
   c. When you squeeze a lemon into half a cup of water, you observe that litmus paper, placed in the solution, turns red.
   d. A can of baking powder should be kept tightly covered when not in use.
   e. Stepping on a burning match puts out the flame.
2. A gas is generated by placing hydrochloric acid on zinc metal. The gas is used to fill a balloon, and then the neck of the balloon is tied.
   a. What is the gas?
   b. What did the balloon do when it was released?
3. Tell what happens in each of the following.
   a. A glowing splint is placed in a bottle of oxygen.
   b. A dish of limewater is exposed to the air.
4. Give a reason for each of the following.
   a. Rags used to wipe up oil paint should be destroyed or kept in a covered metal container.
   b. A match is scratched in order to light it.
   c. A candle will burn for only a short time when placed in a closed vessel.
   d. It is dangerous to close the door of a garage in which there is a car with the engine running.
   e. A camp fire should always be put out.
   f. Water should not be used to try to extinguish burning oil.
   g. Wood shavings burn faster than does a block of wood.
5. Describe a practical way of extinguishing each of the following.
   a. a grass fire in a field
   b. a camp fire that is to be abandoned
   c. a puddle of burning oil near a building
   d. a cigarette butt in the woods
   e. a burning dress on a child

6. Explain how you can either prove or disprove the following.
   a. Carbon dioxide helps fires to burn.
   b. Oxygen is necessary for combustion.
7. Give an example of each of the following.
   a. a fuel used in the home
   b. a gas used in some fire extinguishers
   c. a noncombustible substance
   d. a substance used to remove small, suspended particles in water
   e. using ocean water as a source of drinking water
8. Suppose you turn a glass jar upside down and set it over a lighted candle. The candle soon stops burning. You then try different jars and different candles, and the same thing always happens. Which of the following can you conclude from this experiment? Give a reason for your conclusion.
   a. The carbon dioxide produced by the burning candle put the flame out.
   b. A candle will not burn without a continuous supply of air.
9. In which case (A or B) will a flame appear at the end of the glass tube? Why?

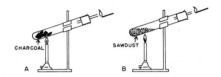

10. What conclusion can you draw from the experiment pictured below?

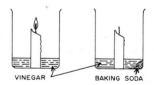

11. Tell whether each of the following practices is good or bad, and why.
    a. Kerosene is added to a fire to make it burn faster.
    b. All the windows are opened after putting out a small fire with a carbon dioxide fire extinguisher.
    c. Ice skates are wiped dry and oiled before they are stored for the summer.
    d. Sulfuric acid is diluted by pouring water slowly into it.
    e. A soda-acid fire extinguisher is used on an electrical fire.
12. State a scientific conclusion based upon the following observation: When a beaker is inverted over a candle flame, moisture collects on the inside surface of the beaker.

13. Each of the following statements is false. In place of the italicized word or expression in each, write a word or expression that will make the statement true.
    a. The freezing point of water under normal conditions is *32° centigrade*.
    b. *Salt* is a good water softener.
    c. Allowing water to seep through layers of sand and gravel is called *aeration*.
    d. Ice will *sink* in water.
    e. In a solution, the solute *will settle out*.
14. Describe an experiment to test the accuracy of the following statements.
    a. Salt lowers the freezing temperature of water.
    b. Rainwater is soft.
    c. Concrete requires water to harden.
    d. Soap is made from fat and lye.
    e. Water expands when it freezes.
15. Describe the water cycle.
16. The following is a description of a procedure performed in a science classroom. Describe what happens and tell why it happens.

    In this order, clean pebbles, coarse sand, and fine sand are placed in a large glass funnel. Muddy water is poured into the funnel, and the water that passes through is collected.
17. Give an example of each of the following.
    a. a common liquid used to dissolve many substances
    b. a method of purifying water
18. Account for the observation that unequal volumes of hydrogen and oxygen are produced during the electrolysis of water.
19. Using the billiard-ball model of the composition of gases, explain why the pressure inside a bicycle tire increases as you pump more air into the tire.
20. Water exists on earth in all three phases.

Unit V.
The Story of Energy

Chapter 25. How We Use Energy

1. SCIENCE, THE STORY OF ENERGY

All the basic ideas in science are related to some principle involving energy. We must understand what energy is, where it comes from, what it can do, and how it changes, in order to fully appreciate the effect of science on our lives.

2. WHAT IS ENERGY?

Energy is the ability to do work. Energy may be either *potential* or *kinetic*. Potential energy is stored energy. Kinetic energy is the energy of motion. A pile driver, when raised to a height, acquires potential energy. When the pile driver drops, its potential energy is changed into kinetic energy. It is the kinetic energy of the pile driver that enables it to do work.

People do work by using the energy they obtain from food. Machines do work by using human energy or the energy contained in fuels provided by humans. Energy is used to exert the force needed to overcome resistance or to produce motion. For example, when you walk, you use energy to overcome the friction (resistance) between the ground and the soles of your shoes.

3. THE SUN—OUR CHIEF SOURCE OF ENERGY

The sun is the source of the energy we obtain from food and fuel. Plants use energy from the sun to manufacture food. Animals feeding on the plants obtain the stored-up energy. The energy in the plants and animals is then passed along to us when we eat these foods.

The energy from the sun is also locked up in fuels, such as coal and oil. Fuels were formed in the earth millions of years ago from the decay of plants and animals. The fuels preserved the energy which these organisms, when living, obtained from the sun.

It has been known for over a century that sunlight can be transformed into electrical energy. To reduce pollution brought on by the use of fossil fuels and to reduce our dependence on oil, *solar energy* is slowly coming into use. Solar electric cells are being used in spacecraft and in areas that are distant from power supplies. The use of large-scale solar power has yet to be achieved because of the practical difficulties involved in the installation. But the manufacture of smaller solar batteries is becoming an important industry.

4. KINDS OF ENERGY

Food and fuel are examples of stored (potential) chemical energy. Yet there are many other kinds of stored energy. Each kind, if properly harnessed, can do work.

Table 25-1. Kinds of Energy and Their Sources

Kind of energy	Source
Heat	Burning fuel
Light (radiant)	Sun, or solar battery
Sound	Vibrations
Mechanical	Gasoline engine
Chemical	Storage battery
Electrical	Generator
Nuclear (atomic)	Reactor

5. ENERGY CHANGES IN AN AUTOMOBILE ENGINE

Many of the happenings around us depend on the fact that energy can be changed, or transformed, from one form to another. For example, the operation of a gasoline engine in an automobile depends on energy transformations. Similarly, the operation of a diesel engine depends on energy transformations.

a. In the Fuel System. Gasoline used in the automobile is obtained from petroleum, a fossil fuel derived chiefly from plant matter. The plants convert the light energy of the sun into chemical energy, and store it. When the gasoline is burned in the cylinders, the chemical energy is changed to heat energy. In the same way, oil is burned in a diesel engine to produce heat energy. In the cylinders, the heat energy is converted into mechanical energy, which powers the vehicle.

b. In the Electrical System. The storage battery transforms chemical energy into electrical energy. The electrical energy is changed to heat energy in the spark plugs, into light energy in the headlights, and into sound energy in the radio. In the generator, mechanical energy of the running engine is changed to electrical energy.

The table below summarizes some important energy transformations.

Table 25-2. Energy Transformations

Energy change	Example
Chemical to electrical	Storage battery
Mechanical to electrical	Generator
Electrical to mechanical	Motor
Sound to electrical, and vice versa	Radio
Light to electrical, and vice versa	Television
Light to heat	Solar heater
Heat to light	Electric lamp
Light to chemical	Photography
Mechanical to heat	Friction
Heat to mechanical	Steam engine
Nuclear (atomic to heat)	Nuclear reactor

6. USING ENERGY

We pay for the direct use of energy. For example, the power companies send us a bill regularly for the use of electricity, or for the use of household fuel, such as oil or natural gas. We also pay for the indirect use of energy. For example, the clothing we wear needs to be manufactured from wool, cotton, or synthetic (laboratory-made) fibers. The cost of our clothing depends not only on the price of the fiber, but also on the energy used in the manufacturing process. When we pay for food, we indirectly pay for the energy used in the preparation of the food.

7. ENERGY UNITS

To pay for energy, we must have some convenient method of measuring the amount of energy used. The amount, or quantity, of energy is expressed by different units that depend on the kind of energy being used. For example, heat is measured in calories, kilocalories, or in BTU's (British thermal units). Electrical energy is measured in kilowatt-hours. You will learn more about these units in a later chapter.

8. CONSERVATION OF ENERGY

Our use of energy shows that energy can be changed from one form to another but that it can neither be created nor destroyed. This is called the *Law of Conservation of Energy*.

When energy appears to be lost, it is really being wasted. For example, when electrical energy is used to power a light bulb, much of the energy is lost, or wasted, as heat. The efficiency of a light bulb depends upon how little energy is wasted as heat.

The Law of Conservation of Energy is one of the fundamental laws of science. This law is actually part of a broader law discussed on page 271.

Multiple-Choice Questions

Write the number preceding the correct answer.

1. The exertion of force requires the expenditure of (1) power (2) work (3) energy (4) food.
2. In order to do work, some machines use the energy contained in (1) air (2) fuels (3) gears (4) friction.
3. The energy contained in all living things can be traced to (1) animals (2) soil (3) the sun (4) water.
4. In the process of manufacturing food, plants (1) create energy (2) destroy energy (3) store the energy of the sun (4) do not require the energy of the sun.
5. The energy contained in fuels is an example of (1) radiant energy (2) chemical energy (3) mechanical energy (4) electrical energy.
6. Of the forms of energy listed, the form most recently discovered and being used by people is (1) sound (2) electrical (3) atomic (4) radiant.
7. When coal is burned, stored energy is released in the form of (1) atomic energy (2) chemical energy (3) mechanical energy (4) heat energy.
8. Energy (1) can be created (2) can be destroyed (3) can always be stored (4) can be transformed from one form to another.
9. The energy that powers an automobile is supplied by the (1) oil (2) gasoline (3) water (4) fan.
10. The type of energy transformation that takes place in a storage battery is (1) heat to mechanical (2) mechanical to electrical (3) chemical to electrical (4) electrical to mechanical.

Modified True-False Questions

If a statement is true, write the word true. *If a statement is false, write the word or expression that must be substituted for the italicized expression to make the statement true.*

1. The ability to do work is known as *force*.
2. In doing work, force is required to produce motion or overcome *resistance*.
3. The energy humans obtain from food can be traced back to *animal life*.
4. Scientists believe that *only some* forms of energy can be utilized by humans.
5. The energy of the sun is being used to operate the new *storage* battery.
6. The energy in the battery of a car is an example of stored *electrical* energy.
7. The reaction that occurs when photographic film is exposed is an example of a change of light energy into *heat* energy.
8. The change of chemical energy to electrical energy often produces light energy and heat energy. This is an example of the conservation of *work*.

Reasoning Questions

Give a reason for each of the following.

1. Solar batteries, thus far, have limited use.
2. During energy transformations, some energy is wasted.
3. The sun is the source of all our energy.
4. Sound is a form of energy.
5. We must learn to conserve energy.

Chapter 26. How We Use Light

1. WHAT IS LIGHT?

The nature of light puzzled scientists for many centuries. Newton, who lived during the 17th century, believed that light was made up of tiny particles, called *corpuscles*. Huygens, another scientist—living at about the same time as Newton—considered light to be made up of *waves*. You can imagine these waves to be very much like the water waves you see when you drop a pebble or a stone into some still water.

Theories are useful only insofar as they explain what you observe. Most of the properties of light—some of which we will consider later—are more satisfactorily explained by the wave theory. However, the particle theory still has some usefulness. We may therefore say that light is a form of energy that consists of particles and waves.

2. HOW DOES LIGHT TRAVEL?

Recall the waves that are produced when a tiny object is dropped into still water. The waves behave in the same manner as do rays of light that come from a source such as a light bulb or a flashlight. From the wave theory, we can say that light waves originate from the source and travel outward (as do water waves) in all directions.

3. THE SPEED OF LIGHT

Attempts to measure the speed of light, as far back as the 16th century, were not successful because light travels short distances almost instantaneously. It became obvious that light must travel at some very great speed. To measure this tremendous speed required the use of very great distances, usually not available on the surface of the earth. Roemer, in 1675, measured the speed of light across the diameter of the earth's orbit around the sun—a tremendous distance. In more recent times, Albert Michelson, an American physicist, measured the speed of light as it was reflected back and forth from a series of mirrors at known distances. Following Michelson, other investigators refined the values for the speed of light. The accepted value for the speed of light in a vacuum is about 186,000 miles per second, or 300,000 kilometers per second.

4. SOURCES OF LIGHT

Light is a form of energy. An energy source is therefore required to produce light. The sun is our great natural source of energy that produces heat as well as light. To account for the sun's energy, many theories have been developed. Most scientists believe that complicated nuclear reactions are responsible for the energy.

Other sources of light need to be manufactured. However, in all cases, some energy source is required to produce the light. For example, the hot filament of an electric light bulb transforms heat energy into light.

5. REFLECTION OF LIGHT

As we have already indicated, only very few objects give off their own light. When you see most objects, you are actually seeing light reflected from the objects. That is why you must provide a source of light in order to see objects in a dark room.

Just as a ball bounces off a wall, so do the tiny particles or waves of light energy bounce off objects receiving light (Fig. 26-1). Notice that the angle at which the light ray (*incident* ray) strikes the mirror equals the angle at which the light ray (*reflected* ray) is reflected. This observation is summarized in the law of reflection: the angle of incidence equals the angle of reflection.

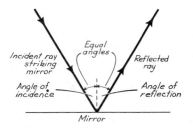

Fig. 26-1. How light is reflected from a flat mirror. The angle at which the light ray is reflected from the mirror is the same as the angle at which the light ray strikes the mirror.

6. REFLECTION IN MIRRORS

Mirrors are polished surfaces which reflect light. If you look into a mirror that is perfectly flat, the image you see will resemble you in all details except one: the image is reversed. The left side of your body appears on the right side of the image.

An image reflected from a curved mirror does not have the same size as the object. Shaving mirrors, for example, produce greatly enlarged images.

7. BENDING OF LIGHT

Light will travel at the same speed in a straight line only so long as the light continues to travel through the same material, called a *medium*. If a light ray passes at an angle from one substance to a substance with a different density, part of the light ray will slow down, and we see the light ray as bent. The bending of light as it goes from one medium into another is called *refraction*. Refraction results when light travels at different speeds in different mediums (Figure 26-2). For example, light travels faster in a vacuum than it does in air, and faster in air than it does in water.

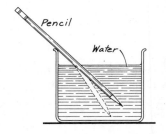

Fig. 26-2. Bending light. Since light travels slower in water than it does in air, the ray of light coming from the air at an angle is slowed down as it enters the water. This results in a change in path of the ray and thus gives the illusion that the pencil is bent or broken.

8. WHAT IS A PRISM?

A *prism* is a piece of solid glass shaped in the form of a triangle. Light entering a prism always bends toward the base of the prism (Fig. 26-3). Because prisms can refract light, they are used in telescopes and other optical instruments.

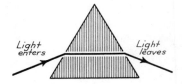

Fig. 26-3. Refraction in a prism. Since light travels more slowly in glass than it does in air, light is refracted when it passes through the prism. How many times is the light refracted?

9. THE SPECTRUM

Lesson 2# answer ⊄

Sunlight appears white, but is actually made up of the colors of the rainbow! These colors are called the *spectrum*. The colors of the spectrum are red, orange, yellow, green, blue, indigo, violet. You can remember these colors if you remember the first letters in ROYGBIV.

10. SEPARATING WHITE LIGHT

White light (sunlight), when passing through a glass prism, comes out of the prism and separates into the colors of the spectrum from red to violet (Fig. 26-4). The spreading out of white light into its component colors is known as *dispersion*. Dispersion occurs because each color travels through the prism at a different speed and bends at a different angle.

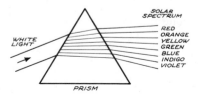

Fig. 26-4. Separating white light

The rainbow, that beautiful band of colors we sometimes see after a rainfall, is caused by dispersion. Each raindrop apparently behaves like a prism, separating the sunlight into the colors of the spectrum.

11. WHAT IS A LENS?

A common optical device used to bend light is a *lens*. A lens is a piece of glass, or plastic, that is not uniform in thickness (Fig. 26-5). A lens that is thicker in the center than at the edges is called a *convex* lens. A lens that is thinner in the center than at the edges is called a *concave* lens.

By refracting the light that passes through them, lenses can either magnify the size of objects or make them appear smaller. A convex lens magnifies nearby objects, while a concave lens always makes objects appear smaller. Lenses are used in eyeglasses, microscopes, cameras, movie projectors, telescopes, and other optical instruments.

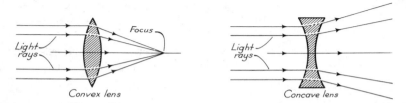

Fig. 26-5. Lenses refract light passing through them. Lenses bend light passing through them. A convex (converging) lens brings light rays to a point, or focus. A concave (diverging) lens spreads light rays. Notice that the light rays that pass through the centers of the lenses emerge unchanged. Why?

12. THE HUMAN EYE

The eyes are located in two hollow, bony sockets in the skull. The eyes are protected by the sockets as well as by the eyelids and the eyelashes. Muscles attach the eyeballs to the sockets and control the movement of the eyes in all directions.

The front part of the eyeball (Fig. 26-6) is the *cornea*. The cornea is a thin, clear layer through which light can pass. Behind the cornea is the colored part of the eye, called the *iris*. In the middle of the iris is the *pupil*, a circular opening which permits light rays to enter the eye.

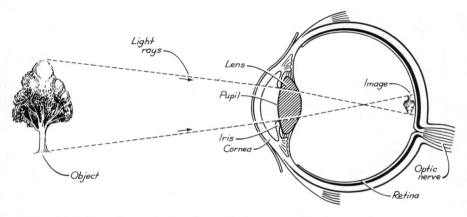

Fig. 26-6. How the eye functions. Light rays coming from an object enter the eye through the cornea, the pupil, and finally the lens. The light rays are bent by the lens to form an inverted image on the retina. The brain reinverts the image.

Muscles in the iris regulate the size of the pupil. In bright light, the muscles make the pupil smaller to permit less light to enter the eye. In dim light, the muscles make the pupil larger to allow more light to enter the eye. Directly behind the pupil is the *lens*, which focuses the light rays on the *retina*, where the image is formed. The retina, the inside lining of the eyeball, consists of nerve cells sensitive to light. The image on the retina causes the cells in the retina to set up a signal which is carried by a large nerve to the brain. The brain interprets the signal and thus makes us aware of what we are seeing.

THE CAMERA RESEMBLES AN EYE

Muscles in the eye can make the lens more convex or less convex. As you look at a nearby object, the lens becomes more convex. When you view a distant object, the lens becomes less convex. As a result, the images are formed directly on the retina and are said to be in focus.

How a camera works. A camera is a lightproof box containing an opening to admit light. As the light strikes a sheet of photographic film, exposure occurs and an image is produced on the film. Developing the film by chemical treatment brings out the image.

The simplest camera is a pinhole camera, where light enters through a tiny opening, or pinhole, which behaves like a lens. A box camera is very much like a pinhole camera. Today's cameras still operate on the same principle but some are fully automatic. That is, the amount of light that enters and the exposure time are set in advance.

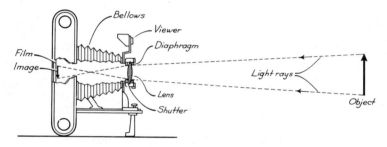

The camera and an eye compared

Camera	Eye
Light enters through the lens and produces an image on photographic film.	Light enters through the lens and produces an image on the retina.
The amount of light admitted is controlled by the diaphragm.	The amount of light admitted is controlled by the iris.
The image is focused by moving the lens nearer to or farther from the film.	The image is focused by the lens. The muscles of the eye automatically change the thickness (convexity) of the lens, permitting the lens to focus properly.

13. COMMON EYE DEFECTS

To some people, nearby objects appear clear, while distant objects appear blurred. Such a person is said to be *nearsighted*. Other persons can see distant objects clearly, but nearby objects are blurred. This person is said to be *farsighted.*

Nearsightedness (also called *myopia*) and farsightedness (also called *hyperopia*) result when the eye fails to focus an image directly on the retina. In such cases the image is blurred. The formation of a blurred image occurs if (*a*) the muscles attached to the lens are too weak to alter the thickness of the lens and so focus it, or (*b*) the eyeball is too long or too short (Fig. 26-7).

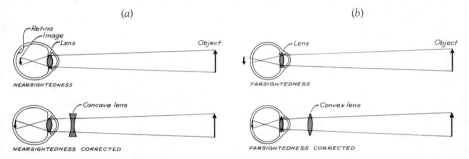

Fig. 26-7. Correcting some eye defects. (*a*) In nearsightedness, the image is formed in front of the retina. The condition can be corrected by using a concave lens which spreads the rays of light apart before they enter the eye. This causes the image to be formed on the retina.

(*b*) In farsightedness, the image would be formed behind the retina. The condition can be corrected by using a convex lens which bends the light rays together before they enter the eye. This causes the image to be formed on the retina.

The defects of the eyes shown in Fig. 26-7 may be remedied by (*a*) exercising the eye muscles to strengthen them, or (*b*) wearing eyeglasses to refract the light rays properly on the retina. In place of eyeglasses, some people wear *contact lenses*, which are worn directly on the cornea.

Another common eye defect is *astigmatism*. Because the lens of the eye is not curved uniformly, objects appear blurred to the individual. Eyeglasses with special lenses or contact lenses are used to correct this condition.

14. CARE OF THE EYES

Like any other part of the body, our eyes must be given proper rest and care. Here are a few good rules to observe.

   a. Make sure you have adequate illumination when reading. Avoid glare. Don't read while in a moving vehicle. Limit television viewing, especially if the picture is not adjusted properly.
   b. Be extremely careful when attempting to remove a foreign object from your eye. Have a physician, or some other competent person, do this.
   c. If eyeglasses have been prescribed for you, use them as directed. In time, you may be able to do without them. Always keep the lenses clean.
   d. Have your eyes reexamined periodically.
   e. If you wear contact lenses, be extra careful in handling and storing them.

15. LIGHT CAN PRODUCE CHEMICAL CHANGES

Light energy from the sun can decompose certain chemicals. Light-sensitive substances are therefore stored in brown glass bottles. If hydrogen peroxide, for example, were kept in a colorless glass bottle, it would slowly lose its strength through chemical change. Exposure to the sun also changes the color of certain dyes. Dyed fabrics will change in color, or fade, due to chemical action over a period of time.

Light energy is used by green plants to manufacture their food. This process, called *photosynthesis*, is discussed on pages 142–143, sections 6–7.

16. PHOTOGRAPHY DEPENDS ON LIGHT

The science of photography depends on the fact that light affects certain silver compounds. The photographic process consists of two steps:

   a. Exposing the film and making a negative of the picture.
   b. Changing the negative into a positive print.

a. Producing a Black-and-White Negative. When the shutter is open, light enters the camera through the lens and strikes the photographic film. The film contains silver compounds which are sensitive to light. Chemical changes occur in those places on the film where the light strikes. These changes cause the silver compounds to deposit silver wherever the film is struck by light.

The exposed film is made into a negative by a process called *developing*. Chemicals in the developing solution produce different shades of gray or black, according to how much light struck the different areas of the film. For example, a white shirt appears black on the negative; a black tie appears white. All the shades of gray are correspondingly produced in reverse on the negative.

b. Making a Black-and-White Print, or Positive. Making the print simply reverses the negative, making the black of the negative appear white and the white appear black (Fig. 26-8). The negative is placed on photographic paper and exposed to light. The black on the negative (corresponding to the white shirt) blocks off the light, while the white on the negative (corresponding to the black tie) transmits all the light. The gray parts of the negative similarly control the amount of light reaching the paper. When the photographic paper is developed, the whites, blacks, and shades of gray appear on the positive as they were in the object photographed.

Negative   **Positive (print)**

Fig. 26-8. Making a print reverses black and white. Black printing appears white on a negative. Making the positive, or print, reverses the process so that the white printing appears black.

c. Color Pictures. Color film contains millions of tiny specks of dyes of three different colors. These colors are blue-violet, green, and red. When exposed to light consisting of these colors, or mixtures of them, the dyes in the film are changed. The final developed picture shows the scene in nearly natural color.

One type of color film is developed directly as a slide, or transparency, for use in a projector. If desired, paper prints can be made from such film. Another type of color film is developed first as a negative and then is printed in color on special photographic paper. The process of making color pictures is so complicated that it cannot usually be carried out at home as black and white pictures can.

d. Instant Pictures. Cameras that take pictures and develop them almost immediately are similar to other cameras. They use a special film package containing the film and rapid-acting developing chemicals in one unit. After a picture is taken, the chemicals are spread over the film while it is still in the camera. After about a minute, the finished print is removed from the camera. In some very recent cameras that take instant pictures, the exposed print is removed from the camera and develops on standing in a few minutes.

Multiple-Choice Questions

Write the number preceding the correct answer.

1. It is impossible to see through a bent piece of metal pipe because (1) lenses bend rays of light (2) light travels in straight lines (3) mirrors reflect rays of light (4) the eye is similar to a camera in many ways.
2. As you read this question, (1) the light is reflected from the paper to your eyes (2) the light is reflected from your eyes to the paper (3) the printed paper gives off light of its own (4) your eyes produce the light needed to see the paper.
3. The bending of light rays as they pass from air into water is called (1) reflection (2) dispersion (3) refraction (4) energy conversion.
4. The breaking of white light into the colors which compose it is called (1) transmission (2) dispersion (3) reflection (4) refraction.
5. A glass prism may be used to (1) reflect light rays (2) break up white light (3) absorb light (4) converge the three primary colors.
6. When a ray of sunlight passing through the edge of an aquarium is broken up into colors, the aquarium is acting as a (1) lens (2) mirror (3) prism (4) rainbow.
7. A convex lens is used in a reading glass because it (1) inverts nearby objects (2) magnifies distant objects (3) magnifies nearby objects (4) reduces nearby objects.
8. Which diagram best represents a cross-section of the lens in a reading (magnifying) glass?

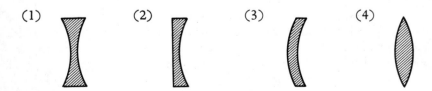

(1)   (2)   (3)   (4)

9. Which part of the eye regulates the size of the pupil? (1) cornea (2) iris (3) lens (4) retina.
10. As a room is darkened, the pupil of the eye (1) becomes larger (2) becomes smaller (3) closes completely (4) shows no change.
11. In each human eye there is a part which acts as a (1) curved mirror (2) flat mirror (3) lens (4) triangular prism.
12. What part of a camera has the same function as the retina of the eye? (1) diaphragm (2) film (3) lens (4) shutter.
13. The purpose of the lens in a camera is to (1) cut out the bright rays of sunlight (2) focus an image on the film (3) keep dust away from the film (4) regulate the amount of light entering the camera.
14. A picture is produced on the film in a camera when the (1) film reflects the light from the object (2) light changes the chemical on the film (3) light changes the film paper to a solid (4) light sticks to the film.
15. If a picture of a snowman is taken, the color of the image of the snowman on the negative will be (1) black (2) blue (3) clear (4) white.
16. Color photography requires (1) special cameras (2) special black and white film (3) film containing a mixture of dyes (4) instant development.

Completion Questions

Write the word or expression that correctly completes the statement.

1. The speed of light in a vacuum is about _____ miles per second.
2. The image you see in a flat mirror is always _____ (*reversed, in the same position as the object*).
3. Light striking a flat mirror is reflected at _____ (*the same, a different*) angle from which it strikes the mirror.
4. The bending of light results from the passing of light from one medium to another medium having a different _____.
5. The colors of the spectrum can be shown on a screen by allowing sunlight to pass through a (an) _____.
6. A lens that brings light to a focus is a _____ lens.
7. Light that enters the eye forms an image on the _____.
8. A person who sees distant objects clearly but nearby objects blurred is said to be _____.
9. To prevent certain chemicals from undergoing chemical changes, they must be shielded from light by being stored in _____ glass bottles.
10. The process by which a negative is made from an exposed film is called _____.

Reasoning Questions

Give a reason for each of the following.

1. It is difficult to measure the speed of light.
2. When a theory can no longer explain a series of observations, the theory must be discarded.
3. Light is both a wave and particle motion.
4. The eye is very much like a camera.
5. A ruler dipping into a glass of water appears broken.
6. Light is refracted as it passes through a prism.
7. The brain reinverts the image formed on the retina.
8. A pinhole camera does not require a lens.
9. A concave lens corrects nearsightedness.
10. The process of photographic developing requires the use of a dark room.

Chapter 27. Molecules in Motion

1. WHAT IS HEAT?

All matter contains *heat* energy. Scientists believe that heat energy comes from the motion of molecules that make up the particles of matter. As the moving molecules collide with one another, heat is produced. Heat is defined as the total kinetic energy that a body possesses. (Recall that the energy of motion is called *kinetic energy*.)

2. WHAT ARE SOME SOURCES OF HEAT?

The various forms of energy can be converted to heat energy.

a. Mechanical Energy. Friction produces heat. For example, rubbing two sticks together may generate sufficient heat to start a fire. Compressing a gas, that is, squeezing the molecules of the gas into a smaller space, also produces heat. This is why the compressor in an air conditioner or in a refrigerator gives off heat.

b. Electrical Energy. Resistance to the passage of an electric current produces heat. This energy change produces heat in electrical devices such as an iron or a toaster. Current-carrying electric wires also generate some heat. Electric power is lost in this way.

c. Chemical energy. Burning produces heat. Stored chemical energy in fuel is converted to heat energy.

d. Radiant Energy. The radiant energy of the sun is changed to heat energy when it strikes the earth. A "burning glass," which is a convex lens, can be used to concentrate the sun's rays sufficiently to start a fire.

Too much sunlight can be injurious to humans, especially to the skin. Excessive and uncontrolled sun-tanning can burn the skin, produce lesions, and even skin cancers. Therefore, exercise great care when you are exposed to the sun for long periods, especially in the summer.

e. Nuclear Energy. Nuclear reactions on the sun are thought to produce the heat of the sun. On the earth, heat produced by the release of nuclear energy can be great enough to vaporize (change to gas) solids like steel and concrete. The heat obtained from nuclear energy can be used to heat buildings, drive engines, and produce electricity.

3. EXPRESSING HEAT: CALORIES AND TEMPERATURE

The amount of heat in a body depends on (*a*) the number of molecules in the body, and (*b*) the rate of movement of these molecules. This is the kinetic energy of the body. The greater the number of molecules and the faster they move, the greater the total heat, or kinetic energy, in the body. Total heat is expressed in *calories*.

The degree of hotness of a body is its *temperature*. One substance may have a higher temperature than another and yet contain less total heat. For example, a glass of boiling water has a higher temperature than a kettle of lukewarm water. But the glass of water has less total heat, or calories, because the glass of water contains fewer molecules than does the kettle of water. Live steam and boiling water both have the same temperature. But in live steam, the water molecules move faster in order to become gaseous. Hence, steam is hotter than boiling water. Both, however, can produce serious burns.

4. MEASURING HEAT

The unit of heat in the metric system is the *calorie*. A calorie is the quantity of heat required to raise the temperature of water 1 C°. Heat is measured in a special container, called a *calorimeter*.

Not all bodies become equally hot with the application of the same amount of heat. For example, suppose 1 calorie of heat is added—first, to 1 gram of water at 15°C; and, second, to 1 gram of alcohol at 15°C. The temperature of the water rises to 16°C, but the temperature of the alcohol rises only to 15.45°C. *Specific heat* is the number of calories of heat required to raise the temperature of 1 gram of a substance, or a body, 1 C°. Thus, the specific heat of water is 1 calorie per gram per Celsius degree, or just shortened to 1, while the specific heat of alcohol is 0.45.

5. MEASURING TEMPERATURE

Temperature is measured with a thermometer and expressed in *degrees*. One type of thermometer contains a liquid that responds to changes in temperature. When a liquid is heated, its molecules move more rapidly, making the liquid occupy a larger volume. This increase in volume is called *expansion*. On the other hand, when the temperature of a liquid is lowered, its molecules move more slowly, causing the liquid to shrink or *contract*. The uniform expansion and contraction of certain liquids in response to heat or cold is utilized in making a thermometer.

Most liquid thermometers contain mercury, a metal that has a silvery color and does not evaporate readily. Alcohol is still used in some thermometers, but its use is limited because alcohol evaporates easily. The use of water in a thermometer is not practical because it does not expand and contract uniformly.

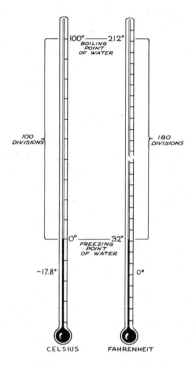

Fig. 27-1. Celsius and Fahrenheit Scales

6. TEMPERATURE SCALES

There are two temperature scales in common use, the *Fahrenheit* and *Celsius* (also called *centigrade*) (Fig. 27-1). The Fahrenheit (F) scale is the one commonly used in the United States. On the Fahrenheit scale, water freezes at 32° and boils at 212°. In the metric system, scientists use the Celsius (C) scale or the Kelvin (K) scale. On the Celsius scale, water freezes at 0° and boils at 100°. On the Kelvin scale, water freezes at 273°K and boils at 373°K. The freezing and boiling points of water are called the *fixed points* of a thermometer.

There are 180 divisions between the freezing point and boiling point of water on the Fahrenheit scale. There are only 100 divisions between these points on the Celsius scale and on the Kelvin scale. One Celsius degree is therefore 1.8 $(\frac{9}{5})$ times as large as a Fahrenheit degree.

To change degrees F to degrees C, use the formula $°F = 1.8 \times °C + 32$. To change degrees C to degrees F, use the formula $°C = \frac{5}{9} (°F - 32)$. To change degrees C to degrees K, add 273° to degrees C.

7. EXPANSION OF SOLIDS

Most solids behave like liquids when heated or cooled. When solids are heated, the increase in molecular motion causes *expansion*. When solids are cooled, the decrease in molecular motion causes *contraction*. These ideas are applied in the following ways:

a. Roads, sidewalks, and railroad tracks are constructed with spacings between sections to allow for expansion during the hot weather.
b. When planning the construction of bridges, engineers take into account the expansion of the bridge in the summer.
c. Telephone and electric wires are strung loosely to permit contraction during the winter.
d. Glass tumblers are made with thin walls so that both the outside and the inside of the tumbler can expand at about the same rate when heated. Thinner glassware, therefore, can generally hold hotter liquids better and safer than thicker glassware.

8. EXPANSION OF GASES

Gases, like most liquids and solids, expand when heated and contract when cooled. For example, upon continued exposure to the sun, automobile tires become hot. The air inside a tire expands and exerts increased pressure on the walls of the tire. Tire manufacturers take this fact into account by making the tire walls strong enough to withstand the increased pressure and prevent the tire from bursting.

9. WHAT IS HEAT TRANSFER?

A heated iron will cool on standing. The lost heat is transferred to the surrounding air. Heat is always transferred from a warmer body to a cooler body.

The transfer of heat is accomplished in three ways: *convection*, *conduction*, and *radiation*.

10. HEAT TRANSFER BY CONVECTION

Heat is transferred through liquids and gases by *convection*. Convection is the transfer of heat by means of currents. For example, when water is heated in a kettle, the water at the bottom of the kettle expands and becomes lighter. The colder water, being heavier, sinks to the bottom and pushes the warmer water up. In this manner, *convection currents* are set in motion. In time, they distribute heat uniformly throughout the water. Convection in gases takes place similarly (Fig. 27-2).

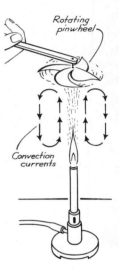

Fig. 27-2. Convection currents transfer heat. The air warmed by the Bunsen flame sets up convection currents that cause the pinwheel to rotate.

11. HEAT TRANSFER BY CONDUCTION

If you hold the handle of a fork and carefully place the tines over a flame, you soon feel the handle getting hot. Heat has been transferred from the tines, or hotter part, to the handle, or cooler part. The transfer of heat through a body from one molecule to another is called *conduction*. Solids, chiefly metals, are good conductors of heat because the particles they contain are packed closely. Liquids and gases are poor conductors because the particles they contain are spread farther apart.

Paper, wool, wood, and asbestos conduct heat slowly and are called *insulators*. Conductors and insulators are used as follows:

    a. Cooking utensils are made of copper and aluminum, which are very good conductors of heat. For insulation, handles are made of wood or plastic.

    b. Insulating materials, such as rock wool and glass wool, are placed between the outside and inside walls of houses. (Asbestos is no longer used because it is thought to be cancer-causing.) Insulation helps keep the house cool in the summer and warm in the winter.

c. Warm clothing is made of such insulating fabrics as wool and flannel to help garments retain body heat. Newer synthetic materials, such as terylene, are also excellent insulators.

12. HEAT TRANSFER BY RADIATION

Heat is also transferred by *radiation*. Radiation is the transfer of heat by the movement of waves through space. In this respect, radiant heat is a form of energy similar to light (Fig. 27-3). Radiant heat energy travels in straight lines at the speed of light, or about 186,000 miles per second in a vacuum. Cooking devices, such as infrared broilers and microwave ovens, use radiant energy to cook foods.

Fig. 27-3. Heat transfer by radiation. The boy is being warmed by the heat distributed by waves.

13. HEATING THE EARTH BY RADIANT ENERGY

Sunlight is the *radiant energy* that heats the earth. Upon reaching the earth, some radiant energy is absorbed by the earth or by objects on the earth, while some radiant energy is reflected back into the atmosphere. Dark, rough surfaces absorb a great deal of heat but reflect very little heat. Light, shiny objects reflect a great deal of heat but absorb little heat.

The amount of heat absorbed by a particular area of the earth depends upon its type of surface.

  a. Dark, wooded areas absorb a great deal of radiant heat but reflect little heat.
  b. Sandy regions absorb little radiant heat but reflect much heat.
  c. Land absorbs heat readily but loses this heat rapidly by radiation. Water, on the other hand, absorbs heat slowly but retains this heat for a long period of time.

Multiple-Choice Questions

Write the number preceding the correct answer.

1. The instrument used to measure temperature is the (1) anemometer (2) barometer (3) hydrometer (4) thermometer.
2. The principle upon which a thermometer works is (1) changes in air pressure (2) evaporation and condensation (3) expansion and contraction (4) reflection.
3. The Fahrenheit temperature that is 50 degrees above the freezing point of water is (1) 18° (2) 50° (3) 82° (4) 262°.
4. The number of divisions between the freezing point and boiling point of water on a Celsius thermometer is (1) 98 (2) 100 (3) 180 (4) 212.
5. The boiling point of water on the Celsius scale is (1) 0° (2) 32° (3) 100° (4) 212°.
6. A long steel suspension bridge sags several inches in summer because (1) greater traffic in summer causes increased weight on the bridge (2) the bridge was not properly constructed (3) the heat causes the steel to expand (4) the steel becomes softer due to the heat.
7. Spaces are left between the cement blocks of a sidewalk to (1) allow for drainage (2) speed drying (3) improve appearance (4) prevent breakage due to expansion.
8. In the summer telephone wires are strung loosely to allow for (1) expansion when heated (2) contraction when heated (3) expansion when cooled (4) contraction when cooled.
9. When boiling water is poured into a cold milk bottle, the bottle will often break because (1) glass is a good conductor of heat (2) milk bottles are made of extremely thin glass (3) the boiling water dissolves part of the glass (4) the inside of the bottle expands faster than the outside.
10. Of the following, the substance that conducts heat most rapidly is (1) copper (2) rock wool (3) glass (4) mica.
11. In making cooking utensils, wooden handles are often used because wood (1) can be shaped easily (2) does not wear out quickly (3) is a poor conductor of heat (4) is lighter than metal.

12. Houses are insulated in order to (1) prevent short circuits (2) lower the humidity (3) beautify the house (4) retain heat.
13. The warmest air in a room is (1) directly below the radiator (2) in the center of the room (3) near the ceiling (4) near the floor.
14. A pinwheel held above a lighted electric lamp rotates because of (1) convection (2) conduction (3) radiation (4) absorption.
15. Heat from the sun reaches the earth by (1) conduction (2) reflection (3) convection (4) radiation.
16. The form of energy most closely related to friction is (1) mechanical (2) electrical (3) radiant (4) atomic.
17. Equal quantities of water at 100°C and steam at 100°C contain (1) the same amount of heat (2) different amounts of heat (3) the same molecules (4) the same kinetic energies.
18. Of the following, the highest temperature is (1) 100°C (2) 373°K (3) 212°F (4) 250°F.
19. Five calories of heat are added to 1 gram of water at 0°C. The temperature of the water rises to (1) 1°C (2) 2°C (3) 5°C (4) 10°C.
20. A fireplace heats a room largely by (1) conduction (2) convection (3) radiation (4) conduction, convection, and radiation.

Completion Questions

Write the word or expression that correctly completes the statement.

1. Heat energy results from the motion of the _____ making up matter.
2. The heat of the sun is believed to result from _____ explosions on the sun.
3. The total heat energy of a body is expressed in units called _____.
4. The temperature of a body is expressed in units called _____.
5. The increase in the volume of a heated liquid or solid is known as _____.
6. _____ is the transfer of heat through a body by the movement of its molecules.
7. A substance, such as wool, which does not conduct heat rapidly is called a (an) _____.
8. _____ is the chief method of transferring heat through liquids and gases.
9. The radiant energy that the earth receives from the sun may be either reflected or _____.
10. Land heats _____ (*more rapidly, slower*) than does water.

Chapter 28. Energy From the Atom

1. SPLITTING THE ATOM

According to the Law of Conservation of Matter, matter, or mass, can neither be created nor destroyed. It was *Albert Einstein*, who, during the early 20th century, developed the idea that matter can be changed into energy. In his now famous equation, $E = mc^2$, where E = energy, m = mass (matter), and c^2 = the velocity of light squared, or $(186,000 \text{ miles/sec})^2$, Einstein showed how mass and energy are related. From the equation, it can be calculated that the conversion of 1 gram of mass yields an amount of energy approximately equal to the energy obtained from the burning of 2,000 tons of gasoline. Thus, a very small quantity of matter can be converted to an enormous amount of energy.

From the relationship between matter and energy, one of the basic laws of science was developed; namely, the *Law of Conservation of Matter and Energy: Matter and energy can neither be created nor destroyed. Matter and energy are interconvertible; that is, one may be converted into the other.*

How can we use the Law of Conservation of Matter and Energy? The energy locked within the atom may be released by splitting the nucleus of the atom into smaller fragments. The total mass of the fragments, however, is slightly less than the mass of the original atom. The loss of mass results from the fact that some matter has been changed into energy (Fig. 28-1).

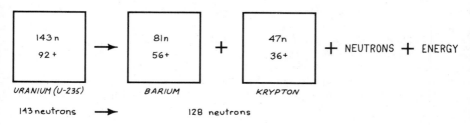

Fig. 28-1. Splitting the nucleus of the uranium atom. When the U-235 nucleus is split, barium and krypton fragments are formed. Note that in these fragments there is a total of 15 fewer neutrons. Some of these neutrons have been converted into energy.

Splitting the nucleus of an atom is called *nuclear fission*. During fission, neutrons are released, which causes further fissions, producing a *chain reaction*. An *uncontrolled* chain reaction takes place in an atomic bomb. A *controlled* chain reaction occurs in an atomic, or nuclear, reactor.

2. WHAT IS AN ATOMIC PILE?

An *atomic pile*, now called a *nuclear reactor*, is a device for changing atomic energy into heat energy (Fig. 28-2). The speed of the reaction is controlled in the reactor in such a way as to produce heat instead of the violent explosion that occurs in the atomic bomb. The heat generated can be used as a source of power in ships, submarines, and airplanes. Nuclear-powered surface ships and submarines are already in use.

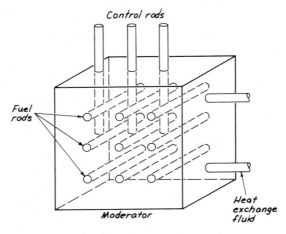

Fig. 28-2. A nuclear reactor is a heavily shielded container consisting of a fuel (U-235 or Pu-239), which undergoes fission. Control rods, made of boron or cadmium, absorb neutrons and control the speed of the fission reaction. A moderator, such as graphite, slows down the neutrons, and the water coolant absorbs the heat of the reaction. The heated water generates steam, which is fed into a turbine to operate an electric generator.

As the supply of naturally occurring fuels, such as coal and petroleum, diminishes, it will be necessary to not only conserve fuels but also to seek other sources. (Read "Fuels and Our World" on page 213.) Nuclear power generators, already in use today, may become the chief power source of the future.

Nuclear generators produce dangerous radiation. How to dispose of it safely has become a very serious problem, especially in areas near reactors. The disposal of nuclear wastes is another kind of pollution that concerns our society. (Read "Handling Nuclear Waste" on page 275.)

3. WHAT IS A FUSION BOMB?

In the *fusion bomb*, light atoms are combined to form heavier atoms. The hydrogen bomb is a fusion bomb in which certain atoms of hydrogen are combined to form helium. In this process there is a small loss of matter, resulting in a tremendous release of energy. It is called a *thermonuclear reaction*, or *hot fusion*. The energy contained in the sun and in other stars is thought to result from the fusion of hydrogen atoms into helium. Claims that fusion can be carried out under laboratory conditions (*cold fusion*) have yet to be accepted by all scientists.

4. DESTRUCTIVENESS OF FISSION AND FUSION BOMBS

Fission bombs have a limited size, while the size of a fusion bomb is unlimited. The explosion of a fission or fusion bomb produces extremely high temperatures, many times as high as the temperature of the sun. The heated air produced sets up violent shock waves, called the *blast effect*. Concrete, for example, can be turned into dust by these shock waves.

In addition to the tremendous heat, atomic explosions release considerable *radiation*. The radiation may consist of neutrons, protons, electrons, helium nuclei, and X-rays. These particles and rays are deadly at short range and are capable of causing serious damage to living things up to two or three miles from the center of the explosion.

5. THE GEIGER COUNTER

A common device for detecting radiation is the *Geiger counter*. By clicking, this electronic instrument not only detects radiation, but also indicates how much radiation is present. The more intense and frequent the clicks, the more radiation is present.

6. CONTROLLING RADIATION

Continued exposure to radiation can destroy bone and blood tissue—and may cause cancer. Radiation can also cause changes in the inherited characteristics of living things. Extreme precautions must be taken by people working with or near sources of radiation. Lead shields, which stop the passage of radiation, are used to protect workers.

The presence of radioactive radon in soil is becoming a serious problem to homeowners. Checking homes for the presence of radon is now considered a wise health measure.

7. USING RADIATION

When controlled, radiation can be of great benefit. Neutron radiation, for example, is used to make certain *radioactive isotopes*, also called *radioisotopes*.

Isotopes are varieties of an element that contain the same number of protons but a different number of neutrons. For example, two common isotopes of chlorine are chlorine–35 (Cl = 35) and chlorine–37 (Cl = 37), shown in Fig. 28-3.

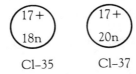

Cl-35   Cl-37

Fig. 28-3. Two chlorine isotopes. Note that each isotope has 17 protons, but Cl-35 has 18 neutrons while Cl-37 has 20 neutrons.

Radioactive isotopes of a given element also have different numbers of neutrons. In addition, radioactive isotopes are unstable. These isotopes break down, or *decay*, to form new elements and different kinds of radiation. The rate of decay (how slow or how fast breakdown occurs) is fixed for a given isotope and is described by the *half-life* of the isotope. Half-life is the time it takes for one-half of a mass of radioactive material to decay. Half-lives can range from billions of years to fractions of a second.

The radiation from the decay of certain radioactive isotopes may be used to destroy diseased body tissue, as in certain cancers. For example, the radioactive isotopes—iodine–131—is used to treat thyroid cancer. The half-life of I–131 is relatively short—about 8 days—so that the body rids itself quickly of this potentially dangerous material.

It is sometimes necessary to follow the course of a series of changes in the body. The introduction of a radioactive isotope, called a *tracer*, allows the researcher to do this by detecting the products of the decay of the isotope.

Knowledge of half-lives of radioactive materials found in the earth's crust has enabled scientists to make more accurate estimates of the age of the earth. For example, the half-life of uranium–238, found in the earth, is about 4.5 billion years. This suggests that the earth is several billion years old.

The radioactive isotope (carbon–14) is found in organic matter. Knowing the half-life of this isotope can be used to date objects found in the earth. Such methods are called *radioactive dating*.

HANDLING NUCLEAR WASTE

Nuclear waste includes all radioactive by-products of a controlled nuclear reaction. These by-products are isotopes of different elements that may remain dangerously radioactive for hundreds and thousands of years. Such isotopes can be lethal to living things. The question facing scientists and citizens alike is what to do with this waste.

In a nuclear reactor, radioactive uranium is placed in groups of tubes called *fuel assemblies*. Fission of the uranium produces radioactive isotopes like plutonium and strontium. These isotopes remain in the fuel assemblies.

Assemblies are replaced about once a year. They are still very hot and must be cooled underwater in storage pools. What, then, is to be done about the nuclear waste remaining in these assemblies?

One idea was to develop commercial reprocessing plants. Waste products would be recycled into fuel for other reactors. Unfortunately, the cost of building the plants is so high that no one has attempted it.

Another proposal suggested burying the waste underground. But no one could guarantee that it would not be disturbed by earthquake or other natural processes.

The Government has not yet decided which plan, if any, to adopt. At this time, nuclear waste is still kept in storage pools on the grounds of nuclear plants.

In Greek mythology, the first mortal woman was named Pandora. She was very curious, and when she came upon a closed box, she felt compelled to open it. Inside the box were all the ills of humanity, from disease to famine, and when the box was opened, they escaped into the world. Pandora was unable to put them back. In creating nuclear waste that cannot easily be disposed, have we also opened a Pandora's Box?

Multiple-Choice Questions

Write the number preceding the correct answer.

1. Matter and energy (1) are unrelated (2) can be created (3) can be destroyed (4) may be converted from one to the other.
2. Tremendous energy results from the conversion of (1) energy into light (2) helium into hydrogen (3) neutrons into protons (4) mass into energy.
3. An element commonly used in fission reactions is (1) radium (2) uranium (3) sodium (4) chlorine.
4. A moderator in a nuclear reactor (1) absorbs neutrons (2) slows down neutrons (3) cools the control rods (4) lowers the cost of the reactor.
5. A device in which a controlled chain reaction is used to change atomic energy into heat energy is the (1) fission bomb (2) fusion bomb (3) nuclear reactor (4) uranium bomb.
6. The radiant energy from the sun is believed to be the result (1) combustion (2) photosynthesis (3) irradiation.(4) nuclear fusion.
7. Atomic radiations may consist of neutrons, protons, and (1) elements (2) X-rays (3) oxygen nuclei (4) calories.
8. An instrument used to detect radiation is the (1) barometer (2) hygrometer (3) Geiger counter (4) thermometer.
9. The metal used to make shields that protect people from harmful radiation is (1) lead (2) uranium (3) mercury (4) cobalt.
10. Of the following, the element that has radioisotopes is (1) helium (2) uranium (3) chlorine (4) magnesium.

Completion Questions

Write the word or expression that correctly completes the statement.

1. _____ is the scientist who proved that matter and energy are related.
2. Nuclear fission involves the _____ of the nucleus of an atom.
3. The type of bomb in which the nucleus is split is a (an) _____ bomb.
4. In the hydrogen bomb, atoms of hydrogen are combined to form the element _____.
5. A hydrogen bomb is an example of a _____ (*fission, fusion*) bomb.
6. The blast effect produced by atomic explosions produces _____ waves.
7. Large doses of radiation may destroy _____ tissue.
8. Atoms of the same element differing only in the number of neutrons are called _____.
9. An isotope that has the same chemical properties as other atoms of the element but which gives off radiations is called a (an) _____.
10. The breakdown of a radioisotope is called _____.

Reasoning Questions

Give a reason for each of the following.

1. Fusion bombs are more powerful than atomic bombs.
2. Neutrons sustain a chain reaction.
3. Tremendous amounts of energy are produced in nuclear reactors.
4. Control rods are required in a nuclear reactor.
5. Neutron radiation is useful.
6. Radioactive isotopes with short half-life are used to treat certain body disorders.
7. Tracers enable researchers to study the course of a reaction.
8. The Einstein equation predicts that a large amount of energy will be formed when a small amount of mass is destroyed.
9. Nuclear reactors employ many safeguards.
10. The presence of radon in soil is a serious problem.

REVIEW OF UNIT V

1. Below is a list of devices that are involved in energy changes. For each, write whether the energy change is (1) electrical to heat (2) electrical to light (3) electrical to mechanical (4) heat to mechanical (5) mechanical to electrical.
   a. electric iron
   b. light bulb
   c. steam engine
   d. electric fan
   e. electric generator
   f. toaster
   g. washing machine
   h. automobile engine
2. Give an example showing where each occurs in the home:
   a. Heat conduction takes place.
   b. Expansion takes place.
   c. Insulation checks the flow of heat.
   d. An electric current is used to produce heat.
3. Explain what happened in each of the following experiments, and tell why it happened.
   a. A flask was filled with colored water, and a stopper with a glass tube was placed in the neck of the flask. The water in the flask was heated.
   b. One end of a glass rod that is held in a flame becomes hot. The other end of the rod, held by the fingers, remains cool. Why?
4. Describe an important application of Einstein's equation.
5. What does the Law of Conservation of Matter and Energy mean?
6. How may nuclear reactors solve our energy problems in the future?

7. *a.* Draw an arrow to show what happens to the ray of light when it strikes mirror *AB*.

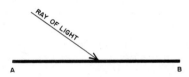

  b. Label the arrows to show which one represents red light and which one represents violet light.

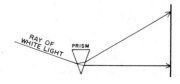

8. Explain each of the following.
    a. A student places a pencil behind a notebook. The pencil cannot be seen.
    b. Light coming from the sun consists of many colors.
    c. Light can be made to bend.

9. A finger was dipped into a glass of water. Then the finger was observed through the side of the glass. What happened? Why did it happen?

10. Continue the rays of light through and to the right of the lens.

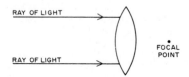

11. In which case (*A* or *B*) will the match light first? Why?

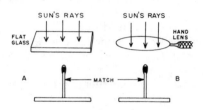

12. Write the names of the colors omitted in the following chart of the spectrum.

13. Explain each of the following.
    a. A pinwheel is placed above a lighted electric lamp and the pinwheel rotates. The pinwheel is then placed beside or below the lamp and the pinwheel does not rotate.
    b. A toy balloon is fastened to the neck of a flask. As the flask is heated, the balloon inflates.
    c. Telephone wires put up in the summer are strung loosely.
    d. While the temperature in a schoolroom may be 72 degrees five feet above the floor, it probably will be less than 72 degrees three feet above the floor.
    e. Water heats faster in a black kettle than it does in a new aluminum kettle.
    f. Many cooking utensils have wooden handles.
    g. Dirty snow melts more quickly than does clean snow.
    h. The liquid in a thermometer goes up as the air becomes warmer.
14. A is a hot radiator in a cool room. The doors and windows are all closed. With arrows, show the paths of the chief air currents in the room. Label the arrows to show which currents are hot air and which are cold air. Explain how these currents heat the room.

15. a. What is the purpose of the lens in a camera?
    b. What is the purpose of the shutter?
    c. What is the purpose of the film?
    d. Why must undeveloped film be kept in the dark?
    e. How is the developed film different from the final picture?

Unit VI.
Magnetism and Electricity

Chapter 29. The Behavior of Magnets

1. IMPORTANCE OF MAGNETISM

The ancient Greeks were among the first people to become aware of naturally occurring rocks that had magnetic properties. The Chinese, during the 10th century, are thought to have used magnetic compasses. Through the years, scientists have provided a better understanding of magnetism. As a result, many devices and machines have been developed that have improved our standard of living. Useful devices such as the compass, electromagnet, electric bell, telephone and telegraph, electric motor, radio, and television depend upon the effects of magnetism. This chapter, which discusses the elementary principles of magnetism, will help you understand the operation of many magnetic devices, as well as the magnetism of the earth itself.

2. WHAT IS A MAGNET?

A *magnet* is a metallic substance capable of attracting iron and certain other metals. A metal that can be made into a magnet or will be attracted by a magnet is a *magnetic substance*. Iron and steel are the most common magnetic substances. Others include cobalt, nickel, and alnico (a manufactured metal consisting mainly of aluminum, nickel, and cobalt).

3. KINDS OF MAGNETS

a. Natural Magnets. A naturally occurring rock, called *lodestone*, has magnetic properties. Lodestone contains an oxide of iron, called *magnetite*. Since lodestone is found in nature, it is known as a *natural magnet*.

b. Artificial Magnets. Certain magnets may be made even stronger than natural magnets. A factory-made magnet is known as an *artificial magnet*. Artificial magnets are usually made from iron, special magnet steel, or alnico, and frequently in the shape of a bar or horseshoe (Fig. 29-1). A compass needle is an artificial magnet. (See Fig. 29-13, page 290.)

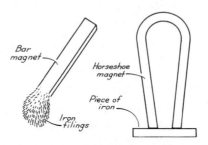

Fig. 29-1. Artificial magnets

4. THE LAW OF MAGNETS

The two ends of a magnet are known as the *poles* of the magnet. One end is called the *north pole* (N), and the other end is the *south pole* (S).

When two magnets are brought close to each other, it will be found that like poles repel each other and that unlike poles attract each other. That is, the N-pole repels the N-pole; the S-pole repels the S-pole; but the N-pole attracts the S-pole, and the S-pole attracts the N-pole. This behavior of magnetic poles is known as the *Law of Magnets* (Fig. 29-2).

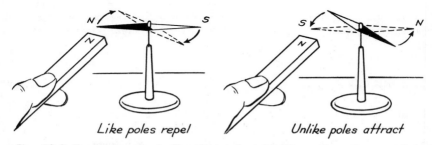

Like poles repel   *Unlike poles attract*

Fig. 29-2. Repulsion and attraction of magnetic poles. The N-pole of the magnet repels the N-pole of the compass needle (which is a magnet), while the N-pole of the magnet attracts the S-pole of the needle.

5. WHAT IS A MAGNETIC FIELD?

We can see from the Law of Magnets that magnetism is a kind of force. Although the magnet does not touch the compass needle, the needle nevertheless moves when the magnet is brought near it. What is this force?

Around every magnet is a region in which the force of the magnet exists. This region is the *magnetic field* of the magnet. In the magnetic field are invisible lines, called *magnetic lines*, or *lines of force*. Although lines of force are invisible, their presence can be mapped by the method shown in Fig. 29-3. The maps reveal that

    a. Lines of force extend from pole to pole of a magnet.

    b. Lines of force are concentrated at the poles. The strength of a magnet is therefore greatest at its poles.

    c. The stronger the magnet, the more lines of force it has and the farther the lines extend outward around the magnet.

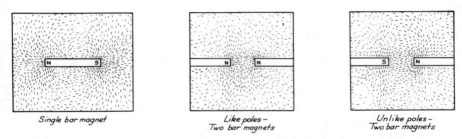

Single bar magnet   *Like poles –*   *Unlike poles –*
                         Two bar magnets   *Two bar magnets*

Fig. 29-3. Mapping lines of force around magnets. The magnets are covered with a clear, stiff plastic sheet. Iron filings are sprinkled on the sheet.Tapping the sheet enables the filings to arrange themselves in definite patterns. These patterns, or maps, indicate the lines of force around the magnets. Note how the patterns show that lines of force between like poles of close-lying magnets repel each other, while the lines of force between unlike poles attract each other.

6. HOW DO WE EXPLAIN MAGNETISM?

Recall that atoms consist of a nucleus around which electrons are in motion. Electrons are thought to possess a property called *spin*, somewhat like a spinning top. A spinning electron has been found to behave like a magnet.

Scientists believe that a magnetic substance is made up of large numbers of atoms, arranged in small groups called *domains*. A domain is a tiny area containing

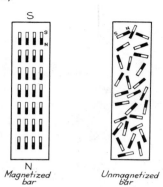

Fig. 29-4. Tiny magnets in a magnetic domain.

atomic magnets. Every one of these atomic magnets, therefore, has an N-pole and an S-pole. When the substance is a magnet, the tiny magnets line up in orderly fashion. All the N-poles of the tiny magnets point in one direction, while all the S-poles point in the opposite direction. When the substance is not a magnet, the tiny magnets in the domain are arranged in a disorganized fashion. The N-poles of some of these magnets face the S-poles of others (Fig. 29-4).

Another way of demonstrating the nature of magnetism is to cut a bar magnet into smaller pieces. Each resulting piece is itself a magnet (Fig. 29-5). When you continue to cut the smaller pieces, you form a domain.

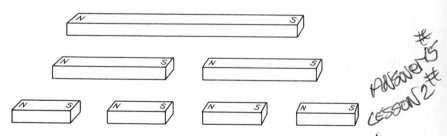

Fig. 29-5. Testing the theory of magnetism. Cutting the bar magnet in half forms two bar magnets. Cutting each of the two bar magnets produces four magnets, and so on, until a domain is formed.

7. HOW CAN WE DEMAGNETIZE A MAGNET?

If a magnet is jarred violently or heated strongly, it loses most or all of its magnetism. The magnetism is lost because the orderly arrangement of the atoms in the magnetic domains is disturbed (Fig. 29-6 on next page).

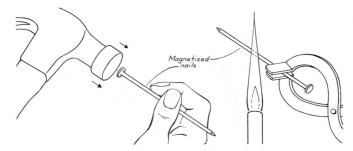

Fig. 29-6. Demagnetizing a magnet. Hammering or heating a magnet, such as a magnetized nail, causes it to lose its magnetism.

8. MAKING MAGNETS

a. By contact. A magnetic substance can be made into a magnet by stroking the substance with a magnet. The rubbing must be done in one direction only so that the magnets in the domains line up properly (Fig. 29-7).

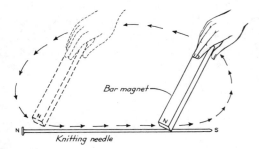

Fig. 29-7. Magnetizing by contact. The steel knitting needle can be made into a magnet by rubbing the needle in one direction with a bar magnet. The stroke is always begun at the same end of the needle. At the completion of each stroke, the magnet is carried through the air back to the starting end of the needle.

b. By induction. A magnetic substance does not actually have to touch a magnet to become magnetized. If a magnetic substance is placed in the magnetic field of a magnet, the substance will become temporarily magnetized (Fig. 29-8). When it is removed from the magnetic field, the substance loses its magnetism.

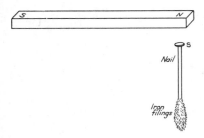

Fig. 29-8. Magnetizing by induction. When the nail is placed in the magnetic field of the bar magnet, the nail becomes magnetized. In the figure, the head of the nail becomes the S-pole. The filings cling to the point of the nail as long as the nail is magnetized. When the nail is removed from the magnetic field, the nail soon loses its magnetism, and the filings drop off.

c. By using electricity. Passing an electric current through a wire sets up a magnetic field around the wire. As long as the electricity flows, the wire behaves like a magnet (Fig. 29-9). This observation was made by the Danish scientist *Hans Christian Oersted* in 1820.

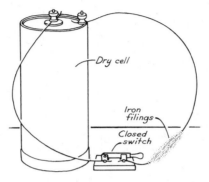

Fig. 29-9. A wire carrying a current behaves like a magnet. When the switch is closed, the iron filings are attracted to the current-carrying wire. The attraction indicates the presence of a magnetic field around the current-bearing wire.

9. MAKING AN ELECTROMAGNET

The magnetic field around a wire carrying an electric current may not be very strong. We can increase the strength of the field by winding the current-carrying wire into the shape of a *coil*. We can further increase the strength of the field by inserting a piece of soft iron, called a *core*, inside the coil. The soft iron core concentrates the lines of force, thereby producing a stronger magnet. A magnet consisting of a current-bearing wire wound around a core is called an *electromagnet*.

In addition to the core, the strength of an electromagnet (Fig. 29-10 on next page) depends on:

    a. The number of turns of wire in the coil. The greater the number of turns, the stronger the electromagnet.

    b. The amount of current in the coil. The greater the amount of current, the stronger the electromagnet.

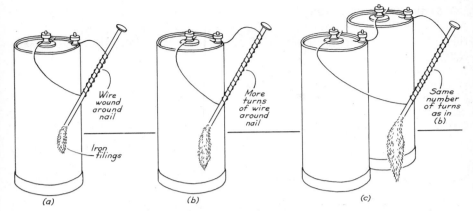

Fig. 29-10. Making an electromagnet stronger. Magnetic force can be increased in two ways. Increase the number of turns of wire as in (*b*), or increase the current as in (*c*).

10. TEMPORARY AND PERMANENT MAGNETS

a. Temporary Magnets. A *temporary magnet* loses nearly all its magnetism quickly. Although soft iron is easily magnetized, it loses its magnetism in a short time. A magnet made of soft iron is therefore a temporary magnet. Electromagnets are also temporary magnets, since they lose their magnetism when the electric current is turned off.

b. Permanent Magnets. A magnet which retains its magnetism for a long period of time is a *permanent magnet*. A magnet made from steel is a permanent magnet. Very strong permanent magnets are made from alnico. Permanent magnets are usually made by placing the magnetic substance in a coil of wire through which a large current of electricity is passed.

11. USES OF MAGNETS

a. Permanent magnets are used in industry to separate magnetic substances from nonmagnetic substances. They are also used to make magnetic compasses.

b. Electromagnets have many more uses than do permanent magnets because the magnetism of the electromagnet can be controlled by varying the current. Very large, powerful electromagnets are used to lift heavy iron and steel objects and move them a distance. Many devices such as the electric bell and the electric motor also employ electromagnets.

12. THE ELECTRIC BELL

The electric bell depends upon the force of magnetism for its operation. When electricity flows through the bell, the *electromagnet* becomes magnetized and draws the soft iron *armature* to it. In the same movement, the *hammer*, which is attached to the armature, strikes the *gong*. As the armature leaves the *contact point*, the circuit is broken and the electromagnet loses its magnetism. The *spring* then pulls the armature back to its original position. The circuit is again closed, the electromagnet is again magnetized, and the action is repeated. The ringing is continuous as long as the circuit is opened and closed (Fig. 29-11).

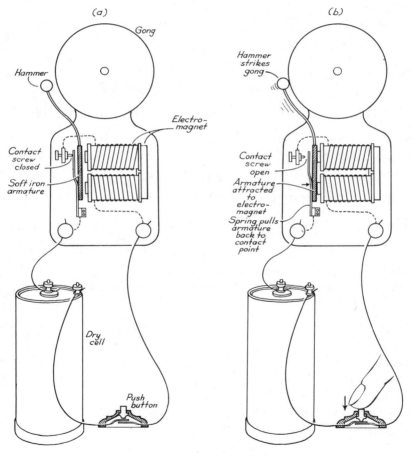

Fig. 29-11. The electric bell in operation

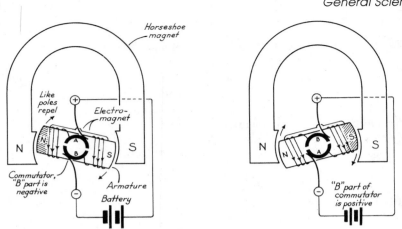

Fig. 29-12. Operation of the electric motor. The polarity of the armature depends upon the direction of the electric current flowing through it. The commutator is used to reverse the direction of current flow in the armature. This causes the polarity of the armature to change. Note that the "B" half of the commutator is in contact first with the negative terminal and then with the positive terminal of the battery. Note also that the shaded part of the armature is first an N-pole and then an S-pole.

13. THE ELECTRIC MOTOR

The electric motor (Fig. 29-12) is a device that converts electrical energy into mechanical energy. A motor contains a stationary horseshoe magnet, called a *field magnet*. (In industrial motors, the field magnet is an electromagnet.) In addition to the field magnet, there is an electromagnet, called the *armature*, which is mounted on a shaft and is free to rotate between the poles of the field magnet. By means of a device called a *commutator*, the motion of the armature is continuous.

The rotation of the armature may be explained by the Law of Magnets: Unlike poles attract; like poles repel.

The polarity of the armature is changed at exactly the correct instant with the aid of the commutator. When this is done, the magnetic poles of the horseshoe magnet repel the like poles or attract the unlike poles of the armature. The alternate attraction and repulsion set up between the poles of the armature and the poles of the field magnet cause the armature to rotate continuously. The shaft of the armature is connected to the device that is being operated by the motor.

THE ELECTRONIC SYNTHESIZER

A guitar produces sound when a string vibrates. The source of sound from a clarinet is a vibrating reed. In an electronic synthesizer, the sound source is a loudspeaker, driven by an alternating current.

By changing the current, electronic synthesizers can be made to mimic the sounds of orchestral instruments or any other natural sound. In addition, the synthesizer can produce sounds that were not possible on traditional instruments. Rock music makes particular use of synthesizers.

The first electronic synthesizer was developed in 1955. Today, smaller synthesizers are available for concert and home use. These portable keyboards are capable of mimicking any number of instruments. In addition, many can simultaneously produce the sound of percussion instruments. This allows the user to play melody and rhythm together. Some of the best known synthesizers are the Moog, the Buchla, and the Synket.

Studio technicians do not necessarily work at a traditional keyboard when composing music. Rather, they may be working with a complex control panel filled with levers and dials. By changing the positions of the controls, they can create the exciting and novel sounds so often heard in rock compositions.

At first, composing music with electronic synthesizers presented a serious problem—how should the electronic music be scored? While traditional instruments produced sounds that could be easily noted on standard music staves, synthesizers produced tones that were never produced before.

The problem was solved when sound recordings gained the right to be copyrighted. A written score became unnecessary unless the composer wanted it.

14. THE MAGNETIC COMPASS

This compass (Fig. 29-13) contains a *magnetic needle* mounted on a pivot and free to rotate *horizontally*. The darker end of the compass needle always points north, while the other end of the needle always points south. The case of the compass is made of a nonmagnetic substance, such as plastic or brass. The dial of the compass is marked off in *points* to indicate direction and degrees. The swing of the needle indicates the location of the magnetic pole attracting the needle.

Fig. 29-13. A magnetic compass

15. THE EARTH IS A MAGNET

Scientists have known for almost four hundred years that the earth is a huge magnet. When a piece of iron, such as an iron fencepost, is hammered, it is magnetized by induction by the magnetic field of the earth.

The magnetic poles of the earth are not located at the true geographic poles (Fig. 29-14 on next page). For example, the north magnetic pole is located in northern Canada, near Hudson Bay, which is almost 1500 miles from the true geographic north pole. Consequently, in most regions, the compass needle does not point to the geographic north pole. To determine true north, navigators must correct their compass readings. Charts issued by the government indicate what corrections are to be made in various locations on the earth.

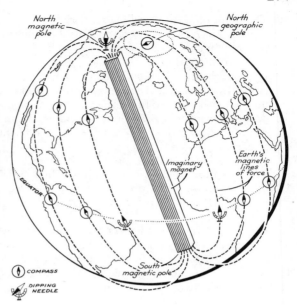

Fig. 29-14. The earth is a magnet. A dipping needle is a magnetic needle free to rotate vertically. Since the needle aligns itself with the earth's lines of force, a dipping needle indicates the direction of these lines around the earth. The lines run from the north magnetic pole to the south magnetic pole. A dipping needle points straight down when held directly above the magnetic north pole.

Multiple-Choice Questions

Write the number preceding the correct answer.

1. Which one of the following substances will not be attracted by a magnet? (1) brass (2) iron (3) cobalt (4) steel.
2. Metal cans will be attracted by a magnet because the can is made chiefly of (1) brass (2) copper (3) iron (4) tin.
3. An example of a natural magnet is (1) hematite (2) limestone (3) lodestone (4) steel.
4. A bar magnet usually has (1) one pole (2) two poles (3) three poles (4) four poles.
5. If the *S*-pole of a bar magnet is brought near the *N*-pole of another bar magnet, the magnets will (1) repel each other (2) lose their magnetism (3) attract each other (4) produce an electric spark.
6. Magnetic lines of force can be mapped with a magnet and (1) aluminum filings (2) iron filings (3) sand (4) shredded paper.
7. A magnet can be produced by (1) heating an iron bar (2) rubbing a pen on your sweater (3) stroking a steel needle with a magnet (4) winding 100 turns of copper wire around a piece of wood.

8. The point of an iron nail placed near the north pole of a magnet (1) becomes a north pole (2) becomes a south pole (3) becomes both a north and a south pole (4) remains unmagnetized.
9. When a compass needle is brought near a wire carrying a current, the needle is (1) deflected (2) demagnetized (3) melted (4) undisturbed.
10. A soft iron core will (1) increase (2) decrease (3) not affect the strength of the magnetic field of a coil of wire carrying a current.
11. A coil of insulated wire wound around a nail and connected to the terminals of a dry cell will (1) act as a magnet (2) give off light (3) make a noise (4) produce a spark.
12. A device that does not contain an electromagnet is the (1) electric doorbell (2) electric motor (3) electric stove (4) telephone receiver.
13. Of the following, the one that transforms electrical energy into mechanical energy is (1) a magnetic compass (2) an electric motor (3) a dipping needle (4) a lodestone.
14. An electric motor is able to operate because electricity (1) magnetizes the armature of the motor (2) is produced by generators (3) produces heat as it passes through wires (4) travels at the speed of 186,000 miles per second.
15. A compass needle can be made of (1) aluminum (2) brass (3) glass (4) steel.
16. Heating a magnet will (1) demagnetize it (2) increase the number of lines of force (3) make it stronger (4) reverse its poles.

Completion Questions

Write the word or expression that correctly completes the statement.

1. The region around a magnet in which the lines of force are found is called the _____.
2. Making a temporary magnet by putting a magnetic substance close to a magnet is known as magnetizing by _____.
3. A permanent magnet can be produced by placing a piece of steel in a coil through which _____ is passing.
4. Clusters of atoms of magnetic substances are called _____.
5. The dark point of the compass needle always points to the _____ magnetic pole.
6. The true geographic poles are _____ (*the same as, different from*) the magnetic poles of the earth.
7. A compass needle free to rotate vertically is called a (an) _____.
8. When the atoms of a magnetic substance are arranged with all their N-poles facing in the same direction, the bar is a (an) _____.
9. Cutting a bar magnet in half produces _____ magnet(s).
10. A magnet can be weakened by _____ or hammering it.

11. The magnetic north pole is located near _____ .
12. To account for magnetism, electrons are thought to possess a property called
_____ .

Modified True-False Questions

If a statement is true, write the word true. *If a statement is false, write the word or expression that must be substituted for the italicized expression to make the statement true.*

1. Alnico is an example of a (an) *natural* magnet.
2. The strength of a magnet is *greatest* at its poles.
3. Magnetizing by induction produces a (an) *permanent* magnet.
4. *Faraday* discovered that a wire carrying an electric current behaves like a magnet.
5. To increase the strength of an electromagnet, use a (an) *steel* core.
6. Both the electric bell and the telegraph contain a (an) *armature.*
7. A dipping needle points straight down when held over the *equator.*
8. In most regions, the compass needle points to the *geographic* north pole.
9. Heating a magnet *increases* its magnetism.
10. In an electric motor, the *commutator* reverses the direction of current flow in the armature.

Reasoning Questions

Give a reason for each of the following.

1. The earth is a magnet.
2. If you drop a magnet, it may lose its magnetism.
3. To keep his or her ship on course, the captain corrects the compass reading.
4. A commutator reverses the direction of the flow of electricity in a motor.
5. Increasing the number of turns of wire increases the strength of an electromagnet.

Chapter 30. The Behavior of Electricity

1. THE ELECTRICAL NATURE OF MATTER

Scientists believe that molecules are the building blocks of all matter. Molecules, in turn, are composed of atoms. Molecules and atoms do not usually have an electric charge.

As we learned in Chapter 20, two types of charged particles making up all atoms are the electron and proton. Atoms also contain uncharged, or neutral, particles called neutrons. An electron has a single negative (−) charge, while a proton has a single positive (+) charge. Thus, we see that the charge of an electron is equal to the charge of a proton.

2. HOW DO ATOMS BECOME CHARGED?

Recall that an atom normally contains an equal number of electrons and protons. Since this is so, the positive and negative charges in the atom neutralize each other, and the atom is said to be *uncharged*, or *electrically neutral*.

Recall also that, under certain conditions, an atom may gain or lose electrons. If an atom gains electrons and thus has more electrons than protons, the atom is *negatively charged*. If an atom loses electrons and thus has fewer electrons than protons, the atom is *positively charged*. All electrical charges in atoms result from the gain or loss of electrons.

3. STATIC ELECTRICITY

Electric charges that collect on the surface of an object and tend to remain there are called *static charges*, and this type of electricity is known as *static electricity*. An object may acquire static electricity as the result of friction between the object and another body.

For example, rubbing a glass rod with silk causes a transfer of electrons from the rod to the silk. Since the glass rod now has fewer electrons than protons, it is positively charged. The silk, having gained electrons, is negatively charged. Fig. 30-1 shows how a plastic comb gets a negative charge.

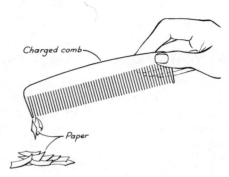

Fig. 30-1. Static electricity. After a plastic comb is rubbed with fur, the comb will attract many kinds of light objects, such as bits of paper. Friction between the comb and the fur causes the transfer of electrons from the fur to the comb. The comb now has an excess of electrons and is charged negatively. It, therefore, attracts the bits of paper. The fur has lost electrons and is charged positively.

Charged comb

Paper

LESSON 2## ANSWER ## 10

4. INSULATORS AND CONDUCTORS

Some materials, called *conductors*, permit electrons to flow freely through them. Most conductors are metals. Examples are silver, copper, aluminum, iron.

Materials which offer resistance to the flow of electrons are called *insulators*. Most insulators are nonmetals. Examples are rubber, cotton, mica, plastic, glass.

Superconductors are substances that conduct electricity with little or no resistance. Very low temperatures are required for superconductivity. There is still much to be learned about superconductivity, and considerable research is going on.

5. EFFECTS OF STATIC ELECTRICITY

As a result of friction, a great number of electric charges may be produced on an object. Such accumulations of charges are more readily produced on insulators than on conductors, where the charges would have a tendency to run off.

Under certain conditions, the number of excess electrons on an object may increase to the extent that they leave the object and move through the air as an *electric spark*. Such sparks may cause considerable damage. For example, trucks riding on rubber tires can build up a considerable charge as the tires rub against the pavement. If the truck contains combustible materials, a spark may cause a fire. Trucks carrying combustible materials are therefore equipped with chains which drag along the ground. The chains conduct the static charges away, thereby preventing the formation of sparks.

Friction between moving air molecules and water vapor molecules may also build up static charges within clouds. When these charges become great enough, there is a discharge of electricity from one cloud to another cloud, or to the ground. Such discharges are called *lightning*. Since metals conduct static charges to the ground, a safe shelter during an electric storm is an automobile. (Read "What Is Lightning?" on page 386.)

6. WHAT MAKES ELECTRICITY FLOW?

Electrons will flow from a point having an excess of electrons to a point where there is a deficiency of electrons. The flow of electrons from one point in a conductor to another is called an *electric current*, or *current electricity*.

How can we keep electricity flowing for as long as we wish? The answer is by maintaining an excess of electrons at one end of the conductor and a deficiency at the other end. This difference in the number of electrons at two points in a conductor is called *difference of potential*, or *electrical pressure*.

7. ELECTRICAL UNITS

A force is required to maintain electrical pressure between two points. This force, called *electromotive force*, or *voltage*, is measured in units called *volts* and abbreviated as E.

The number of electrons passing a given point in a conductor in a given time is called *amperage*, or *current*. The unit used to measure current is called the *ampere*, abbreviated as I.

Electrons flowing through a conductor encounter some *resistance* due to friction. Electrical resistance is measured in units called *ohms*, named after the German physicist Georg Ohm, and abbreviated as R. Ohm's law relates volts, amperes, and ohms: volts equals amperes times ohms, or $E = I \times R$.

8. THE ELECTRIC CIRCUIT

An *electric circuit* consists of a source of electrical pressure, a conductor through which the electricity can flow, and a device using the current, which offers resistance to the flow. Electricity will flow only through a complete, or *closed*, circuit (Fig. 30-2 on next page). An electric circuit is closed if the electrons can flow back to their source. Conversely, a circuit is incomplete, or *open*, if the electrons are unable to flow back to the source. To permit electrons to flow back to the source in a complete circuit, an electric cord consists of two wires. The electrons are brought to the device by one wire and returned through the resistance to the source by the second wire.

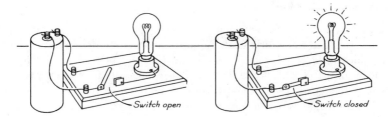

Fig. 30-2. A closed circuit. Closing the switch completes the circuit, providing a path for the electrons to flow back to their source.

9. CHEMICAL ENERGY IS CHANGED TO ELECTRICAL ENERGY

Under certain conditions, chemical energy can create a difference of potential and cause electrons to flow. Devices in which chemical reactions produce a difference of potential are called *electrochemical cells*, or *cells* for short. There are two common types: the *dry cell* and the *storage cell*, also referred to as *batteries*.

10. THE DRY CELL

A *dry cell* consists of a zinc container, a carbon rod, and a black paste of chemicals. The paste is made up of ammonium chloride (sal ammoniac), manganese dioxide, and powdered carbon. Chemical reactions produce an excess of electrons around the zinc and a deficiency of electrons around the carbon. This causes a flow of electrons from the negative zinc container to the positive carbon rod (Fig. 30-3).

The electrical pressure, or voltage, of a new dry cell is $1\frac{1}{2}$ volts. Dry cell batteries are used in flashlights, electric bells, and portable radios, and in many mechanical toys.

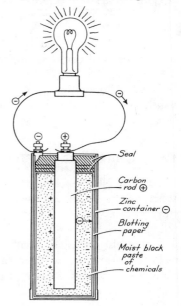

Fig. 30-3. The dry cell. The difference of potential at the two terminals causes electrons to flow, thus lighting the bulb.

11. THE LEAD STORAGE CELL

The *lead storage cell* consists of lead plates (negative) and lead dioxide plates (positive) suspended in sulfuric acid. As in the case of the dry cell, chemical reactions produce an excess of electrons around the lead plates and a deficiency of electrons around the lead dioxide plates. This causes a flow of electrons from the negative lead plates to the positive lead dioxide plates. The voltage of a new storage cell is about 2 volts. When a greater voltage is required, cells are connected in groups of three and are referred to as *storage batteries*. Storage batteries (Fig. 30-4) are used in automobiles to supply the necessary electrical power for many of the car's necessities, such as the lights, radio, and ignition system.

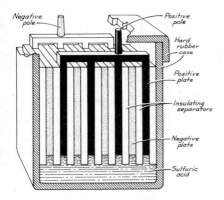

Fig. 30-4. The storage battery. Insulating separators between the negative lead plates and positive lead dioxide plates prevent the plates from touching each other and thus causing a short circuit. An electric current is produced by the reaction between the lead plates, the lead dioxide plates, and the sulfuric acid.

As the battery is used, the plates are changed chemically. To restore the plates to their original composition, the chemical reaction in the storage battery is reversed—a process called *charging*. Since water may be lost during operation of the battery, additional water must be furnished. Some of today's storage batteries are sealed to prevent water loss and thus reduce maintenance problems. A lead storage battery can generate hydrogen gas, so flames should be kept away from the battery.

12. RECHARGING THE STORAGE CELL

Storage cells (as well as dry cells) become weaker upon standing and upon usage. When any chemicals are used up, the cell goes "dead" and can no longer deliver current. Storage cells can be *recharged* by causing electrons to flow back into the cell. These electrons reverse the chemical reactions and restore some of the used-up chemicals to their original condition. In the automobile, an electric generator recharges the battery while the automobile is in operation. The ability to recharge a storage cell makes it the most valuable of our electric cells.

BROWNOUTS AND BLACKOUTS

We depend on a ready supply of electricity in our daily lives. While electric stoves and overhead lights require electric power at only certain times of the day, other devices, like the refrigerator, use electricity almost constantly. It is the task of the electric power company to see that there is enough electricity available.

Electricity is produced by one or more generating plants. Sometimes, however, the demand for electricity is much greater than normal, as on a hot summer's night when everyone has his or her fan or air conditioner on. Such increased demand may put a great strain on the generating plants.

At such times, the company may decide to decrease the voltage of electricity in selected areas. The flow of electricity, like the flow of water, can be increased or decreased when necessary. If this happens, electricity remains available, but lights may not seem as bright as usual, and air conditioners may blow cool, not cold, air. Such a situation is called a *brownout*.

Sometimes, equipment in the generating plant or along the transmission lines breaks down, and a blackout occurs. In a *blackout*, no electricity is available at all. Depending on where the breakdown of equipment occurred, a blackout may affect only one home, one side of the street, one community, or one entire section of the country. In general, the closer the breakdown is to the generating plant, the greater the area affected.

For most of us, a brownout or blackout is a short-term inconvenience. We rely on the electric company to return power to normal levels quickly. Perhaps we realize once again just how much we depend on electricity.

13. OTHER CELLS

As our civilization continues to grow, we find ourselves facing shortages of electrical energy. (Read "Brownouts and Blackouts" on the preceding page.) Newer means of producing electricity are constantly being sought. Among these are alkaline cells, fuel cells, solar cells, and nickel-cadmium batteries.

    a. *Alkaline cells* resemble dry cells but contain potassium hydroxide in place of the black paste in the dry cell. Potassium hydroxide, being more efficient than the black paste, gives the alkaline cell many times more life than the dry cell.

    b. In a *fuel cell*, a gas such as hydrogen (the fuel) is burned, or oxidized. In this process, electrons are released and permitted to flow through a circuit.

    c. In a *solar cell*, an electric eye changes light energy from the sun into electrical energy. To gather enough light to produce adequate amounts of electricity, many solar cells are used together.

    d. *Nickel-cadmium* storage batteries are much like lead storage batteries but contain potassium hydroxide in place of sulfuric acid. These batteries can also be recharged and sealed airtight, thereby increasing their usefulness.

14. GROUPING CELLS

Cells may be connected in groups to provide more current, more voltage, or both. Cells are grouped in a *series* or a *parallel* combination (Fig. 30-5).

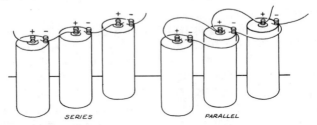

Fig. 30-5. Cells in series and in parallel. *Series:* The total voltage of the series combination is three times that of one cell. The total current is the same as one cell. *Parallel:* The total voltage of the parallel combination is the same as one cell. The total current, however, is three times that of one cell.

15. SERIES AND PARALLEL CIRCUITS

    a. In a *series circuit*, the electricity flows through each and all the electrical devices before returning to the source. If there is a break in any part of a series circuit, or if an appliance is turned off, the entire circuit becomes opened and the electricity no longer flows.

b. A *parallel circuit* consists of a number of branches, each of which is independently connected to the source. If there is a break in a parallel circuit, only that branch is affected. All other branches remain closed, and thus the electricity continues to flow through them. For this reason, all electrical appliances in the home are wired in parallel (Fig. 30-6).

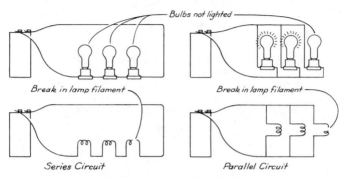

Fig. 30-6. Lamps in series and in parallel. If even one lamp is turned off in the series circuit, the entire string of lights goes out. In the parallel circuit, if one bulb is turned off, the others will remain lighted. Note that electricity will flow through each branch of the parallel circuit except the branch that is broken.

Series and Parallel Combinations

Series	*Parallel*
(1) Unlike terminals are connected. The negative zinc terminal of one cell is connected to the positive carbon terminal of the next cell.	(1) Like terminals are connected. All the negative zinc terminals are connected together and all the positive carbon terminals are connected together.
(2) The remaining positive and negative terminals of the cells are connected to the device using the current.	(2) The positive and negative terminals of the last cell are connected to the device using the current.

Advantage

Cells in series deliver more voltage than does a single cell. For example, if a single dry cell produces 1.5 volts, two of these cells in series produce 3 volts.	Cells in parallel provide greater current, but do not increase voltage. For example, if each of three cells delivers one ampere of current, connected in parallel the three cells deliver 3 amperes of current.

16. ELECTRICAL SYMBOLS

Following are some electrical symbols used by scientists and technicians.

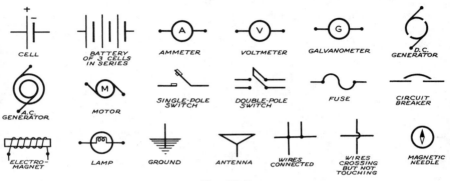

Fig. 30-7

17. MEASURING AN ELECTRIC CURRENT

Weak electric currents can be detected and measured by a *galvanometer*. This is a device making use of the magnetic effect of electricity. The galvanometer consists of a coil free to rotate between the poles of a permanent horseshoe magnet (Fig. 30-8). A spring and a pointer are attached to the coil. When the circuit is closed, the coil becomes an electromagnet. The attraction between the opposite poles of the permanent magnet and the electromagnet moves the pointer across the scale. When the circuit is opened, the spring pulls the pointer back to the zero position. The stronger the current, the greater is the deflection, that is, the movement of the pointer.

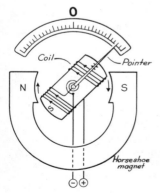

Fig. 30-8. The galvanometer. Electricity passing through the coil magnetizes it. The resulting magnetic poles of the electromagnet are attracted by the unlike poles of the horseshoe magnet. The pointer attached to the coil moves across the scale.

18. THE ELECTRIC GENERATOR

In the previous chapter, we learned that electricity, when passed through a wire, causes the wire to behave like a magnet. Around 1830, the English scientist *Michael Faraday* showed by experiment that the reverse is also true. A magnetic field moved back and forth over a wire causes electricity to flow through the wire (Fig. 30-9).

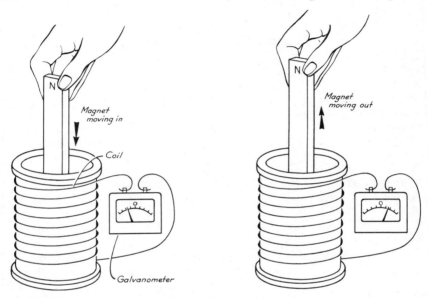

Fig. 30-9. Principle of the generator. As the magnet moves into the coil, the galvanometer pointer moves in one direction. As the magnet is withdrawn from the coil, the pointer moves in the opposite direction. This indicates a flow of electrons first in one direction and then in the opposite direction. This kind of current is called alternating current (AC). Some large commercial generators are designed to make the current flow in one direction only, producing direct current (DC).

In *electric generators*, or *dynamos*, moving coils of wire cut the lines of force of a magnet. A generator thus produces electricity. The greater the number of lines of force cut by the coil, the greater is the flow of electricity. Commercial generators contain an armature consisting of many coils of wire moving rapidly between the poles of powerful magnets. Steam turbines or waterfalls are used to supply the mechanical energy necessary to rotate the coils. Generating stations are therefore located near sources of waterpower, such as Niagara Falls and dams like the Grand Coulee. Generating stations in other localities use nuclear fuels or fossil fuels to provide the steam for turbines.

19. THE TRANSFORMER

Electrical transmission lines carry high-voltage AC efficiently from generating stations. Before this high voltage can be used in our homes, however, the voltage must be lowered, or stepped down. A device which reduces high-voltage AC to a lower voltage AC is a *transformer*. Transformers can also be constructed to raise, or step up, voltage.

Multiple-Choice Questions

Write the number preceding the correct answer.

1. When a comb attracts bits of paper, the comb is (1) charged (2) uncharged (3) magnetized (4) demagnetized.
2. A good conductor of electricity is (1) aluminum (2) glass (3) paper (4) rubber.
3. Of the following, the best conductor of electricity is (1) iron (2) copper (3) tin (4) zinc.
4. Which one of these is the safest place to be during a thunderstorm? (1) in an automobile (2) in an open field (3) in a lake (4) under a tree.
5. An electric current consists of a flow of electrical particles called (1) neutrons (2) protons (3) electrons (4) neutrinos.
6. The unit of electrical pressure is called the (1) ampere (2) current (3) meter (4) volt.
7. What is the approximate voltage of a new dry cell? (1) 1 (2) $1\frac{1}{2}$ (3) 3 (4) 6.
8. The metallic case of a dry cell is made of (1) aluminum (2) copper (3) iron (4) zinc.
9. A dry cell is safe to experiment with because it (1) has a strong casing (2) has a low voltage (3) is easily carried (4) is small.
10. In an electrical current, where the difference of potential is 6 volts and the resistance is 0.5 ohm, the current equals (1) 3 amps (2) 12 amps (3) 5.5 amps (4) 15 amps.
11. A generator is a device used to (1) store an electric current (2) detect an electric current (3) produce an electric current (4) store charges.
12. If the removal of one lamp from a string of Christmas tree lights causes the rest of the lamps to go out, the lamps are connected (1) in parallel (2) in series (3) to a generator (4) without a fuse.
13. The type of circuit in which it is possible for one branch not to operate without affecting the rest of the circuit is called (1) a parallel (2) a series (3) a fluorescent (4) a short circuit.
14. A transformer (1) changes voltage (2) filters a current (3) generates a current (4) serves as a fuse.

Completion Questions

Write the word or expression that correctly completes the statement.

1. Negatively charged particles are called _____.
2. Charges that collect and remain stationary on the surface of an insulator are called _____.
3. An electric spark is the rapid movement of _____ through the air.
4. The unit used to express the strength of an electric current is the _____.
5. The resistance offered by a conductor to the flow of electrons is measured in units known as _____.
6. The negative terminal of a dry cell is the metal _____.
7. Dry cells are connected in _____ when a greater voltage is required.
8. An instrument used to detect and measure tiny electric currents is the _____.
9. A generator is a device which changes mechanical energy to _____ energy.
10. A current in which the electrons flow first in one direction and then in the opposite direction is called a (an) _____ current.

Matching Questions

Match the items in column A with those in column B.

Column A	Column B
1. made up of atoms	*a.* storage cell
2. excess of electrons	*b.* single path circuit
3. cotton	*c.* incomplete circuit
4. can be charged	*d.* dry cell
5. carbon rod	*e.* negatively charged
6. series circuit	*f.* voltage
7. parallel circuit	*g.* insulator
8. electric generator	*h.* molecules
9. difference of potential	*i.* branched circuit
10. open circuit	*j.* dynamo

Reasoning Questions

Give a reason for each of the following.

1. Electrical charges result from the gain or loss of electrons.
2. A safe place during an electric storm is an automobile.
3. The storage cell is usually more valuable than the dry cell.
4. Grouping cells in series increases voltage.
5. A galvanometer must contain a spring.
6. Dynamos contain electromagnets.
7. A chemical reaction can produce an electric current.
8. Atoms are electrically neutral.
9. Trucks carrying combustible materials are equipped with chains which drag along the ground.
10. When the resistance of a circuit containing a dry cell increases, the current that the cell can deliver decreases.
11. An unused dry cell slowly loses power.
12. House appliances are connected in parallel.
13. Generators are located near sources of waterpower.
14. Alkaline batteries are superior to dry cells.
15. Lighted matches should be kept away from lead storage batteries.

Chapter 31. Putting Electricity to Work

1. ELECTRICAL RESISTANCE

The inner surface of a pipe opposes the flow of water through the pipe. Similarly, the interior of a wire opposes the flow of electrons through the wire. This opposition, or electrical friction, is called *resistance.*

The resistance to a flow of electrons through a wire depends upon:

a. Kind of Wire. The arrangement of atoms in metals affects the resistance of the metal. Wires of silver and copper have low resistance, while wires of tungsten and nichrome have high resistance.

b. Thickness. Increasing the number of paths through which electrons can flow decreases resistance. Thus, resistance decreases with the thickness of the wire. Thickness provides more paths. The thicker the wire, the lower is its resistance.

c. Length. The greater the distance that electrons flow through a metallic wire, the greater is the resistance of the metal. Thus, resistance increases with the length of the wire.

2. HEAT AND LIGHT FROM ELECTRICITY

Resistance, or electrical friction, produces heat as electricity flows through a conductor. The greater the resistance, the greater the amount of heat formed in the circuit. Increasing the current also increases the amount of heat in a circuit.

Resistance is put to work for us in a number of ways:

a. In Heating Devices. Electric toasters, irons, stoves, and heaters contain coils of nichrome wire, a metal of high resistance and relatively low cost. Resistance to electric current causes this wire to glow red and give off much heat.

b. In Lighting Devices

(1) The Incandescent Lamp. This lamp (Fig. 31-1 on next page) consists of a glass bulb filled with inert (noble) gases, such as argon or krypton. Within the bulb is a very thin tungsten filament, which is a high resistance wire with a very high melting point. When the circuit is closed, the filament becomes so hot as to give off light. Such a glowing wire is called *incandescent.* The inert gases in the bulb prevent the filament from burning out (evaporating) too quickly when heated to incandescence.

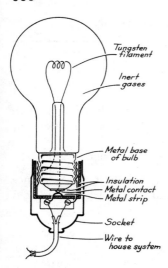

Fig. 31-1. The incandescent lamp

(2) *The Fluorescent Lamp.* This lamp (Fig. 31-2) is a glass tube, containing a filament, the inside of which has been coated with special fluorescent chemicals. In addition, the lamp contains an inert gas and some mercury vapor. When electricity passes through the filament, it becomes hot and causes the mercury vapor to give off ultraviolet rays. These rays strike the fluorescent coating, making it glow. The color of the light depends on the type of chemical coating used. Fluorescent lamps give off less heat but produce more light for less money than do ordinary incandescent lamps.

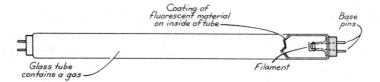

Fig. 31-2. The fluorescent lamp

3. OVERHEATING IN A CIRCUIT

Excessive heat resulting from increased electrical resistance and increased current can cause damage, usually fires. *Overheating* of an electric circuit comes about when more electricity flows through a circuit than the wire is able to carry safely. There are two common causes of overheating.

a. Overloading the Circuit. There is a maximum amount of current that an electrical circuit can carry safely. An excessive current, or flow of electrons, will cause the circuit to become *overloaded*. The wires may overheat and cause the insulation to burn. To prevent overloading the circuit, the wiring system must be designed to carry safely enough current to all the electrical devices desired. This may be done by installing several separate circuits in a home or factory.

b. Short Circuit. Defects in wiring may allow the flow of electrons to take a shorter path than the circuit was designed for. The shorter path decreases the length of the wire and decreases its resistance. Thus, in a *short circuit*, there is a greater electron flow (more current) than the wire can safely carry. As a result, the wires may become overheated. A frequent cause of a short circuit is worn, frayed insulation, which allows bare wire to touch some metallic object.

4. FUSES AND CIRCUIT BREAKERS

a. A *fuse* contains a small strip of metal that melts at a lower temperature than will the other wires in the circuit. A fuse is connected in series with each branch of a house circuit (Fig. 31-3). Therefore, the same amount of electricity that passes through the house circuit passes through the fuse. If an excessive amount of electricity flows through a circuit, the heat produced may cause the fuse metal to melt. The circuit then breaks, and the electricity stops flowing, thus preventing the circuit from overheating. A fuse or other type of circuit breaker is therefore an important safety device that must be present in all electrical circuits.

Fuses are rated according to the amount of current they will carry before melting. A fuse having a metal strip with a higher melting point than the conducting wires is useless. This is why using a coin in place of a fuse is a dangerous practice. The circuit wires would overheat before the fuse wire or the coin melts.

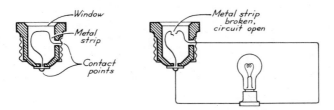

Fig. 31-3. How a fuse works. When the metal strip of the fuse melts, the circuit is broken. The electricity can no longer flow.

b. A *circuit breaker* employs an electromagnet to open a circuit when the flow of electricity becomes too great. A circuit breaker is really an automatic switch that opens when too much electricity flows as a result of an overloaded or short circuit. Thus, a circuit breaker acts like a fuse. Circuit breakers are replacing fuses in modern wiring systems.

5. SAFETY RULES WHEN USING ELECTRICITY

a. Check all electric wires to be sure the covering is not broken. The covering insulates the wire and prevents short circuits.

b. Do not plug too many devices into one outlet because this will overload the circuit.

c. To remove an electric plug from an outlet, firmly grasp and pull the plug itself. Do not pull on the wires because you may pull them out of the plug and cause a short circuit.

d. Always use fuses or circuit breakers with the proper amperage (current) rating. Avoid substitutes, such as a coin.

e. Electrical repairs should be done only by qualified electricians. Before any repair can be made, the main electrical switch must be opened.

f. Do not handle electrical equipment or touch electric light switches when you are taking a bath, or when your feet are in water, or when your hands are wet. The water, which contains dissolved minerals, makes you a conductor of electricity. People are needlessly electrocuted each year through failure to observe this simple precaution.

6. HOW DOES RADIO WORK?

a. Electrical Waves. When someone in a radio studio speaks into a microphone, the sound waves from his or her voice strike a sensitive part of the microphone that changes the sound into *electrical voice waves* (Fig. 31-4). If the same

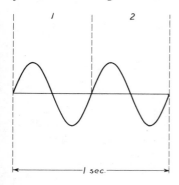

Fig. 31-4. Electrical voice waves produced by a hum. Two full waves are shown. One *hertz* equals one complete wave per second. In this example, the frequency of the wave is 2 hertz.

person hums a steady low note, the voice wave produced differs from the wave produced by a steady high note in a very important respect. The high-pitched note produces a wave of higher frequency (more waves per second) than does the wave from a low-pitched note (Fig. 31-5).

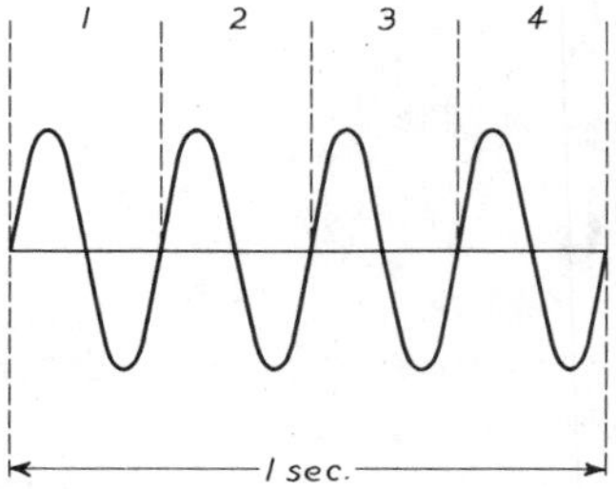

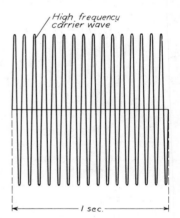

Fig. 31-5. Electrical voice waves produced by a whistle. Four full waves are shown. If these four waves are formed in 1 second, we say that the wave has a frequency of 4 hertz.

Voice waves travel readily along wires, but they cannot be broadcast as such in radio programs. To send voice waves from one place to a distant location, it is necessary to have the voice waves ride piggyback on another kind of electrical wave, called a *radio*, or *carrier*, *wave* (Fig. 31-6). The carrier wave is generated by a special device, called a *transmitter*. The carrier wave differs from the voice wave in that the carrier wave has a frequency several thousand hertz or more.

Fig. 31-6. A carrier wave. In a carrier wave, many more complete waves are formed in each second as compared to a voice wave. Thus, a carrier wave has a much higher frequency than a voice wave.

b. Transmitting Radio Programs. The electrical voice wave is sent from the studio where the microphone is located to the transmitting station where the carrier wave is produced. Here the two waves are mixed together and strengthened, or *amplified*, by transistors and vacuum tubes. The strong carrier wave with the voice wave riding piggyback (Fig. 31-7 on next page) is then sent out in all directions in space by a tall, tower-like *antenna*, or *aerial*, located near the transmitter building.

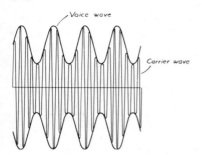

Fig. 31-7. Amplitude modulation (AM): The broadcast radio wave showing the voice wave carried with it. This final wave is said to be *amplitude modulated* (that's what "AM" stands for). "Amplitude" means "size." The diagram shows how the voice wave changes or modulates the amplitude of each successive little wave in the carrier to achieve the piggyback condition.

c. How FM Differs from AM. You probably have a radio of your own that can receive either AM or FM broadcasts. In FM, the same kind of carrier is generated by the transmitter, but the voice wave mixes with the carrier in an entirely different way. Instead of changing the amplitude of the carrier wave, the voice wave is made to change the frequency of the wave sent out from the antenna. This is why FM stands for *frequency modulation*. In FM, the voice wave can ride along on the carrier just as well as it can in the AM system (Fig. 31-8).

Both the AM and FM carriers travel through space at the enormous speed of 186,000 miles per second. At this speed, any one of these waves can go around the entire earth seven times in a single second!

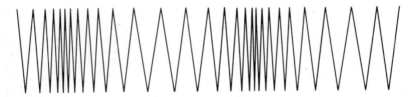

Fig. 31-8. Frequency modulation (FM): A frequency modulated (FM) carrier. Instead of changing the amplitude of the carrier as in AM, the voice wave causes changes in the frequency of the carrier. The voice wave is just as easily separated from the carrier at the receiver as in the case of AM.

d. Receiving AM and FM Radio Programs. When the radio wave reaches your radio receiver, it sets up a very weak electrical wave in the set's receiving antenna. The electrical wave is then amplified by one or two transistors and then fed to a special transistor called the *demodulator*. The demodulator's principal task is to separate the voice wave from the carrier wave. After it does this, it discards the carrier and leads the voice wave to several additional amplifiers. The strengthened voice wave coming from the last amplifier feeds into the loudspeaker. This converts the electrical voice waves into the sound waves that you hear.

Why don't you hear all the radio programs coming from all the different radio stations at the same time? If you glance at the radio program page in your newspaper, you will see that each AM and FM radio station is assigned a very definite frequency by the Government. Every radio has built into it a frequency selector, called a *tuner*, located between the antenna and the demodulator. When you turn the tuning knob on your radio, you are operating the tuner. At any one setting on the dial, the tuner selects only one particular frequency, rejecting all others. Only the chosen frequency is allowed to move on to the demodulator. Thus, you hear only the radio program you selected on your dial.

e. The Advantage of FM. An AM radio receiver cannot receive FM broadcasts, and an FM receiver cannot receive AM broadcasts. It happens that noise waves, due to static electricity in the air, or other disturbances, closely resemble AM radio waves but are not at all like FM waves. Since an FM receiver does not respond to AM waves, it does not reproduce noise waves and therefore gives you noise-free reception of your favorite programs.

7. HOW DOES TELEVISION WORK?

a. Television Waves. The television wave that reaches your home consists of two separate parts: (1) An FM wave that carries the sound part of the program and (2) an AM wave that brings the picture into your home. The sound part of your television set is nothing more than an ordinary FM receiver tuned to the frequencies used for the sound portion of the television broadcast. Most of the space inside the cabinet of your TV set is occupied by electrical parts that enable you to receive the picture on your screen.

b. Forming the Picture at the Studio. The picture-forming process starts with the television *camera*, which contains a special vacuum tube capable of changing the light and dark areas of the scene into *electrical picture waves*. The camera tube has the same kind of job as the microphone in a radio station except that it handles light waves instead of sound waves. In the camera tube, the scene being televised is broken down into horizontal lines of light and dark in a process called *scanning*. A separate set of picture waves is formed for each line of the scene that is scanned, one after the other. These are then sent out over wires to the transmitting station, which is generally located at some distance from the studio.

c. Transmitting Television Programs. The picture waves that arrive at the transmitter are then mixed with the television carrier; this carrier is identical in nature to the kind used for radio broadcasts. Again, the picture waves are piggybacked on the carrier, which spreads out in all directions at a speed of 186,000 miles per second. The sound is transmitted at the same time so that both parts of the program arrive at your television receiver together.

d. Receiving Television Programs. Your TV set contains two separate and distinct receivers: one for the FM sound part of the program and the other for the AM picture part of the broadcast. Since each receiver responds only to its own kind of wave, the sound and picture are automatically separated as they come down the antenna into the tuner. The voice waves proceed through the FM receiver to the loudspeaker as described previously.

Suppose there are four television transmitters broadcasting in your area. Each one has a different carrier-wave frequency, so that your tuner can select only one of these for reproduction. Just as in the radio-receiving process, the picture waves are separated from the carrier in the demodulator, the carrier is discarded, and the picture waves alone are amplified. When these waves have been made strong enough, they are fed to the *picture tube*, where they are converted into scanned lines on the screen, each line being composed of light and dark areas. These lines follow one another so rapidly from the top to the bottom of the screen that your eye combines them into a complete picture. There are 32,500 of these lines, or more, formed during every second that the television receiver operates!

8. TRANSISTORS

Electronic devices, from the time they were first invented, were powered by vacuum tubes. These tubes permitted current *rectification* (change from AC to DC) and *amplification* (change in volume). These devices were generally large and bulky because of the size and number of vacuum tubes that they employed. In addition, the tubes could break easily or develop leaks, so that constant maintenance and repair of the equipment became necessary. Furthermore, vacuum tubes required considerable power to operate.

In the early 1940's, *semiconductors*—substances with electrical properties between those of conductors and nonconductors (insulators)—were developed. Semiconductors contain the elements silicon and germanium, and are moderate conductors of electricity. The introduction of impurities, such as arsenic or boron, alters the electrical properties of semiconductors and makes them useful for rectification and amplification. Around 1950, this modified semiconductor became known as a *transistor*.

Because transistors are very small and can control the current in a circuit, as well as its direction, with less power, transistors have replaced vacuum tubes in many electronic devices. Where the device needs to be small, as in hearing aids, for example, transistors have become invaluable. Radio and television, as well as sound and picture recording devices—audiocassettes and VCR's (videocassette recorders)—employ transistors, also called *solid state* components.

The latest development in transistor circuitry is the use of tiny silicon *chips* designed to replace individual transistors. Tremendous numbers of chips, taking up very little room, can be mounted on circuit boards. The growth of computers is linked to these techniques.

Multiple-Choice Questions

Write the number preceding the correct answer.

1. Opposition to the flow of electricity through a conductor is known as (1) voltage (2) amperage (3) resistance (4) magnetism.
2. The factor upon which the resistance of a wire does *not* depend is (1) length (2) thickness (3) kind of insulation (4) kind of wire.
3. Heat is produced in an electric bread toaster because (1) electricity can produce heat (2) electricity is hot (3) electromagnetism heats the bread (4) a wire is coiled around an insulator.
4. An electric lamp produces light because (1) electricity is bright and yellow (2) the bulb is filled with argon (3) the interior of the bulb is a partial vacuum (4) the wire in the bulb is heated.
5. Fluorescent lamps produce light by the glowing of the (1) filament (2) chemical which covers the inside of the tube (3) gas which fills the bulb (4) glass.
6. An electric fuse will probably burn out when (1) an electric coffee maker is used with no water in it (2) an electric iron is used too long (3) a penny is used in place of the fuse (4) too many electric devices are attached to one outlet.
7. When too much electricity is flowing through a wire, it is automatically shut off by a (1) fuse (2) generator (3) meter (4) push-button switch.
8. An electric fuse "blows" when there is a short circuit because (1) the electricity gets too hot (2) the electricity produces enough heat to melt the wire in the fuse (3) the fuse has been weakened by age (4) less electricity goes through the fuse.
9. The wires that carry electric current in your home are made of (1) copper (2) iron (3) lead (4) rubber.
10. Insulation is placed on electric wires to (1) help the electricity flow smoothly (2) make them look better (3) prevent a short circuit (4) protect the wire from oxidation.
11. A wise rule to follow in the home is to (1) place coins behind burned-out fuses (2) pull electric plugs from wall outlets by the cord (3) use many electrical devices on one circuit to save electricity (4) use no electric cords with broken insulation.

12. Before an electrician makes repairs to a house circuit, the safe thing for him to do is (1) pull the main electrical switch (2) remove all burned-out lamps (3) turn out the lights (4) wash his hands.
13. Radio waves that carry voice waves are called (1) transmitters (2) detectors (3) carriers (4) amplifiers.
14. A television wave consists of (1) an FM wave only (2) an AM wave only (3) an FM wave and an AM wave (4) two FM waves.
15. The advantage of FM radio transmission over AM transmission is that FM (1) is cheaper (2) cuts out static noises (3) can be sent over greater distances (4) can transmit pictures.
16. A unit of frequency is the (1) ampere (2) volt (3) ohm (4) hertz.
17. Transistors are superior to vacuum tubes because transistors (1) require little maintenance (2) use more power (3) use less power (4) are safer.
18. Semiconductors contain the elements silicon and (1) copper (2) silver (3) carbon (4) germanium.
19. Solid state components do *not* use (1) vacuum tubes (2) silicon chips (3) transistors (4) semiconductors.
20. An example of an inert gas used in an incandescent lamp is (1) helium (2) argon (3) radon (4) chlorine.

Completion Questions

Write the word or expression that correctly completes the statement.

1. The resistance of a wire _____(*increases, decreases*) with an increase in the length of the wire.
2. The high-resistance coils of a toaster are made of the metal _____.
3. The filament of an electric light bulb is made of the high-resistance metal _____.
4. When a wire is heated to the temperature where it glows, the wire is said to be _____.
5. A circuit in which too many appliances are connected to one outlet is said to be _____.
6. When a flow of electricity takes a shorter path than the circuit was wired for, a (an) _____will result.
7. A fuse is always connected in _____(*series, parallel*) with the branch of the circuit it is to protect.
8. Radio waves travel at a speed of _____miles per second.
9. The part of the radio transmitter which changes sounds into electrical signals is the _____.
10. The TV carrier-wave frequencies of different stations are separated in your TV set by the part called the _____.

REVIEW OF UNIT VI

1. A pupil hangs a bar magnet from a ring stand so that it can swing freely in a horizontal position. The N-pole of a second bar magnet is brought near one end of the suspended magnet. The end of the suspended magnet swings away. Was it the N-pole or the S-pole that swung away? Why?

2. Explain how you would make each of the following devices.
   a. an electromagnet
   b. a magnetic compass
   c. a permanent magnet, using a steel knitting needle and a permanent magnet
   d. a dipping needle

3. Explain how each of the following devices operates.
   a. an electric bell
   b. an electric motor

4. Complete the drawing below of an electromagnet.

5. Below are five diagrams. For each diagram, state whether the magnetic pole marked X is stronger, weaker, or equal in strength to the pole marked Y.

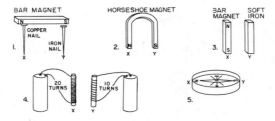

6. Name the unmarked pole of magnet 2.

7. Name the unmarked pole of magnet 2.

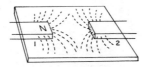

8. In the diagram below, the parts of the circuit have been lettered *A-E*. List each item of equipment (*A-E*) that shows its place in the circuit.

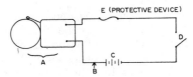

E (PROTECTIVE DEVICE)

9. The five questions below relate to drawings *A* and *B*. Write the word which will correctly complete each statement.
   a. The dry cells in *A* are connected in _____.
   b. The dry cells in *B* are connected in _____.
   c. The three dry cells in *A* have a total voltage of _____ volts.
   d. The three dry cells in *B* have a total voltage of _____ volts.
   e. The lamp that glows more brightly is in the circuit labeled _____.

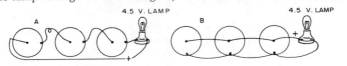

4.5 V. LAMP   4.5 V. LAMP

10. Below are the electric lamps and their sockets that can be installed in a doll's house. Show how they may be connected to the dry cells so that either lamp may be unscrewed without putting out the other one.

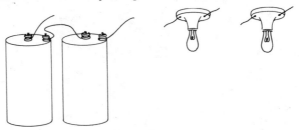

11. Suppose a dry cell, a switch, and an electric lamp are connected, as shown in the diagram below. When the switch is closed, the lamp does not light. Name at least two things that might be done to find out what is wrong.

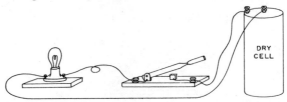

DRY CELL

12. Sketch in the missing part of the diagram of a complete electric circuit, and write the name of the missing part.

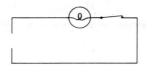

13. Complete this circuit so that the greatest amount of light will be obtained from the cells shown.

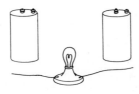

14. Either explain in one or more sentences how you would correct the diagram below, or redraw the diagram correctly.

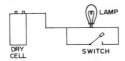

15. Draw lines to indicate wires connecting lamp *B* in parallel with lamp *A*.

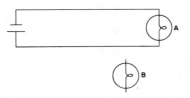

16. *a.* How many wires are there in an electric cord leading to an electric lamp? Why?
    b. What is the purpose of the covering on an electric wire?
    c. Describe the best way to remove the plug on the end of an electric cord from an electric outlet.
    d. Explain why one should not run an electric cord under a rug to a lamp.
    e. Explain why it is dangerous to put pennies behind worn fuses.

Unit VII.
Overcoming Gravity and Friction

Chapter 32. How Gravity Is Useful to Us

1. WHAT IS GRAVITY?

Force is a push or pull that a body exerts. The force of attraction that the earth exerts on all objects is called *gravity*. Although gravity cannot be seen, it can be felt. For example, gravity pulls all matter to the center of the earth, and the pull of gravity keeps us from falling off the earth. Because of gravity, dropped objects always fall to the earth. Gravity causes the atmosphere to remain with the earth. Gravity also makes water flow downhill. The earth's gravity is great enough to influence the motions of the other planets, as well as the motion of the moon.

2. FALLING BODIES

The early Greeks, led by Aristotle, were interested in falling bodies. They reasoned, but did not test their reasoning, that a heavy object would fall to the ground sooner than would a lighter object if both were dropped from the same height at the same time. This belief persisted for some 2,000 years until it was disproved by the experiments of Galileo, an Italian scientist, at the beginning of the 17th century. Galileo is thought to have dropped a 10-pound ball and a 1-pound ball, at the same time, from the top of the Leaning Tower of Pisa. Both balls—the heavier one and the lighter one—hit the ground at the same instant.

During the middle of the 17th century, Sir Isaac Newton, a British scientist, discovered the laws of motion that bear his name. Based upon experimentation, these laws describe the effect of forces on both stationary and moving bodies. Newton's laws also explain how falling bodies behave. As you continue your work in science, you will study these laws and their many applications.

3. MASS AND WEIGHT

Recall that mass is the amount of matter that a body contains. The mass of a given body, therefore, always remains the same.

Recall also that weight is the pull of gravity on a given mass. As the pull of gravity decreases—for example, in a space vehicle—the weight of the body also decreases. On earth, however, at any given location, as at sea level, the force of gravity does not change very much. Hence, the mass of a body and its weight are about the same. In this book, we will use mass and weight interchangeably with the understanding that we are dealing with a single location.

4. HOW IS GRAVITY MEASURED?

You have learned that the pull of gravity on an object determines the weight of the object. Thus, when you measure the weight of an object on a scale, you are really measuring the pull of gravity on that object. The force of gravity is expressed in units of weight, such as grams, kilograms (1,000 grams), or pounds.

a. The Spring Balance. Objects may be weighed on various kinds of scales. One type of scale commonly employed to weigh small objects is the *spring scale*, also called a *spring balance*. A given weight attached to the spring will stretch the spring a given distance. If the weight is doubled, the spring will stretch twice as much (Fig. 32-2 on next page). The amount of stretch, therefore, is proportional to the weight of the object, or the force of gravity.

b. The Platform Balance. To weigh objects with a greater degree of accuracy than can be obtained with a spring balance, scientists use the *platform balance*. It is also known as the *equal-arm balance*. This scale (Fig. 32-1) consists of an arm balanced on a pivot point. A pan is found at each end of the arm.

The platform balance really measures the mass of a body, but since mass and weight are approximately equal at any given location, this balance also measures the weight of the body.

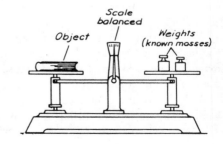

Fig. 32-1. The platform balance. The object being weighed is placed on one pan. Weights (masses) are placed on the other pan. When the pointer stops swinging and is at the center of the scale, the pull of gravity is the same on both sides.

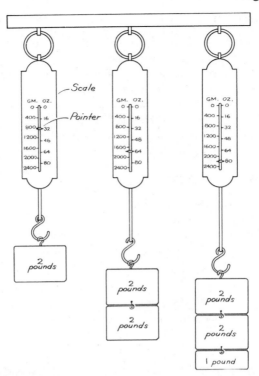

Fig. 32-2. The spring balance. The pointer attached to the spring moves along the scale, indicating the weight of the object being measured.

5. UNITS OF MEASUREMENT

In the past, two common systems of measurement were used: the *metric system* and the *English system*. In the metric system, units for a given measurement are related by multiples of 10; that is, this system uses decimals to convert larger to smaller units. The metric system is, therefore, simpler to use because of the ease of conversion.

In 1960, international scientific societies renamed the metric system to become the *International System of Units*, abbreviated SI. In 1975, Congress authorized the extended use of SI for the United States. In time, it is expected that all nations will use the International System.

Length, weight, and volume are some common units of measurement. How these units are related in both systems of measurement is shown in Table 32-1. The ease in changing metric units is shown in Table 32-2. (See tables on next page.)

Table 32-1. English and Metric (SI) Equivalents

English system	Metric system
Length	
1 inch	2.54 centimeters (cm)
1 foot	30 centimeters
1 yard	0.9 meter (m)
1 mile	1.6 kilometers (km)
Weight	
1 ounce	28.3 grams (g)
1 pound	454 grams
2.2 pounds	1 kilogram (kg)
Volume	
1 pint	0.47 liter (L)
1 quart	0.95 liter
1 gallon	3.8 liters

Table 32-2. How Some Metric Units Are Related

Prefix	Meaning	Unit (length)	Decimal Notation	
		meter	1 meter	= 1.0 meter
deci	one-tenth	decimeter	1 decimeter	= 0.1 meter
centi	one-hundredth	centimeter	1 centimeter	= 0.01 meter
milli	one-thousandth	millimeter	1 millimeter	= 0.001 meter
kilo	one thousand times	kilometer	1 kilometer	= 1,000 meters
mega	one million times	megameter	1 megameter	= 1,000,000 meters

Prefix	Meaning	Unit (weight)	Decimal Notation	
		gram	1 gram	= 1.0 gram
deci	one-tenth	decigram	1 decigram	= 0.1 gram
centi	one-hundredth	centigram	1 centigram	= 0.01 gram
milli	one-thousandth	milligram	1 milligram	= 0.001 gram
kilo	one thousand times	kilogram	1 kilogram	= 1,000 grams
mega	one million times	megagram	1 megagram	= 1,000,000 grams

6. FORCE AND WORK

Gravity affects all objects on the earth. To lift or push objects, a force must be exerted to overcome the resistance (force) of gravity. The push or pull exerted against gravity is called *effort force*.

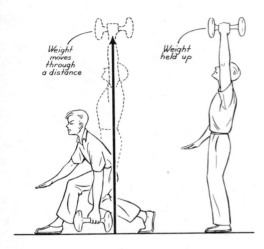

Fig. 32-3. Doing Work. The boy is doing work when he exerts a force and moves the weight a given distance. He is not doing work when he is merely holding the weight.

If you exert a force on a weight (the resistance) and succeed in moving the weight a given distance, you have done work (Fig. 32-3). Thus, work (W) equals force (f) × distance (d), or $W = fd$. This relationship is called the *Law of Work*.

In the metric system, force is measured in *newtons* (N). One newton is equal to a force of approximately 0.224 pound. How big is a newton? A 135-pound person weighs about 600 newtons (N).

7. MACHINES HELP PEOPLE

A *machine* is a device that helps a person work more efficiently and more comfortably. A machine, however, turns out the *same* amount of work that is put into it, or: *work output equals work input (Law of Machines)*. In actuality, a machine turns out a little less work than what was put into it because some force is required to overcome friction. It is the way the work is done that makes a machine useful. Machines do work in three ways:

a. A machine increases or multiplies force. Examples of such machines are the lever, the inclined plane, the wheel and axle, the pulley, and the jackscrew.

b. A machine increases speed. Machines that increase the rate of doing work consist of various gear combinations.

c. *A machine can change the direction of a force to suit one's convenience.* The pulley is a common device that can change the direction of the applied force. It can also be used to multiply force.

8. TYPES OF MACHINES

a. The Lever. The *lever* is a bar free to rotate around a fixed point, called a *fulcrum*, or *pivot*. The fulcrum can be placed at any position along the bar. However, the closer the fulcrum is to the object (resistance), the less force (effort) is required to move the object. This is so because the effort exerted now moves a great distance (input work), while the resistance moves a short distance (output work). Thus, the lever multiplies force at the expense of distance.

Notice in Fig. 32-4 (*a*) that, as the resistance (5 coins) moves 2 cm, the effort (1 coin) moves 10 cm. In (*b*), the resistance (200 kg) moves 0.3 m while the effort (20 kg) moves 3 m. In each case, work output equals work input. Examples of levers (*c*) include shears and scissors, the seesaw, crowbar, wheelbarrow, nutcracker, pliers, shovel, and the forearm of a person.

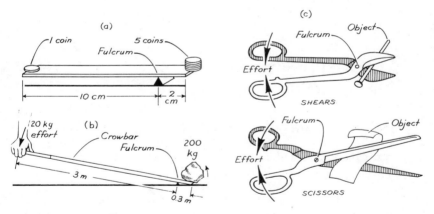

Fig. 32-4. The lever at work. (*a*) One coin placed 10 centimeters from the fulcrum balances five similar coins 2 centimeters from the fulcrum.

(*b*) The 20-kilogram effort acting 3 meters from the fulcrum can raise the 200-kilogram weight resting on the bar 0.3 meter from the fulcrum. With this lever, work is done with one-tenth of the force otherwise needed to lift the weight.

(*c*) Each half of a pair of shears or scissors is actually a lever. As the object being cut is moved closer to the fulcrum, less force is required to cut the object. Shears, because they cut heavier objects, require a longer effort arm than do scissors.

b. The Inclined Plane. Have you ever noticed how a heavy crate is raised from a sidewalk onto a truck that has no lifting platform? The crate is pushed up a plank from the sidewalk to the truck. Such a plank is called an *inclined plane*. The longer the plane for any given height, the less steep it is. The smaller the angle the plane makes with the ground, the less force is required to move the object. Thus, the inclined plane decreases effort at the expense of distance. In Fig. 32-5(*a*), the resistance (400 lb) moves 3 ft (work output) while the effort (100 lb) moves 12 ft (work input). Examples of the inclined plane (*b*) are a ramp, stairs, knife edge, ax, wedge, chisel, and a road up a hillside.

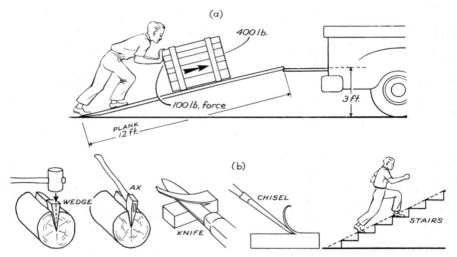

Fig. 32-5. The inclined plane at work. (*a*) The 100-pound force must be exerted through a distance of 12 feet along the plank to raise the 400-pound crate 3 feet above the ground. (*b*) Various uses of the inclined plane.

c. The Wheel and Axle. The *wheel and axle* consists of a large wheel mounted on a thin axle (Fig. 32-6 on next page). During a complete revolution, a force applied to the wheel travels a distance equal to the circumference of the wheel. At the same time, the weight moves through a distance equal to the circumference of the axle. Because of this, a small force exerted on the wheel can move a large weight attached to the axle. However, the force moves a great distance compared to the short distance moved by the weight (Law of Machines). Thus, the wheel and axle multiplies force at the expense of distance. The antique coffee grinder, doorknob, and steering wheel are examples of the wheel and axle.

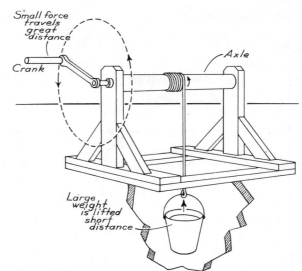

Fig. 32-6. The wheel and axle at work. The wheel and axle is a lever revolving around a pivot at the center of the axle.

d. The Jackscrew. The *jackscrew* is a combination of two machines, an inclined plane and a lever (Fig. 32-7). The part of the machine called the *screw* is an inclined plane wound around a cylinder; the handle and movable head together form the lever. Examples of jackscrews are automobile and house jacks, carpenter's vise, and wine press.

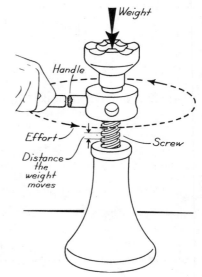

Fig. 32-7. The jackscrew at work. The effort, applied to the handle, travels a great distance in making one complete turn. The weight is raised only a small distance by the screw. The distance the weight travels equals the distance between two adjacent threads of the screw.

e. The Pulley. The *pulley* is a grooved wheel mounted on an axle. When in use, a cord is run around the wheel (Fig. 32-8). Friction between the cord and the groove makes the wheel turn on the axle. Pulleys may consist of more than one wheel, and may be fixed or movable, depending on their use. A pulley may be used to multiply force, or change the direction of a force.

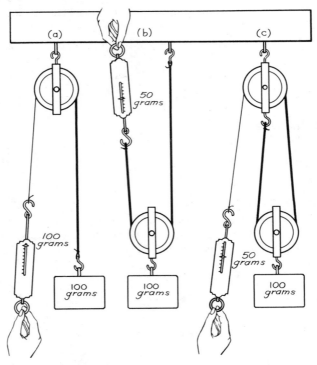

Fig. 32-8. Pulleys at work. The darker parts of the cord indicate the strands supporting the weight in each case. Count them. *(a) Single fixed pulley:* One strand supports the weight. The force is not multiplied, but the direction in which the force is exerted is changed.

(b) Single movable pulley: Two strands support the weight. Therefore, the force is multiplied by 2. Note that an effort of 50 grams overcomes (lifts) a resistance of 100 grams.

(c) One fixed and one movable pulley: Since two strands support the weight, the force is multiplied by 2. In addition, the direction of the force is changed by the single fixed pulley.

The extent to which a pulley can multiply force depends upon the number of strands of cord actually supporting the weight. (The number of strands is referred to as the *mechanical advantage* of the pulley.) However, when the force is multiplied, it is accomplished at the expense of the greater distance through which the force is exerted (Law of Machines).

Pulleys are used by painters to raise scaffolds, by riggers to lift heavy weights, and in power shovels, derricks, flagpoles, and elevators.

f. Gears. *Gears* are applications of the wheel and axle. Combinations of gears are used to multiply force or to increase speed, as in the bicycle and automobile. For example, in Fig. 32-9, one revolution of the large gear will cause four revolu-

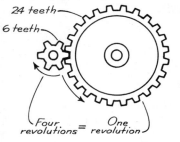

tions of the small gear, thus increasing speed. However, if the effort is applied to the small gear, four revolutions of the small gear will cause the large gear to revolve once. In this case, the force is multiplied four times (24 ÷ 6) at the expense of speed. In the home, gears are used in egg beaters and in electric and wall-type can openers.

Fig. 32-9. Gears

Multiple-Choice Questions

Write the number preceding the correct answer.

1. The attraction of the earth for all objects is called (1) density (2) pressure (3) gravity (4) barometer reading.
2. The amount of attraction exerted by the earth on an object can be obtained by finding the object's (1) pressure (2) texture (3) buoyancy (4) weight.
3. The pull of gravity is measured in units called (1) kilometers (2) miles per hour (3) pounds (4) quarts.
4. The prefix *kilo* equals (1) 1000 (2) 0.001 (3) 0.01 (4) 100.
5. Of the following, a machine does *not* (1) multiply force (2) increase speed (3) change the direction of a force (4) increase work.
6. A machine consisting of a bar which can rotate around a fulcrum is a (1) wheel and axle (2) lever (3) cylinder (4) screw.
7. An example of a lever is the (1) ramp (2) seesaw (3) knife blade (4) saw.
8. A pulley is frequently used (1) in a doorknob (2) in some windows (3) to make an ironing board open (4) to make a window shade roll.
9. The principle of a wheel and axle can be demonstrated by using (1) two pencils and a book (2) a windowpole (3) a pencil sharpener (4) a piece of chalk attached to a string.

10. A jackscrew is a combination of an inclined plane and a (1) wheel and axle (2) gear (3) lever (4) pulley.

11. By using a single fixed pulley, one can (1) multiply the effort force by 2 (2) increase the amount of work (3) change the direction in which the effort force is applied (4) increase the effort force as well as change its direction.

12. The diagram shows the use of a (1) lever (2) pulley (3) screw (4) wedge.

13. How many times a pulley multiplies a force depends on (1) how fast it is being used (2) how large the force is (3) the number of strands holding up the weight (4) the size of the pulley wheel.

14. Gears are forms of the (1) wheel and axle (2) pulley (3) jackscrew (4) lever.

15. Gears are used in a bicycle to (1) change the direction of motion (2) create energy (3) increase the force on the pedals (4) increase the speed at which the wheels turn.

Completion Questions

Write the word or expression that correctly completes the statement.

1. To go to the moon, a rocket ship must first overcome the gravitational attraction of the _____.

2. A balance containing two equal arms is called a (an) _____ balance.

3. If a force has been used to lift an object, _____ has been accomplished.

4. The general term given to a device which can be used to multiply a force is a (an) _____.

5. The doorknob is an example of a machine called a (an) _____.

6. A board is used to roll a barrel from the ground onto a truck. If a longer board is used, the force necessary to roll the barrel is _____ (*decreased, increased*).

7. An ax is an example of the simple machine called the _____.

8. If three strands of rope of a pulley support a weight, the force is multiplied by _____.

9. The metric unit of length about half the size of an inch is the _____.

10. The number of times a pulley system multiplies force is known as _____.

Modified True-False Questions

If a statement is true, write the word true. *If a statement is false, write the word or expression that must be substituted for the italicized expression to make the statement true.*

1. Water will not flow uphill because of *gravity*.
2. *Work* is required to overcome resistance.
3. Machines multiply *work*.
4. Machines may *increase* speed.
5. An example of a lever is a (an) *hammer*.
6. The wheel and axle multiplies force at the expense of *time*.
7. The *metric* system of measurement is more widely used than the English system.
8. An automobile jack is an example of a (an) *wheel and axle*.
9. A spring scale is *more* accurate than a platform balance.
10. To cut metal, shears have a (an) *long* effort arm.

Reasoning Questions

Give a reason for each of the following:

1. Machines do not decrease work.
2. The metric system is convenient.
3. Mass and weight are the same at sea level.
4. A scissors is an example of a lever.
5. Newton's laws of motion are still valid today.
6. In a machine, work output equals work input.

Chapter 33. Using and Reducing Friction

1. WHAT IS FRICTION?

Every surface, however smooth, contains minute irregularities. When you move one surface over another, the irregularities rub against one another and offer resistance to the movement. The resistance which results from the rubbing together of two surfaces is called *friction*. Two important factors on which the amount of friction depends are (*a*) the weight (mass) acting on each of the surfaces, and (*b*) the nature of the surfaces (Fig. 33-1).

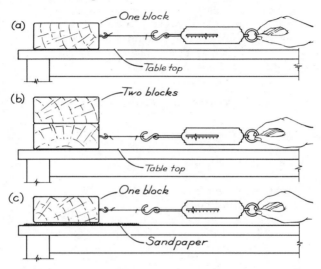

Fig. 33-1. Factors determining friction. It takes more force to pull the double block (*b*) over the table top than to pull the single block (*a*). It also takes more force to pull the single block over the sandpaper (*c*) than over the table top.

When the work output of a machine exactly equals the work input, the machine is said to be 100% efficient. More often, the work output is less than the work input because some of the effort force is used to overcome friction. For example, in Fig. 32-5(*a*), on page 326, an effort force of 100 lbs moving a distance of 12 ft is required to lift the 400-lb resistance a distance of 3 ft. If the surface of the plank were rough, it would require more than 100 lbs to move the resistance along the plank. Thus, the input work would become greater than the output work, reducing the efficiency of the machine. Machines are therefore less than 100% efficient.

2. UNDESIRABLE EFFECTS OF FRICTION AND THEIR REMEDIES

In many instances, friction creates problems. Although friction cannot be eliminated completely, it can be reduced.

a. When one object is to be moved over another object, enough force must be exerted to overcome not only the resistance of the object, but also the resistance of friction.

b. Friction causes excessive heat and wear of metal parts.

How to Reduce Friction. *Sliding* friction may be changed to *rolling* friction. The object to be moved may be placed on wheels. Examples are skates, bicycles, and automobiles. In these machines, roller bearings and ball bearings are also used to reduce friction (Fig. 33-2).

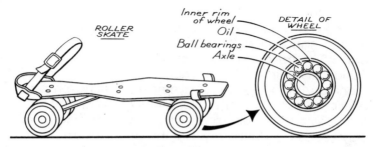

Fig. 33-2. Reducing friction by the use of bearings. The inner rim of the wheel and the outer edge of the axle rotate on very smooth ball bearings that are lubricated. Friction is greatly reduced by this combination.

Friction between surfaces is reduced when they are smoothened. This can be done by polishing, and by using lubricants (Fig. 33-3 on page 335). In the automobile engine, for example, cylinder and piston surfaces are polished smooth, and oil is used to reduce friction between the piston and the cylinder wall. This is why engine oil must be changed regularly, since old engine oil loses its effectiveness after a while.

3. USING FRICTION

Friction is absolutely essential to us in many ways. We could not walk if there were not sufficient friction between the soles of our shoes and the ground. Stationary objects would not stay fixed if it were not for friction. The operation of brakes in automobiles depends upon friction. The heat generated by friction may be used to ignite matches. (Read "Friction and Sports" on next page.)

FRICTION AND SPORTS

All sports involve movement of some kind. And where there is movement, there is friction. In order to better their performance, athletes must take steps to use friction to their advantage.

One of the most obvious steps is the use of the sneaker. These sport shoes with rubber soles create a great amount of friction when they come into contact with a playing surface. Basketball players, for example, who need to stop and turn quickly will not do too well if they find themselves slipping and skidding across the court.

There are many other instances where increased friction can benefit athletic performance. While this can often be accomplished simply by keeping the hands dry, athletes can choose from a number of techniques. For example, gymnasts working on parallel bars cannot afford to lose their grip. For that reason, they cover their hands with chalk. The chalk not only keeps the hands dry, but the gritty texture of the chalk prevents slipping on the wooden bars.

Billiard players also chalk the tips of their cues so that they may control the billiard balls better. In fact, every sport that requires holding on to something benefits when the athlete has increased friction in some way.

But there are many other sports that require the freest movement possible. In those activities, athletes must lessen friction to achieve their best performance. Swimmers may even go so far as to shave their heads and bodies in order to reduce friction while in the water.

One of the more common examples of reducing friction comes from skiing. Skis move easily over snow when they are waxed. After much use, the waxy coating wears off and the skier begins to notice that he or she is not going as fast as customary. Rewaxing the skis solves the problem.

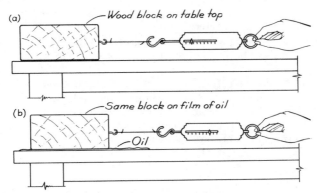

Fig. 33-3. Reducing friction by lubricating the surfaces. Oiling the surfaces of moving parts creates a smooth film between the parts, thus reducing friction. Less force is required to pull block (*b*) than to pull block (*a*).

4. FRICTION IN LIQUIDS AND GASES

Liquids and gases also cause friction. Barnacles on the bottom of a boat will increase friction between the boat and the water. Air friction causes meteors and artificial satellites to burn up as they enter the earth's atmosphere. Air friction slows down airplanes. Designers constantly strive to make airplane surfaces as smooth as possible to reduce friction.

Objects that move through air encounter air resistance. In outer space, however, there is so little friction that space vehicles can travel without additional force to overcome friction. Upon reentry to the earth's atmosphere, friction slows down the spacecraft. Considerable heat is generated and special heat shields are required to protect the craft and its occupants.

Multiple-Choice Questions

Write the number preceding the correct answer.

1. The movement of one object over another is slowed down by (1) gravity (2) pressure (3) friction (4) heat.
2. If a spring balance is attached to a small toy car, the reading of the scale on the balance will be least when the car is (1) dragged on its side (2) dragged upside down (3) lifted straight up by the balance (4) moved forward on its wheels.

3. Friction between automobile tires and the road is increased by the use of (1) grease (2) oil (3) sand (4) water.
4. Oil is put on the bearings of wheels to (1) give the wheels more force (2) increase the leverage of the wheels (3) prevent sparks of static electricity (4) reduce friction.
5. Friction can be reduced by (1) substituting sliding friction for rolling friction (2) substituting rolling friction for sliding friction (3) roughening the surfaces in contact (4) increasing the area of the surfaces in contact.
6. In addition to resisting the movement of one object over another, friction also produces (1) pressure (2) heat (3) gravity (4) work.
7. Friction is not necessary to (1) stop a car (2) unlock a door (3) keep an engine running (4) row a boat.

Modified True-False Questions

If a statement is true, write the word true. If a statement is false, write the word or expression that must be substituted for the italicized expression to make the statement true.

1. Friction is the *resistance* to the movement of one surface over another.
2. The amount of friction depends on the *masses* of the objects in contact and the nature of the surfaces.
3. One effect of friction is that it *roughens* the surfaces of moving parts.
4. *More* friction is produced when an object is rolled over a surface than when it is dragged.
5. A lubricant is used to *increase* friction between two moving surfaces.
6. Ball bearings are used to *reduce* friction between moving parts.
7. Friction between two objects produces *heat*.
8. The operation of automobile brakes depends on the effect of *friction*.
9. When a boat moves through water, friction is *not* produced.
10. Airplanes are designed with *rough* surfaces to decrease friction.

Applications of Principles

Select those statements from this group that are true and explain why each is true.

1. Friction depends upon the kinds of surfaces in contact with one another.
2. A mirror is almost a frictionless surface.
3. Friction may cause metal parts to wear away.
4. Rolling friction is greater than sliding friction.
5. The production of heat by friction is sometimes desirable.
6. Air friction slows down a moving car.
7. As a spaceship reenters the earth's atmosphere, tremendous heat is generated.

Chapter 34. How We Use Buoyancy

1. WHAT IS DENSITY?

Density is the mass of a given volume of matter, or

$$\text{Density} = \frac{\text{mass}}{\text{volume}}.$$

The volume of matter can be expressed in any cubic unit of length, in either the metric (SI) or English system. Some units of volume are the cubic centimeter and cubic foot. One cubic centimeter of water has a mass of one gram; its density in metric units is therefore one gram per cubic centimeter, or 1 g/cm^3. Measured in English units, one cubic foot of water weighs 62.4 pounds. The density of water is therefore 62.4 pounds per cubic foot.

2. WHAT IS PRESSURE?

Pressure is the force exerted on a given unit of area, such as a square centimeter or a square inch. The force of gravity is responsible for pressure. Both water and air exert pressure as a result of the pull of gravity (Fig. 34-1).

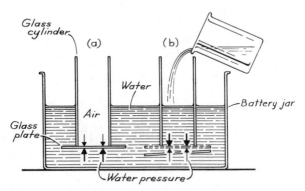

Fig. 34-1. Water exerts pressure. (*a*) The upward pressure exerted by the water in the battery jar is greater than the downward pressure of the air in the cylinder. Thus, the glass plate stays in place.

(*b*) The plate falls off when the height of the water inside the cylinder reaches the height of the water in the battery jar. In the cylinder, the combined downward pressure of the water and the air is greater than the upward pressure of the water in the battery jar.

3. WHAT DETERMINES WATER PRESSURE?

Water exerts pressure on the surfaces of all objects immersed in it. The amount of pressure exerted by water on a given surface of an object depends on the depth of an object in the water. The deeper an object is in water, the greater the pressure on the object. At a depth of 4,500 feet, the pressure of water is 62.4 lbs/ft^3 × 4500 feet, or about 280,000 pounds per square foot. This pressure is about the same as one ton of water on every square inch of surface. The water pressure at any given depth is the same in all directions (Fig. 34-2).

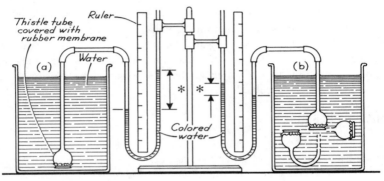

* indicates membrane pressure

Fig. 34-2. Pressure depends on depth. The pressure on the membrane of the thistle tube is indicated by the difference of the levels of the colored water in the two columns of the U-tube. The deeper the thistle tube is held in the water, the greater is the pressure exerted by the water on the membrane of the tube. By turning the thistle tube in all directions at a given depth, we see that at any given depth the water pressure is the same in all directions.

4. BUOYANT FORCE

The upward force which a liquid exerts on an object immersed in it is called the *buoyant force*. Since this upward force supports part of the weight of an immersed object, an object weighs less in a liquid than it does in air (Fig. 34-3 on next page). The weight an object appears to lose in a liquid is equal to the weight of the liquid it displaces. The weight of the displaced liquid determines whether an immersed object will sink or float in a liquid.

The laws of buoyancy were first stated by the Greek scientist Archimedes about 240 B.C.

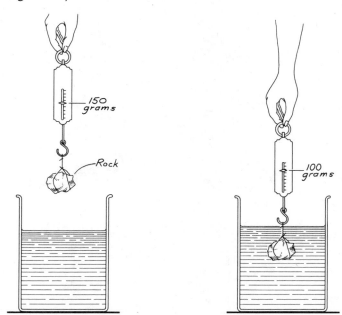

Fig. 34-3. Buoyant force. The same rock weighs 50 grams less when immersed in water.

5. SINKING BODIES

If a rock is dropped into water, it will sink. Any object will sink in a liquid if the weight of the object in air is greater than the weight of the liquid it displaces (Fig. 34-4). In terms of density, objects denser than water will sink in water.

6. FLOATING BODIES

An object will float in a liquid if the object displaces a weight of the liquid equal to its own weight. This is the same as saying that an immersed object floats when its weight is just balanced by the buoyant force of the liquid. In terms of density, an object less dense than water will sink until it displaces a weight of water equal to its own weight. Then the object will float in the water. (See Fig. 34-5.)

A floating object will float higher in a denser liquid than in a less dense liquid. When a ship moves from fresh water to salt water, the ship rises higher in the salt water. The denser the liquid, the greater the buoyant force it can exert.

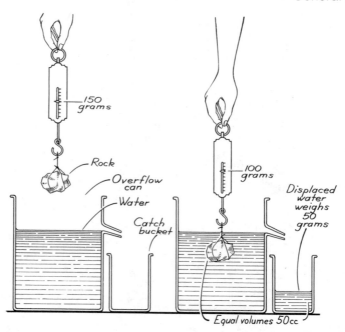

Fig. 34-4. Why an object sinks. Note that the weight of the rock in air, 150 grams, is greater than the weight of water the rock displaces (buoyant force), which is 50 grams. The rock therefore sinks.

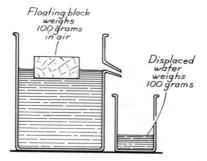

Fig. 34-5. Why an object floats. The wooden block is placed in the overflow can, and the displaced water is caught in the catch bucket. Since the weight of the block in air is the same as the weight of the displaced water, the block floats. Note that part of the floating block must be under water so that there is some displacement.

7. APPLYING BUOYANCY TO A SUBMARINE

Submarines depend on buoyancy. In order for a submarine to sink, it must weigh more than the water it displaces. When a submarine dives, water is admitted into special tanks to increase the submarine's weight. In order to surface, the process is reversed. Water is pumped out of the submarine by compressed air until the buoyant force of the water equals the weight of the submarine and its contents.

8. AIR BUOYANCY

Archimedes' principle more precisely applies to *fluids*—matter that flows. Fluids, therefore, include gases as well as liquids. This means that air can exert an upward push, or buoyancy, on objects immersed in air. (See page 347, section 8.)

Suppose a scale reads your weight as 125 pounds. Is 125 pounds your true weight or is it more, or less, than your true weight? Remember the rock that lost weight when immersed in water (Fig. 34-3 on page 339). The density of air is much less than the density of water, so the buoyant force is also much smaller. Your weight in air is, therefore, a little less than what it would be in an airless medium.

Multiple-Choice Questions

Write the number preceding the correct answer.

1. The mass of matter in a given volume is called (1) gravity (2) pressure (3) density (4) buoyancy.
2. The force that an object exerts on a given unit of area is called (1) weight (2) volume (3) density (4) pressure.
3. As an object sinks deeper in water, the pressure of the water on the object (1) decreases (2) increases (3) remains the same (4) first increases then decreases.
4. At any given depth, the pressure exerted by water is (1) greater downward than upward (2) greater sideways than downward (3) greater upward than downward (4) the same in all directions.
5. An object immersed in water displaces a volume of water (1) equal to its own volume (2) less than its own volume (3) greater than its own volume (4) equal to its own weight.
6. A sinking object (1) displaces a weight of liquid equal to its own (2) displaces a weight of liquid less than its own (3) displaces a volume of liquid greater than its own (4) displaces a volume of liquid less than its own.
7. An object floating in water displaces (1) its own weight (2) less than its own weight (3) more than its own weight (4) less than its own volume.
8. One factor which determines the amount of buoyant force exerted by a liquid on an object submerged in it is (1) the size of the container (2) the density of the liquid (3) the shape of the container (4) the pressure of the liquid.
9. A submarine will submerge if the buoyant force of the water is (1) less than the submarine's weight (2) greater than the submarine's weight (3) equal to the submarine's weight (4) equal to the volume of water displaced by the submarine.

10. To make a submarine rise to the surface, (1) water must be forced out of the submarine (2) water must be pumped into the submarine (3) the submarine must be made less buoyant (4) air must be pumped out of the submarine.

Completion Questions

Write the word or expression that correctly completes the statement.

1. The density of water is _____ pounds per cubic foot.
2. As you go deeper into water, the pressure on your body _____ (*increases, decreases, does not change*).
3. The density of an object that sinks in water is _____ (*greater than, less than*) the density of water.
4. A ship _____ (*floats higher, sinks deeper*) as it enters the St. Lawrence River from the Atlantic Ocean.
5. A dense liquid exerts _____ (*more, less*) buoyant force on a given object than does a less dense liquid.

Problems

1. An object weighs 500 grams in air and loses 100 grams when submerged in water.
   a. Will the object float or sink in water? Why?
   b. What is the volume of the object?
2. An object weighs 100 pounds in air and 6.4 pounds in water.
   a. What is the volume of the object?
   b. What is the density of the object?
3. An object exerts a force of 10 newtons.
   a. What pressure does the object exert on an area of 2 cm^2?
   b. On an area of 0.2 cm^2?

Reasoning Questions

Give a reason for each of the following:

1. Archimedes' principle applies to air as well as to water.
2. An object immersed in a liquid less dense than water weighs more than the same object immersed in water.
3. As the area of a body immersed in water increases, the pressure on the body decreases.
4. A cubic centimeter of mercury has a greater mass than the same volume of water.
5. A body must first sink a little before it can float in a liquid.

Chapter 35. Transportation

The world has become a smaller place because of the more efficient means of communication and transportation. Countries thousands of miles apart can engage in conversation within seconds. The automobile and the airplane have reduced traveling time from days and weeks to minutes and hours. In the next century, we can expect further improvements that will bring the peoples of the world even closer.

The first automobile engine, built around a hundred years ago, was crude and little was expected of it. At about the beginning of the 20th century, the first practical gasoline engine was built.

THE AUTOMOBILE

1. THE GASOLINE ENGINE

The *gasoline engine* is an internal combustion engine; that is, fuel is burned inside the engine. The steam engine, on the other hand, is an external combustion engine where power is generated outside the engine. The gasoline engine is made up of a number of closed *cylinders*: usually four, six, or eight. Each cylinder (Fig. 35-1) contains a movable *piston*. A cylinder also contains two *valves*, one of which admits fuel and air, while the other permits the exhaust gases to escape. The mixture of gasoline and air is ignited in the cylinder by a spark, causing an explosion that moves the piston up and down. The up-and-down motion of the piston is changed to circular motion with the aid of rods connected to the *crankshaft*.

Gasoline is the most common engine fuel. Another fuel, used in diesel engines, is oil.

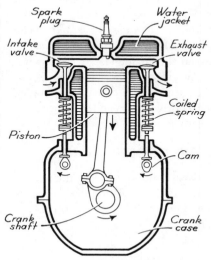

Fig. 35-1. A cylinder of the gasoline engine

343

In a diesel engine, unlike the gasoline engine, the fuel-air mixture is compressed sufficiently to ignite it. Improvements have been made in engine fuels, and additives have been developed that make for a smoother ride. Further, more complete combustion of fuels has lowered the operating cost of the engine. (Read "Electric and Solar-Powered Cars" on next page.)

2. THE ELECTRICAL SYSTEM

The electrical energy of an automobile is obtained from a 6-volt or 12-volt storage battery containing plates of lead and lead dioxide immersed in sulfuric acid. (See page 298.) During operation of the engine, some water is used up, so additional water must be provided to maintain the proper acid concentration. In new type batteries, the components are sealed and require little maintenance. Some new-type batteries also contain nickel-iron components.

The battery supplies the necessary power for lights, the radio, and other electrical devices. The battery, together with the spark coil and condenser, supplies to the spark plugs the electricity necessary to ignite the mixture of gasoline and air in the cylinders. The battery is recharged by the generator while the engine is running. The armature of the generator is rotated by the operating engine.

3. TRANSMITTING POWER TO THE WHEELS

The motion of the piston, resulting from the explosions of the fuel-air mixture, produces power. In *standard-shift*, or *manual-transmission* cars, this power is transmitted to the rear wheels through the action of a friction clutch, gears, and driveshaft. In cars having *automatic transmission*, there is no direct connection between the engine and the rear wheels; the friction clutch of the standard shift is replaced by a device containing oil and gears that shift automatically according to the speed of the car. Power may also be transmitted to the front wheels (front-wheel drive) or to all four wheels (four-wheel drive). These improvements give the engine more pulling power.

4. THE COOLING SYSTEM

Heat produced by the burning fuel causes expansion of the metal parts of the engine, thus increasing undesirable friction. Heat also hastens rusting. The engine, therefore, must be cooled so that it may operate efficiently and not wear out rapidly.

ELECTRIC AND SOLAR-POWERED CARS

The automobile is an essential part of life in the modern world. We depend on the car for our work and our play. Unfortunately, the automobile is also one of the major sources of air pollution. It is imperative, then, for scientists and engineers to search for new sources of energy for the car.

Surprisingly, electric cars were developed in the late 1890's. These early models were fairly easy to operate, ran quietly, and did not pollute. Even so, few went faster than 20 mph and had to have the batteries recharged every 50 miles.

After the gas shortage of the mid-1970's and the passing of stricter anti-pollution laws, engineers began to reconsider the electric car as the automobile of the future. While current models can still travel only about 60 miles before batteries must be recharged, they can move much faster. Present research is focused on developing improved batteries that last longer.

Solar energy has also been considered as a fuel source for the automobile. Unfortunately, capturing solar energy depends on some conditions that are beyond human control: time of day, season of the year, latitude, and amount of sky cover, or clouds.

On a clear day, with the sun directly overhead, a square meter of ground receives no more than 1000 watts of energy. Scientists have tried to concentrate this energy by using parabolic mirrors to create solar furnaces. Such mirrors concentrate sunlight and can raise temperatures as high as 4900°F (2700°C). Using a form of this technology in a solar-powered car, however, has not yet been achieved.

Water and other coolants are poured into the radiator. They are circulated in passageways throughout the operating engine by means of a *water pump*. The heated water returns to the radiator where it is cooled by air currents aided by the action of a fan. The coolant also prevents the water from freezing in the winter and thus cracking vital metal parts.

5. THE BRAKES

Automobiles are equipped with *four-wheel brakes*. When you step on the brake pedal, the braking system provides a braking action on all four wheels at once. In drum brakes, this action is produced by the friction of the brake linings pressing against the brake drum (Fig. 35-2). In disc brakes, the braking action is produced by brake linings that press against a disc.

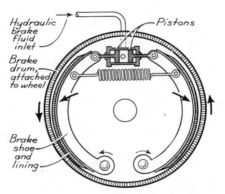

Fig. 35-2. The brake depends on friction

6. FOR SAFE CARE AND OPERATION OF AUTOMOBILES

Automobile accidents have caused more deaths in the United States than all our wars combined. Most accidents would be prevented if drivers practiced greater care. The following suggestions will contribute toward greater safety on the road.

- a. Observe all traffic suggestions and regulations.
- b. Make sure the car is mechanically perfect. Have the lights, windshield wipers, steering wheel, and brakes checked regularly.
- c. Always fasten your seat belt or shoulder harness and insist that all other riders in the car do the same.
- d. Excessive speed is the major cause of accidents. Slow down and stay within posted speed limits.
- e. Practice courtesy and consideration.

AIRCRAFT

7. KINDS OF AIRCRAFT

At the beginning of the 20th century, the Wright brothers made the first airplane. Today, many commercial aircraft fly between 300–600 miles per hour, and *supersonic* planes travel at speeds greater than the speed of sound (about 750 miles/hour at 0°C). In 1970, the *Concorde*—a supersonic jet—crossed the Atlantic Ocean in about three hours. Modern planes span continents, and rocket ships have reached the moon with speeds exceeding that of sound, while the future holds promise of interplanetary travel.

There are two kinds of aircraft:

   a. lighter-than-air: balloons and dirigibles.
   b. heavier-than-air: airplanes, helicopters, jets, rockets.

8. WHAT MAKES A DIRIGIBLE RISE?

A *dirigible* is filled with helium, which is a gas less dense than air. The dirigible has a large volume and therefore displaces a large volume of air. The displaced air weighs more than the dirigible and its contents, which include sandbags used as ballast. The buoyant force exerted by the displaced air on the dirigible causes the craft to rise and remain aloft. In effect, the dirigible floats in an ocean of air. Release of some helium lessens the buoyant force and the dirigible descends.

9. WHAT MAKES AN AIRPLANE FLY?

For a plane to fly, it must produce forces called *lift* and *thrust*. These forces overcome the pull of gravity and the resistance of air friction.

a. Lift. *Lift* is an upward force that balances and sometimes even exceeds the downward force of gravity (Fig. 35-3 on next page). Lift is produced by the design of the wing, the top surface being curved and the bottom surface being flat. Air, forced over the wing by the forward motion of the plane, thus moves more rapidly over the curved top surface than it does over the flat bottom surface. This causes a decrease in air pressure above the wing and an increase in air pressure below the wing. The difference in pressures produces the upward force, *lift*, that supports the plane in air.

Paper strip

Fig. 35-3. How lift is developed. When you blow across the top of a strip of paper, the paper is forced upward. This takes place because the high velocity of the air moving across the top of the paper lowers the air pressure above the paper. Normal air pressure then lifts the paper.

Lift is increased by tilting the forward edge of the wing slightly upward and by increasing the air speed of the plane (Fig. 35-4).

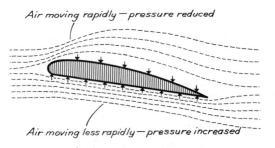

Air moving rapidly — pressure reduced

Air moving less rapidly — pressure increased

Fig. 35-4. Increasing lift

b. Thrust. In order for air to move past the wing and create lift, an airplane must be in motion. This motion is brought about by a forward push called *thrust*, which is supplied by a jet engine or a fast-turning propeller rotated by a gasoline engine. The rotating propeller advances into the air in the same manner that a screw advances into wood.

10. FORCES ACTING AGAINST AN AIRPLANE

a. Weight. The weight of the plane tends to pull it to the ground. Making planes of lightweight metal, such as aluminum, reduces the weight of the aircraft.

b. Drag. Drag tends to retard the movement of a plane through the air. Drag is caused by the resistance of the plane to the moving air and by the friction between the air and the surface of the plane. Streamlining the plane and smoothing its surfaces reduce drag.

11. CONTROLLING AND OPERATING AIRPLANES

a. Fuselage. This is the body of the plane, housing the control instruments, the crew, passengers, and freight (Fig. 35-5).

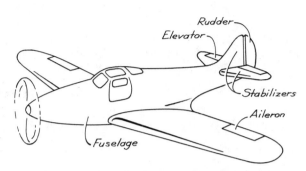

Fig. 35-5. Structures of an airplane

b. Ailerons. These are two horizontal, movable flaps, each hinged to the rear (trailing) edge of a wing. Moving an aileron changes the curvature of the wing. When one aileron is raised, the aileron on the other wing is lowered. Moving the ailerons causes a plane to "bank," or make sharp turns. When both ailerons are lowered, they slow the plane down before landing.

c. Stabilizers. These are vertical and horizontal flaps in the tail assembly which help keep the plane flying on a steady keel.

d. Rudder. This is a vertical, movable strip attached to the fin. The rudder is used in steering the airplane while it is moving on the ground. When flying, the rudder is used together with the ailerons for turning, without skidding or slipping.

e. Elevators. These are two horizontal, movable flaps. One elevator is hinged to the rear edge of the left side of the horizontal stabilizer, and another is hinged to the right side. Raising the elevators raises the nose of the plane and allows it to climb. On the other hand, lowering the elevators causes the plane to descend.

12. THE HELICOPTER

In a *helicopter*, the overhead rotor (horizontal propeller) consists of long, slender blades which rotate in a horizontal direction. Each blade is actually a wing. When the blades are set at a certain angle, they provide the lift needed to keep the plane aloft. When the blades are set at a different angle, they also provide the thrust required to move the plane forward or backward through the air. A helicopter also has a small tail propeller which rotates vertically. The tail propeller helps guide the craft and keeps the fuselage from turning in a direction opposite that of the overhead propeller.

Helicopters do not need runways. They can take off and land vertically. They can hover over a given location. For this reason, helicopters are useful in providing transportation for short distances over crowded areas. They are also useful in rescuing people marooned in places difficult to reach by other means.

13. WHAT IS A JET?

Jet planes do not obtain their thrust by a propeller. Instead, thrust is obtained by the action of escaping gases—according to a law of physics first stated by Sir Isaac Newton: *Every action has an equal but opposite reaction* (Fig. 35-6).

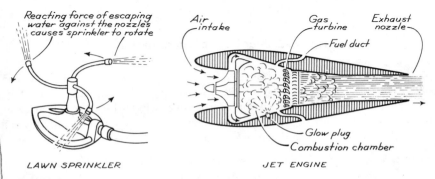

LAWN SPRINKLER   JET ENGINE

Fig. 35-6. Action and reaction. The same force that operates the rotary lawn sprinkler shoots the jet plane across the skies.

Special fuels burned in jet engines form extremely hot gases which expand tremendously. The movement of the hot gases escaping from the rear of a jet engine (action) causes movement (reaction) in the opposite direction. This reaction, the thrust, pushes the plane forward. Jet planes may attain tremendous speeds, exceeding that of sound.

Modern jet planes, such as the Douglas DC 10 and the Boeing 747, can carry over 300 passengers and crew more than 7,000 miles without refueling.

14. SAFETY IN AIR TRAVEL

Despite fatal crashes from time to time, air travel, in terms of numbers alone is probably safer than any other means of travel. Highly trained personnel such as air traffic controllers (ATC), aided by accurate weather data and a variety of instruments, continue to make air travel safer each day. The use of the safety belt prior to takeoff and landing has also increased safety. This practice has been adopted for use in automobiles. Radar guides the plane in blind flying at takeoff and landing, during fog or storm, and over hills and mountains.

Multiple-Choice Questions

Write the number preceding the correct answer.

1. The energy that propels an automobile is stored up in the (1) battery (2) gasoline (3) motor (4) wheels.
2. The fuel in a car is burned in the (1) cylinders (2) cams (3) valves (4) pistons.
3. Electrical energy required to operate a car is supplied by the (1) spark coil (2) clutch (3) dry cells (4) battery.
4. The power generated by a gasoline engine is transmitted to the wheels by the (1) pistons (2) cylinders (3) generator (4) driveshaft.
5. Water that is heated in the engine of a car is cooled in the (1) pistons (2) generator (3) cams (4) radiator.
6. A lighter-than-air craft is the (1) helicopter (2) airplane (3) dirigible (4) glider.
7. An airplane is able to fly because (1) it is heavier than air (2) it is lighter than air (3) it is made of aluminum (4) moving air can lift things.
8. The force which a moving airplane produces to overcome the downward pull of gravity is (1) lift (2) thrust (3) drag (4) friction.
9. When a pilot wishes to bank or turn a plane, he uses the rudder and the (1) elevators (2) fuselage (3) stabilizers (4) ailerons.
10. Horizontal structures found in the tail of a plane which are needed to keep a plane on an even keel when in flight are the (1) rudder (2) ailerons (3) stabilizers (4) elevators.
11. A pilot can make a plane climb by moving the (1) ailerons (2) wing flaps (3) elevators (4) stabilizers.
12. The type of plane that can land most easily on the flat roof of a building is (1) an amphibian (2) a bomber (3) a jet plane (4) a helicopter.
13. The principle that every action has an equal but opposite reaction was first stated by (1) Einstein (2) Newton (3) Ford (4) Edison.
14. A jet plane is moved forward by the thrust produced by (1) a gasoline motor (2) a piston (3) a propeller (4) hot gases.
15. When an airplane starts to come down for a landing, the passengers should (1) fasten their safety belts (2) get their baggage (3) put on their coats (4) stand in the aisle.

Completion Questions

Write the word or expression that correctly completes the statement.

1. While the engine of a car is operating, the _____ is charging the battery.
2. The substance most commonly used as a cooling agent in cars is _____.
3. Braking action in a car is the result of _____ between the brake lining and the drum.
4. The dirigible and the _____ stay aloft because they are lighter than air.
5. A dirigible floats in air because of the _____ force exerted by the air.
6. When air flows over the curved upper surface of a wing, the pressure above the wing is _____ (*increased, decreased*).
7. Planes that travel at speeds greater than the speed of sound are called _____.
8. Friction between a moving plane and air results in a force known as _____.
9. A type of aircraft that can rise vertically is the _____.
10. A jet plane operates on the principle that every action has an equal but opposite _____.
11. The gasoline engine is an example of an _____ (*internal, external*) combustion engine.
12. In place of gasoline, a Diesel engine uses _____.
13. In an automobile, the coolant is in the _____.
14. Examples of heavier-than-air aircraft are the airplane and the _____.
15. The downward force in an airplane is provided by its _____.

Reasoning Questions

Give a reason for each of the following.

1. A cylinder of a gasoline engine must contain two valves.
2. Dry cells are not used in the electrical system of an automobile.
3. A transmission system is necessary in an automobile.
4. The action of a brake depends on friction.
5. Excessive speed is the major cause of automobile accidents.
6. Curving the top surface of an airplane wing increases lift.
7. Jet planes do not require propellers.
8. Water must be added to a storage battery occasionally.
9. The world is becoming a smaller place.
10. Additives improve the quality of gasoline used in an engine.

Chapter 36. Exploring Space

1. THE SPACE AGE

Humans entered the Space Age on October 4, 1957, when Soviet scientists succeeded in sending an artificial satellite, called *Sputnik I*, into orbit around the earth. As Sputnik I continued to orbit the earth, it lost altitude until it burned up from atmospheric friction.

On January 30, 1958, the United States placed its first satellite, *Explorer I*, into orbit. Since that time, Soviet, American, and other scientists have launched hundreds of space devices.

On July 16, 1969, *Apollo 11* was launched and on July 20th, Neil Armstrong became the first human to touch the soil of another heavenly body—the moon. Since that time, there have been other launchings, all successful with the exception of the *Challenger*, which exploded in air, killing its occupants.

Astronauts have traveled to the moon, landed on it, walked on it, and have returned to earth. More recently, spaceships, containing electronic and photographic equipment only, have been sent to Venus, Mars, and even farther into space. Important information has been sent back to earth revealing details, never before known, about these planets. (See pages 423–425, sections 6–9.) Someday, astronauts may make such trips. All of these achievements have been made possible by the development and application of rockets, which are used to propel spaceships.

2. WHAT IS A ROCKET?

A *rocket* is a streamlined projectile which propels itself by the thrust produced from burning fuels. Although rockets have been known for centuries, the first practical rockets were developed during World War II. A rocket engine operates on the same principle as does a jet engine, but with one important difference. Although both engines carry fuel, a jet uses oxygen from the atmosphere, while a rocket carries its own oxygen supply. The oxygen supply may be either in the form of a liquid or a solid combined with other elements. Rockets are therefore able to travel in the upper atmosphere, where there is little oxygen, and in outer space, where there is none.

Rockets require extremely rapid burning, which produces tremendous amounts of energy. Easily combustible materials, like alcohol or gasoline, and liquid oxygen are common rocket fuels. Great care must be taken in the storage and handling of these materials.

3. MULTISTAGE ROCKETS

We have learned that gravity is the force that the earth exerts on all objects. Scientists have determined that in order for an object to break away from this gravitational pull and continue in flight, an object must travel at a speed of at least seven miles a second. To attain this speed, a rocket must overcome air resistance and gravity. The weight of the rocket and the heavy load of fuel required have made it impossible for a single rocket to leave the earth's atmosphere. The required speed is obtained by using a combination of several rockets, called a *multistage rocket*. This rocket consists of two, three, or four rockets, called *stages*, properly assembled. When the fuel in a stage is consumed in flight, the stage is separated and dropped off. The remaining stages are lighter in weight and can travel at even a higher speed. The final stage is much lighter than the original rocket and requires little fuel to maintain a high speed.

4. PUTTING A SATELLITE INTO ORBIT

If a rocket is aimed so that the last stage is moving at the proper speed in a direction parallel to the earth's surface, an object carried by the rocket will circle the earth. Such an object circling the earth is an *artificial satellite*. Its path around the earth is called its *orbit*, which is shaped like an ellipse.

5. WHY SATELLITES REMAIN IN ORBIT

As a satellite is fired from the last stage of a rocket, the satellite tends to travel outward in a straight line, somewhat like a bullet fired from a gun. The effect of gravity, however, is to pull the satellite toward the center of the earth. The net effect of the outward and downward motions is to produce a state of balance. It is this state of balance which allows the satellite to remain in its orbit. As the satellite continues to orbit, its speed is lessened by air friction. The satellite now orbits in a continuing smaller circle until it eventually drops to the earth.

6. VALUE OF ARTIFICIAL SATELLITES

The first satellites that were placed in orbit were launched just to see whether the task could be done. Since then, satellites loaded with various instruments have been placed into orbit for research purposes. At present, many types of satellites are orbiting the earth. Among these are weather satellites, communication satellites, astronomical observatory satellites, and navigation satellites.

a. Weather Satellites. These satellites have taken pictures of clouds and storms from over 500 miles above the earth. Some weather satellites send back information about conditions in the atmosphere. With the help of such satellites, scientists of the Weather Bureau are able to provide us with more reliable weather forecasts than ever before.

b. Communication Satellites. These satellites orbit thousands of miles above the earth. Such satellites make it possible to transmit radio and television communications to all parts of the world at the same time. Thus, we are able to see on our television screens live programs taking place in Europe and Asia.

c. Astronomical Satellites. Astronomers have made many important discoveries with the aid of telescopes. However, the envelope of air around the earth limits what astronomers can see because the air blocks or distorts light and other rays that come to us from distant parts of the universe. By placing telescopes and other instruments into orbit as satellites, many interesting discoveries have been made. (See "How Vast the Universe?" on page 457.)

d. Navigation Satellites. These satellites provide a worldwide system by which ships and planes can determine their exact positions. Navigation satellites are equipped with radio transmitters that send signals to the surface of the earth.

7. THE CONQUEST OF SPACE

In 1962, the United States sent a ship carrying an astronaut into space. The ship orbited the earth three times at altitudes ranging from 86 to 141 miles above the surface. After the third orbit, the ship returned safely.

In 1969, American astronauts reached the moon, approximately 240,000 miles away from the earth. The dream of conquering space had been realized.

In 1972, the crew of *Apollo 17* explored the surface of the moon on foot and in a wheeled vehicle. They remained on the moon longer than any astronauts before them.

8. THE FUTURE OF SPACE EXPLORATION

Astronauts have reached the moon and explored its surface. Many specimens of moon rocks and soil have been brought back to earth for scientific study. Where do we go from the moon? What plans are there for future space flights?

The National Aeronautics and Space Administration (NASA) is the Government agency responsible for the further conquest of space.

a. Skylab. This project established a space station that served as a laboratory in space. Scientists lived in it for long periods of time. While there, they conducted numerous experiments designed to benefit mankind.

Some experiments carried out in Skylab dealt with studies of the earth's resources and environmental conditions. Others may deal with using the sun's energy for the production of electric power without depending on our natural resources and without polluting the earth's atmosphere. Still other experiments may deal with laying the groundwork for future interplanetary missions that might take months or years to accomplish.

b. Space Shuttle. This project has developed a spaceship that goes out into space, returns to earth, and is used over again.

A space shuttle makes it possible to place in orbit as many types of satellites as desired. In addition, a space shuttle makes possible the repair of satellites that have broken down.

Is it possible that a moon base and a flight to Mars by astronauts may become realities before very long? Time and ingenuity will decide.

Multiple-Choice Questions

Write the number preceding the correct answer.

1. The region in which people can obtain most information about heavenly objects is (1) the earth (2) the atmosphere (3) outer space (4) the stratosphere.
2. A rocket can travel in outer space because it (1) uses oxygen of the atmosphere (2) is weightless in space (3) carries its own oxygen supply (4) does not require oxygen.
3. A rocket consisting of a number of rockets joined together is known as a (1) jet (2) satellite (3) projectile (4) multistage rocket.
4. An object shot into space to circle the earth is called (1) a star (2) an artificial satellite (3) an asteroid (4) a meteorite.
5. An artificial moon will continue in flight if a balance is established between the forward motion of the object and (1) the earth's gravity (2) air resistance (3) thrust (4) air speed.
6. Explorer I was (1) a moon ship (2) a natural satellite (3) an artificial satellite (4) an orbit.
7. Weather satellites have enabled us to (1) make weather to order (2) make better weather forecasts (3) reach Mars (4) clear clouds from airports.
8. Seeing television pictures of foreign events while they are happening is made possible by (1) astronomical satellites (2) the moon shots (3) communication satellites (4) navigation satellites.

Completion Questions

Write the word or expression that correctly completes the statement.

1. The burning of fuels provides the _____ necessary to propel a rocket.
2. Before a rocket can leave the atmosphere, it must overcome the _____ pull of the earth.
3. The path in which an artificial satellite circles the earth is known as its _____ .
4. In outer space, the speed of a satellite is reduced by _____ .
5. The development of spaceships resulted from improved _____ .
6. The first practical rockets were developed during _____ .
7. Rocket fuels contain a combustible and _____ .
8. The first artificial satellite launched was called _____ .
9. The first American astronaut to set foot on the moon was _____ .
10. Rockets, unlike jet engines, carry their own _____ .

REVIEW OF UNIT VII

1. Describe one practical use of (*a*) a pulley, (*b*) an inclined plane, (*c*) a wheel and axle, (*d*) a jackscrew, (*e*) a windlass.
2. In the two figures below, indicate the weight at B that will exactly balance the weight at A.

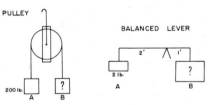

3. Imagine that in each diagram below both A and B are moving. For each diagram, write A if A would move farther, write B if B would move farther, or write *equal* if A and B would move equal distances.

4. Write the letter *a*, *b*, *c*, or *d* that correctly completes the statement or answers the question.

a. At what point on side B does a 50-pound child have to sit to balance the child on side A? (*a*) 1 (*b*) 2 (*c*) 3 (*d*) 4.

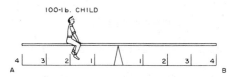

b. When gear A is driven in the direction shown, gear B will turn in the (*a*) same direction at a slower speed (*b*) same direction at a faster speed (*c*) opposite direction at a slower speed (*d*) opposite direction at a faster speed.

c. Which of the following weights is the most that a 120-pound boy or girl could lift using this pulley? (*a*) 10 pounds (*b*) 60 pounds (*c*) 100 pounds (*d*) 200 pounds.

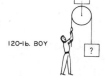

5. Give an example of each of the following.
   a. a form of inclined plane found in the home
   b. a machine or other device containing a gear
   c. a device which uses a pulley

6. The closer that a piece of heavy cloth is to the pivot of a pair of shears, the easier is the cutting. Explain.

7. Explain the operation of a spring-balance.

8. A pupil pulls on a spring balance attached to a 10-pound box and slides the box over the floor a few feet. Next he pulls the box over a row of round pencils. The readings of the spring balance are compared. Which reading is greater? Why?

9. Explain why an automobile skids more readily on a wet road than on a dry road.

10. Give an example of:
    a. a use of friction
    b. a substance used to decrease friction

11. Tell why the following statement is false: When a stone is being lifted, it feels heavier while it is under water than while it is in the air.

12. Give a reason for each of the following.
 a. As a ship sails into a river from the ocean, it sinks lower in the water.
 b. A boat that is heavily loaded sinks deeper into the water than an empty boat.
 c. A gallon of sea water weighs more than a gallon of fresh water.

13. The following devices are parts of an airplane. Select five and give the use of each.

 a. propeller   e. ailerons
 b. rudder   f. stick
 c. wings   g. compass
 d. elevators   h. altimeter

14. Name a type of airplane that:
 a. can ascend vertically
 b. has an engine but no propeller

15. Explain what a pilot must do to make an airplane do each of the following.
 a. turn right
 b. dip the right wing

16. The following questions refer to a powered model airplane.
 a. If there were a strong wind from the north and you did not wish the plane damaged by landing too fast, in which direction should you land the plane?
 b. If a carbon dioxide cylinder were fastened to the plane for propulsion, what part of the plane would not be needed for flight?

17. Why has the manufacture of jet planes for airlines overtaken the manufacture of propeller-driven planes?

18. Explain why a jet plane, like those used in transatlantic travel, does not go into orbit.

19. Why are the Skylab and the Space Shuttle projects important for the future of space travel?

Unit VIII.
Living in an Ocean of Air

Chapter 37. What the Atmosphere Is Like

1. THE AIR AROUND US

We are living at the bottom of an ocean of air that extends upward about 900 kilometers, or over 500 miles. This blanket of air, called the *atmosphere*, serves to keep the earth warm. The atmosphere consists of many different layers, chief among which are the *troposphere*, the *stratosphere*, and the *ionosphere*. Differences in temperature separate the layers although the divisions are not sharp (Fig. 37-1 on next page).

a. The Troposphere. This is the part of the atmosphere closest to the earth; it is the air layer in which we live. The troposphere rises to a height of about 20 kilometers (12 miles). The temperature of the troposphere drops as we go higher. The portion of this layer nearest us is the *tropopause*, and most of the mass of the atmosphere (nitrogen and oxygen gases) is found here. Just below the tropopause, strong winds (up to 500 miles/hour) blow from west to east, which make up the *jet stream*. Aircraft try to ride on these winds to conserve fuel. The jet stream also influences the movement of air masses that determine our weather.

b. The Stratosphere. This layer of the atmosphere contains very little air and extends to a height of about 30 kilometers (18 miles) above the troposphere. In this layer, the ultraviolet radiation of the sun reacts with oxygen and changes it to ozone. Recall from Chapter 4 that the *ozone layer* (pages 38–39) shields the earth from the penetrating and harmful ultraviolet rays of the sun. It is extremely important to maintain the thickness of the ozone layer so that living cells are not damaged or destroyed by the rays. The propellants used in spray cans that eventually are expelled into the air have been found to reduce the ozone concentration of the atmosphere. Stringent regulations have been set up to curb this threat to the environment. Above the stratosphere, temperatures can drop as low as $-100°C$.

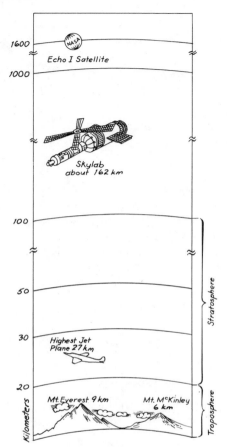

Fig. 37-1. Layers of the atmosphere

c. The Ionosphere. This is the outermost region of the atmosphere where the gases are very thin. In the top layer of the ionosphere, called the *thermosphere*, temperatures may rise to several thousand degrees Celsius. Here, the ultraviolet radiation converts the gas molecules into charged particles called *ions*. These ions have electrical properties which make them useful in radio communication, worldwide. It is thought that the electrical properties of this layer explain the presence of that startling and beautiful display in the sky, called the *aurora borealis*.

The outermost portion of the earth's atmosphere extends many hundreds of kilometers. This region is referred to as the *exosphere*, beyond which lies *outer space*.

2. COMPOSITION OF THE AIR

Air is a mixture of gases (Fig. 37-2), consisting approximately of:

Oxygen—20%
Nitrogen—79%
Carbon dioxide, noble gases (argon, neon), water vapor—1%

Air also contains solid particles, such as dust, smoke, and other pollutants, depending on the locality.

3. OXYGEN

Oxygen is a colorless, odorless gas that can be extracted commercially from the air. Oxygen supports combustion. A glowing splint will burst into flame in the presence of pure oxygen. This property is used for testing the presence of oxygen.

Oxygen is necessary for all living things. Human beings are constantly inhaling air containing oxygen. In the lungs, the oxygen is taken out of the air by the hemoglobin in the blood and is distributed throughout the body. Without oxygen, living things cannot survive.

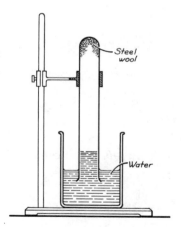

Fig.37-2. Determining the composition of air. Moist steel wool rusts, using up most of the oxygen in the tube. Water rises to occupy the place of the oxygen. The gas above the water is largely nitrogen. Note that nitrogen occupies about four-fifths (about 80%) of the height of the test tube.

4. NITROGEN

Nitrogen is a colorless, odorless gas that does not support combustion. Nitrogen is removed from the air, used by plants and animals, and then—after a series of events—returned to the air. Fig. 37-3 pictures the steps of the *nitrogen cycle.*

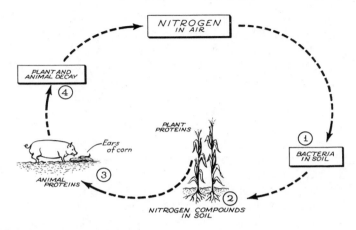

Fig.37-3. The nitrogen cycle. This cycle shows how nitrogen is first consumed and then restored to the air and soil. The nitrogen may be used by a number of different animals and plants before the cycle is completed.

① Certain bacteria in the soil convert nitrogen of the air into nitrogen compounds, which plants need for growth.

② Green plants extract nitrogen compounds from the soil and use them to form *proteins.*

③ Proteins are passed to animals, including humans, when the plants are eaten.

④ When plant and animal matter decays, certain bacteria liberate nitrogen compounds, and other bacteria liberate nitrogen. This bacterial action returns nitrogen to the air and soil.

5. CARBON DIOXIDE

Carbon dioxide is a colorless, odorless gas that does not support combustion. Carbon dioxide is identified by the fact that it turns limewater milky. Carbon dioxide is a product of combustion as well as a product of plant and animal respiration. Carbon dioxide is used by green plants in the process of photosynthesis. (See page 143.) Large quantities of carbon dioxide, produced from burning coal, are responsible for the *greenhouse effect.*

THE GREENHOUSE EFFECT

It is interesting to speculate how the earth's atmosphere might have been formed. One theory, proposed by an American scientist—Harold Urey—supposes that the atmosphere was once made up of a number of gases, including *ammonia* (a compound of nitrogen and hydrogen), *methane* (a compound of carbon and hydrogen), and *water vapor* (a compound of hydrogen and oxygen).

Because of its closeness to the sun (compared to other planets), the earth's atmosphere was subjected to ultraviolet radiation. In a series of complex chemical changes taking millions of years, the composition of the atmosphere began to change. Nitrogen, oxygen, and carbon dioxide were formed and blanketed the earth. Lighter hydrogen gas escaped into the upper atmosphere. A layer of ozone (formed from oxygen) also appeared in the upper atmosphere. Ozone absorbs ultraviolet, thereby preventing ultraviolet from entering the atmosphere where it may burn living things.

As life-forms evolved, nitrogen and oxygen were consumed, but these gases later reappeared as products of growth and development. Carbon dioxide was used by green plants but was re-formed by respiration and the burning of fuels. Thus, the composition of the atmosphere remained stable. As the human population began to grow, however, the demand for fuels increased tremendously, and more and more carbon dioxide was expelled into the atmosphere. A serious problem, called the *greenhouse effect*, began to develop. Why?

As we discussed earlier, carbon dioxide and other gases behave much like the glass shield of a greenhouse. The glass allows the sun's rays to enter the greenhouse. At the same time, the glass prevents some of the heat from escaping. As a result, the greenhouse becomes hot. On the earth, as the amount of carbon dioxide increases, more and more heat from the sun is trapped by the atmosphere, and the temperature on the earth's surface rises. Although the heat increase is slow, if unchecked, the average temperature of the earth could increase by several degrees over a period of a hundred years.

Recall that the effect of a steady temperature rise on the earth's surface could have disastrous consequences. Glaciers might melt and raise ocean levels sufficiently to threaten coastal cities. They may have to be abandoned. Temperatures on earth might become unbearably hot. The added heat would affect plant and animal life as well as humans, and might even challenge their existence.

The increased use of fossil fuels such as coal, natural gas, and petroleum is largely responsible for the accumulation of carbon dioxide in the atmosphere. How to control and limit the burning of these fuels is one of the most important problems we face. How we deal with this situation may determine how long living things, as we know them today, can inhabit the earth!

6. RARE GASES

The rare gases, also called *noble* gases, in the atmosphere are largely argon, neon, and very small amounts of helium, krypton, and xenon. Argon is used in incandescent bulbs, and neon is used in neon lamps and signs. Helium, the lightest noninflammable gas, is used in dirigibles.

7. WATER VAPOR

Water vapor, or moisture, exists in the atmosphere as an invisible gas lighter than air. Water vapor in the atmosphere is also called *humidity*. The amount of water vapor in the air is constantly changing and in a greater percentage than that of any of the other gases. Water vapor gets into the air in many ways.

   a. The surface layers of large bodies of water are constantly *evaporating* as a result of the action of the sun and wind.
   b. Plants give off water vapor by the process of *transpiration*.
   c. Water is one of the products formed from the *burning* of common fuels.
   d. Water vapor is given off in the process of *respiration*.

8. EVAPORATION

The process by which water changes from liquid to vapor is called *evaporation*. Several factors affect the rate at which evaporation takes place.

a. Temperature. An increase in the temperature of the water, or the air around the water, speeds evaporation. Electric and gas dryers use hot air to dry laundry.

b. Area Exposed. The greater the area of water exposed, the faster the rate of evaporation. Wet clothes dry faster when spread out.

c. Wind. As water evaporates, the air above the water becomes filled (saturated) with water vapor. Evaporation then slows down. Winds blow the saturated air away, permitting more water to evaporate. Thus, wet clothes will dry faster on a windy day than on a calm day.

d. Humidity. The presence of water vapor in the atmosphere slows down further evaporation. The drier the air, the faster will water evaporate.

9. WHAT MAKES WATER VAPOR CONDENSE?

If water were to evaporate continuously from the lakes, rivers, and oceans, all bodies of water in time would become dry. This does not happen because evaporated water condenses and eventually returns to its source. This series of changes, called the *water cycle*, was discussed on page 225.

The process by which a vapor changes back to a liquid is called *condensation*. When warm, moist air is cooled sufficiently, condensation takes place in the form of a liquid or solid (Fig. 37-4). The temperature at which water vapor in air condenses is called the *dew point*.

Fig. 37-4. Principle of condensation. If you allow a metallic container filled with ice cubes to stand in a room, water droplets will form on the outside of the container. This occurs because the cold surface of the container cools the air near it, causing the water vapor to condense.

Multiple-Choice Questions

Write the number preceding the correct answer.

1. The layer of the atmosphere in which we live is the (1) ionosphere (2) stratosphere (3) troposphere.
2. Above the stratosphere, temperatures can drop as low as (1) 0°C (2) −50°C (3) −100°C (4) −273°C.
3. Life in the stratosphere is not possible because of the (1) great heat (2) insufficient oxygen (3) great amount of moisture (4) excessive dryness.
4. Most of the mass of the atmosphere is located in the (1) troposphere (2) ionosphere (3) stratosphere (4) jet stream.
5. Air is a (1) single gas (2) compound of two gases (3) compound of three gases (4) mixture of several gases.
6. The most abundant gas in air is (1) carbon dioxide (2) nitrogen (3) oxygen (4) water vapor.

7. A rare gas present in the atmosphere is (1) oxygen (2) nitrogen (3) radon (4) neon.
8. The gas in air that is necessary for burning is (1) argon (2) neon (3) nitrogen (4) oxygen.
9. The gas that bacteria extract from air and change into a form which plants can use is (1) oxygen (2) carbon dioxide (3) argon (4) nitrogen.
10. The gas in air that is used by green plants to make food is (1) oxygen (2) nitrogen (3) argon (4) carbon dioxide.
11. Water vapor is (1) an invisible gas (2) an invisible liquid (3) a visible gas (4) a visible liquid.
12. The part of air that shows the greatest variation in percentage is (1) carbon dioxide (2) nitrogen (3) oxygen (4) water vapor.
13. Water vapor enters air by the process of (1) condensation (2) evaporation (3) humidity (4) reflection.
14. When we exhale on a cold morning, we often see (1) our breath (2) carbon dioxide from our breath (3) tiny droplets of water from our breath (4) water vapor.
15. Moisture collects on the inside of kitchen windowpanes in winter because (1) cold air condenses the water vapor in warm air (2) cold air evaporates the water vapor in warm air (3) cold glass attracts water (4) cold glass sweats.

Completion Questions

Write the word or expression that correctly completes the statement.

1. The layer of the atmosphere in which daily changes of weather take place is the _____.
2. The layer of the atmosphere which has electrical properties is the _____.
3. The _____ is the portion of the atmosphere containing the ozone layer.
4. The gas that makes up about one-fifth of the air is _____.
5. The atmosphere consists principally of the gases _____ and _____.
6. Oxygen is obtained commercially by extracting it from _____.
7. The decay of plant and animal matter restores the gas _____ to the air.
8. The moisture in air is called _____.
9. Air that holds as much water vapor as it can is said to be _____.
10. The process by which water vapor settles out of the air as a liquid is known as _____.

Chapter 38. The Characteristics of Air

1. AIR HAS MASS

Because many gases are invisible, we are likely to forget that they are a form of matter, occupying space and having mass (Fig. 38-1).

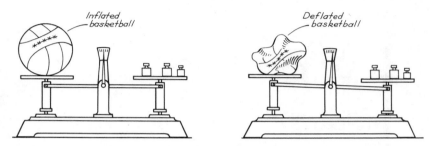

Fig. 38-1. Determining the mass of air. A ball filled with air has a mass slightly more than an empty ball, proving that air has mass.

2. AIR EXERTS PRESSURE

Pressure is a push or pull exerted by a mass on a given unit of area. Since air has mass, it exerts pressure on all objects exposed to it. At sea level, normal atmospheric pressure is about 15 pounds per square inch of surface. This means that about 20 tons of air are constantly pushing against all surfaces of our bodies. We are able to survive this mass because the outward and inward pressures are balanced, or equalized. For example, our chest is not crushed because the air inside the chest is pushing outward with the same pressure as the air outside the chest is pushing inward.

3. THE MERCURY BAROMETER

A *barometer* is an instrument used to measure the pressure exerted by the atmosphere. The first *mercury barometer* was made by Torricelli in 1643. At sea level, normal air pressure supports a column of mercury approximately 30 inches, or about 76 centimeters, high (Fig. 38-2 on next page). The height of the mercury column changes with changes in pressure. When the air pressure decreases below normal, the mercury falls below 30 inches in the tube; when the air pressure increases above normal, the mercury rises above 30 inches in the tube.

Since mercury is about 14 times as dense as water, air pressure will support a taller column of water. At sea level, the water column supported by normal air pressure equals about 34 feet.

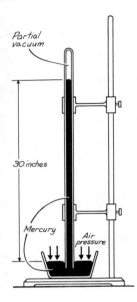

Fig. 38-2. The mercury barometer. Air pressure against the mercury in the dish supports the mercury in the tube. The mercury drops in the tube until the pressure of the mercury column equals the pressure of the air. The space above the mercury now contains very little air and is called a *partial vacuum*.

4. THE ANEROID BAROMETER

Air pressure can be measured by another type of barometer, called an *aneroid barometer*. As this barometer does not contain a liquid, it is more convenient to handle. An aneroid barometer consists of a small metal chamber from which most of the air has been removed. The top of the chamber moves inward or outward depending on changes in atmospheric pressure. Air pressure is read from a pointer moving across a scale, calibrated in inches of mercury.

5. ALTITUDE AFFECTS ATMOSPHERIC PRESSURE

Since air exerts pressure, the greater the mass of an air column, the more pressure it exerts. The farther down we go in our ocean of air, the greater the column of air above us and therefore the greater the pressure on our bodies. The farther up we go, the shorter becomes the column of air above us and the lower is the pressure.

Atmospheric pressure on mountain peaks is less than it is in valleys. For approximately every 1,000 feet of elevation above sea level, there is a drop in pressure equal to a one-inch drop in the mercury column of a barometer. At 18,000 feet above sea level (about 3½ miles up), the air pressure is about half the pressure at sea level. A special type of aneroid barometer, an *altimeter*, is used to measure altitude above sea level.

6. PUTTING COMPRESSED AIR TO WORK

Since air is highly elastic, it can easily be compressed by exerting pressure on it. This principle is the basis of the operation of a bicycle pump (Fig. 38-3), air brakes, blowers, and sprayers.

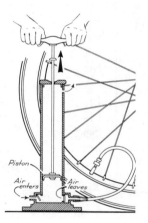

Fig. 38-3. The bicycle pump. The pump is a cylinder in which is placed a tightly fitting piston. The pump is fitted with an inlet valve and an outlet valve. As the piston rod is pulled up, air enters the cylinder through the inlet valve, while the outlet valve remains shut. On the downstroke, the inlet valve closes and the compressed air leaves through the outlet valve.

7. PUTTING DECREASED AIR PRESSURE TO WORK

We have seen that air is forced out of a compression pump when the pressure in the pump is greater than the pressure outside. Whenever there is a difference in air pressure between two places, air will move from the place of greater pressure to the place of lesser pressure. By decreasing the air pressure in a device, the movement of air produced by the greater atmospheric pressure can be used to help us to do work. This principle is used in the operation of the soda straw, medicine dropper, lift pump, and vacuum cleaner. (Read "The Vacuum Cleaner," on next page.)

THE VACUUM CLEANER

If your weekly chores include cleaning the carpets, chances are you use a vacuum cleaner. This useful appliance, developed around 1900, uses suction to pick up dirt and dust from floor surfaces. It can also clean furniture, curtains, and even clothing, if you have the right attachments.

The vacuum cleaner has two basic parts—a fan and a dirt-collecting bag. The fan is similar to the circulating fans you use to cool yourself in hot weather, but with a few changes.

If you hold a piece of paper in front of a circulating fan, it will be blown away from the fan. If you hold the same paper behind the fan, it will be pulled toward the blades. The bend of the blades and the direction of their rotation are responsible for such exhaust and suction properties.

In a vacuum cleaner, the fan is positioned so that the suction is directed toward the surface being cleaned. The exhaust is directed into the collecting bag. By increasing the speed of the fan, greater suction and exhaust are created.

Vacuum cleaners come in two basic models. *Canister vacuums* have a long flexible hose and nozzle attached to the canister body. The fan is in the canister, below a collecting bag. When the machine is turned on, suction is created in the hose and nozzle. By moving the nozzle back and forth over a surface, you loosen dirt and dust, which are then pulled into the hose and deposited in the collecting bag.

Upright vacuums have a collecting bag connected to a large cleaning head. The fan is in the head and makes the appliance fairly heavy. The cleaning head cannot be moved rapidly over a surface as the canister's nozzle can. Upright vacuums have a built-in agitator—a series of revolving brushes—to help loosen the dirt before being drawn into the machine.

8. THE SODA STRAW

When you insert a straw into a liquid and suck on one end of the straw, the liquid rises. This results from the fact that as you remove the air from the straw, the air pressure in the straw is reduced. The greater atmospheric pressure outside the straw then forces the liquid up into the straw. The liquid stops rising when you stop sucking, because the pressure inside the straw becomes the same as the outside atmospheric pressure.

Similar to the operation of the soda straw is the medicine dropper, which employs a rubber bulb to remove the air from the tube.

9. THE LIFT PUMP

A *lift pump* is a machine used to pump water from a well. The principle of operation of the lift pump (Fig. 38-4) is similar to that of the soda straw. The

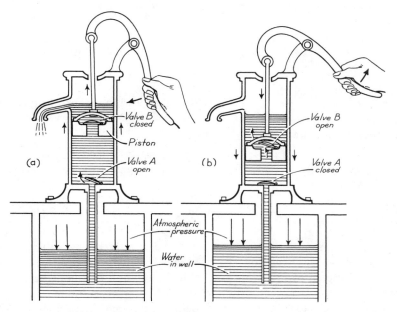

Fig. 38-4. The lift pump in operation. (*a*) The pressure is reduced in the piston chamber when the piston is moved upward. Air pressure forces the water to open valve *A* and enter the chamber while valve *B* remains closed.

(*b*) When the piston is moved downward, valve *B* opens while valve *A* closes. This causes the water trapped in the chamber to flow above valve *B*. When the piston is next moved upward, the water above valve *B* is lifted to the spout and flows out.

removal of air by the action of a piston causes air pressure to be reduced in the upper part of the pump. The outside air forces water into the pump to balance the decrease in air pressure. Valves in the pump prevent the water from flowing back into the well. Since air pressure can support a column of water about 34 feet high, lift pumps theoretically will not draw water from depths greater than 34 feet. However, since pumps are not mechanically perfect, lift pumps will not draw water above a height of about 30 feet.

LESSON 3# ANSWER # 3

10. HEATING OF AIR CAUSES MOVEMENTS OF AIR

Air expands when heated because its molecules move about faster and spread out farther. As warm air expands, it becomes less dense and is therefore lighter than cold air. The warm air then rises above the cold air. When the heavier, colder air moves in to occupy the space left by the warm air, the cold air pushes the warm air upward. The cold air becomes warmed and then rises. The moving currents of air produced by heating are called *convection currents* (Fig. 38-5).

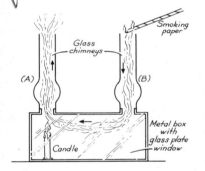

Fig. 38-5. Convection currents in air. As the air (in chimney A) above the candle is heated, it becomes lighter. In chimney B, smoke produced by the burning paper is carried downward by the cooler, heavier air. The smoke is then forced upward together with the warmed air in chimney A.

11. VENTILATION

In order for a room to be properly ventilated, it must have a constant supply of fresh air. Natural circulation of air in the home (Fig. 38-6 on next page) is achieved by keeping windows open at both the top and bottom. The cooler air enters the room through the opening at the bottom of the window. The cool air forces the warm air upward and out of the room through the opening at the top of the window.

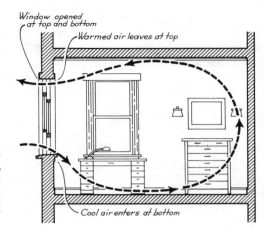

Fig. 38-6. Ventilating a room. Air currents can be produced by opening a window at both the top and bottom. Circulation of air results from cool air entering at the bottom of the window and warm air flowing out at the top.

12. HEATING SYSTEMS

Convection currents are employed to heat the home. In *hot-air* heating systems (Fig. 38-7), air is warmed in a jacket surrounding the furnace. The warmed air then rises by convection through ducts into openings, called *registers*, located in the floors or walls of the rooms. The warm air enters the rooms and rises to the ceilings. As the air cools, it settles and passes through other registers into pipes which lead the air back to the furnace to be reheated.

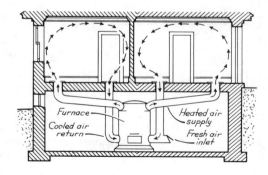

Fig. 38-7. Hot-air system. The arrows show warm air rising to the ceiling of the rooms. When the air cools, it falls and returns to the furnace to be reheated.

In *hot-water* and *steam-heating* systems (Figs. 38-8 and 38-9), the radiators are heated by the hot water or steam circulating through them. The radiators then heat the air near them. As the heated air rises, it is circulated by means of convection currents.

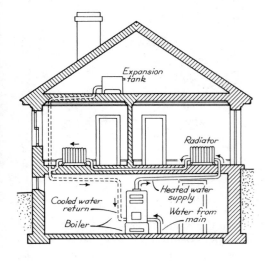

Fig. 38-8. Hot-water system. After being heated in the boiler, the hot water rises. After being cooled in the radiators, the cool water sinks to be reheated in the boiler.

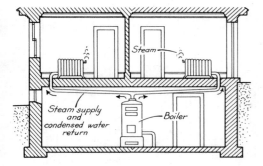

Fig. 38-9. Steam-heating system. Steam rises into the radiators where the steam condenses. The warm water returns to the boiler to be reheated.

Some homes are heated by electric panels located in ceilings or near the floor. The panels radiate heat that spreads throughout the room, generally by convection.

A disadvantage of home-heating systems is that the air they heat may become too dry for comfort. Dry skin, chapping, and nasal irritation may result. This dryness can be overcome by placing a container of water on the radiator to moisten the air or by using *humidifiers*, which blow moisture into the air.

13. AIR-CONDITIONING

Air-conditioning means cleaning the air and providing the proper temperature and humidity. Large air-conditioning units can cool the air of a building in the summer and warm the air in the winter. The air is also filtered, and moisture is added or removed, to insure comfort. Small air conditioners may be used in cars or in individual rooms, usually in the summer, to lower the temperature. Such air-conditioning units are really room refrigerators in the sense that they can maintain a fairly constant and desired temperature.

14. THE THERMOSTAT

A *thermostat* consists of a metal bar, called a *compound bar*, composed of two strips of different metals joined together (Fig. 38-10). Heating the bar causes the two metals to expand at different rates, bending the bar in one direction. Cooling the bar causes the two metals to contract at different rates, bending the bar in the opposite direction.

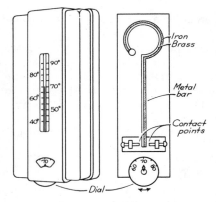

Fig. 38-10. A thermostat

The thermostat automatically controls the temperature of the air in a room as follows: When the temperature drops below the setting on the thermostat, the bar contracts and touches an electric contact. This closes the circuit and turns on the furnace. When the temperature rises to the setting on the thermostat, the bar expands and touches the opposite contact. This turns off the furnace.

15. INSULATING A HOUSE

Such substances as rock wool, glass fibers, and cork are *insulating* materials. When a home is constructed, insulating materials are placed in the walls, floors, and roof. The purpose of insulation is to reduce heat transfer into a house in the summer and out of the house in the winter.

Insulating materials are also used in the walls of refrigerators, around furnaces and steam pipes, and around the walls of picnic jugs.

Asbestos is no longer used as an insulating material because inhaling asbestos fibers is thought to cause lung cancer.

Multiple-Choice Questions

Write the number preceding the correct answer.

1. An instrument used to measure atmospheric pressure is the (1) anemometer (2) barometer (3) hygrometer (4) thermometer.
2. The height of a column of mercury that can be supported by normal air pressure at sea level is about (1) 15 inches (2) 30 inches (3) 30 feet (4) 34 feet.
3. The height of the column of mercury in the mercury barometer depends on the (1) amount of mercury in the dish (2) height of the glass tube (3) diameter of the tube (4) pressure of the air.
4. An altimeter is an instrument that (1) measures height above sea level (2) measures amount of rainfall (3) indicates the percentage of water vapor in the atmosphere (4) measures the wind velocity.
5. The elasticity of air allows it to be easily (1) expanded (2) compressed (3) measured (4) moistened.
6. The bicycle pump is an example of (1) an altimeter (2) an aneroid barometer (3) an exhaust pump (4) a compression pump.
7. Compressed air is used in operating (1) a soda straw (2) a lift pump (3) air brakes (4) a medicine dropper.
8. By decreasing the air pressure, air can be made to move from (1) a low pressure region to a high pressure region (2) a high pressure region to a low pressure region (3) a high pressure region to another high pressure region (4) a region of low pressure to a region having the same pressure.
9. When you drink soda through a straw, the liquid rises because of (1) adhesion (2) atmospheric pressure (3) capillary action (4) leverage.
10. Decreased air pressure is used to (1) operate a lift pump (2) inflate a football (3) operate a door check (4) operate an electric fan.
11. If a bottle is lowered mouth downward into a jar of water, (1) a small amount of water will flow into the bottle (2) the bottle will burst (3) water will flow into the bottle until it is completely filled (4) water will flow into the bottle until it is nearly filled.
12. The heating of air produces moving currents of air known as (1) descending air (2) convection currents (3) ventilation (4) radiation.
13. A room may be properly ventilated by opening a window from (1) the bottom only (2) the top only (3) both the top and the bottom.
14. Both hot-water and hot-air heating systems heat a home by (1) air conditioning (2) ventilation (3) convection currents (4) compression.
15. A thermostat is used to (1) regulate the humidity (2) measure the air pressure (3) purify the air (4) regulate the temperature.

Completion Questions

Write the word or expression that correctly completes the statement.

1. Since air is a form of matter, it occupies _____.
2. Because air has mass, it exerts a push, known as _____, on all surfaces.
3. A column of water about _____ feet high can be supported by normal air pressure at sea level.
4. An instrument, without liquid, used to measure air pressure is the _____ barometer.
5. Air pressure at the top of a mountain is _____ (*greater than, less than*) the air pressure in a valley.
6. There is a decrease of about 1 inch in the height of the mercury column with an increase in elevation of about _____ feet.
7. Air can be compressed by exerting _____ on it.
8. Keeping air in circulation in order to freshen the air in a room is called _____.
9. Proper temperature and moisture control can be maintained in a room by the use of a (an) _____.
10. _____ materials prevent some loss of heat from a house.

Matching Questions

Match the items in column A with those in column B.

Column A	Column B
1. normal air pressure at sea level	*a.* altimeter
2. mercury barometer	*b.* medicine dropper
3. aneroid barometer	*c.* registers
4. reduced air pressure	*d.* expansion tank
5. convection currents	*e.* compound bar
6. hot-air heating system	*f.* Torricelli
7. hot-water heating system	*g.* insulator
8. rock wool	*h.* ventilation
9. thermostat	*i.* 15 pounds per square inch
10. compressed air	*j.* air brakes

Chapter 39. Understanding the Weather

1. WHAT IS WEATHER?

Weather describes the daily condition of the atmosphere in any given place. The conditions of the atmosphere which determine weather are:

- *a.* temperature
- *b.* pressure
- *c.* humidity
- *d.* wind speed and direction
- *e.* type and amount of precipitation

2. HOW THE ATMOSPHERE IS HEATED

Changing conditions of the air in the troposphere determine our weather. The lower troposphere is warmer than the upper troposphere because:

- *a.* The lower portion is denser than the upper, and therefore absorbs more of the sun's heat.
- *b.* The lower portion is in contact with the heated surface of the earth and therefore has more heat transferred to it from the earth. As the warmer air rises and the cooler air settles, convection currents are set up. Convection, therefore, is the chief method of heating the atmosphere.

3. FACTORS AFFECTING AIR TEMPERATURE

Some of the factors affecting the temperature of the atmosphere are:

a. Time of Day. Since the sun is the chief source of the earth's heat, the earth is warmer during daylight hours. Local conditions, such as clouds, may prevent some of the sun's rays from reaching the earth, thus lowering the air temperature.

b. Season. During the summer months, the temperature of the air is higher because the earth is receiving more heat from the sun. Not only are the days longer, but also the region is exposed to the direct rays of the sun.

c. Location. Places near the equator receive the direct rays of the sun, while regions near the poles receive slanting rays. The temperature of the air near the equator is therefore higher than near the poles.

Land becomes heated faster than does water, and land loses heat faster than does water. Thus, the temperature of the air above land during the day is higher than the temperature of the air above water, and the air over the land at night is usually cooler than the air over the water.

d. Altitude. Air is warmer at lower altitudes than at higher altitudes. The temperature of the air decreases about 3 Fahrenheit degrees for each 1,000 feet of altitude.

4. AIR PRESSURE

The pressure of the air depends on both the temperature and the amount of water vapor in the air. Since warm air is lighter than cold air, warm air produces a lower pressure than does the same amount of cold air. Also, moist air is lighter than dry air and produces a lower pressure than does dry air. Therefore, as air of differing temperature and humidity moves into an area, the pressure in the area changes.

Changes in atmospheric pressure are indicated by changes in the barometer reading. When the air pressure decreases, the barometer reading falls. When the air pressure increases, the barometer reading rises. These changes are carefully observed by weatherpeople to help them forecast weather.

Since decreasing air pressure indicates the presence of warm, moist air, a falling barometer usually forecasts warm, rainy weather. Increasing air pressure indicates the presence of cold, dry air. A rising barometer, therefore, generally forecasts cool, fair weather. *Hight*

An area of low pressure is described as a "low," or L, and an area of high pressure as a "high," or H. A low-pressure area contains warm, moist air. A high-pressure area contains cold, dry air. Since these pressure areas travel across the United States in almost fixed paths, they can be used to predict the weather for short periods of time, usually from 24 to 48 hours.

5. HUMIDITY

Humidity refers to the amount of water vapor present in the air. The amount of water vapor the air can hold depends mainly on the air temperature. The higher the temperature of the air, the more water vapor it can hold. When air has the maximum amount of water vapor it can hold at a given temperature, the air is said to be *saturated*. This temperature is called the *dew point*. Cooling below the dew point produces condensation.

When we compare the actual amount of water vapor in the air with the maximum amount of water vapor the air can hold at that temperature, we obtain a percentage known as the *relative humidity* of the air. Suppose a given amount of air can hold 10 grams of water but has only 5 grams of water. The relative humidity is then 50%. Relative humidity is another factor in forecasting weather. For example, if the relative humidity reaches 100 percent, the water vapor may condense to form clouds or fog, or fall to the earth as rain or snow, depending on the temperature.

Humidity affects our comfort. At room temperature, a relative humidity of about 60% is comfortable. We are more uncomfortable on hot, humid days than on hot, dry days. When the air is saturated, perspiration evaporates from our body too slowly for comfort. When the air is dry, however, evaporation takes place more rapidly. Since evaporation has a cooling effect, we feel more comfortable.

6. HOW WE MEASURE RELATIVE HUMIDITY

The instrument used to measure relative humidity is the *hygrometer*, also known as the *wet- and dry-bulb thermometer*. The hygrometer consists of two thermometers (Fig. 39-1). One thermometer, the wet bulb, has a piece of wet cloth around its bulb. The temperature recorded by this thermometer depends on the rate of evaporation of water from the cloth. The other thermometer, the dry bulb, has no cloth around it and therefore records the air temperature.

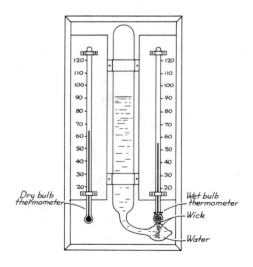

Fig. 39-1. The hygrometer

As a result of evaporation, the temperature indicated by the wet-bulb thermometer is usually lower than the temperature indicated by the dry bulb. The greater the difference in readings between the two, the lower the relative humidity. When both thermometers register the same temperature, the relative humidity is 100 percent and no further evaporation takes place. Special charts (Table 39-1) enable us to determine the relative humidity from the wet-and-dry-bulb thermometer readings.

Table 39-1. Relative Humidity (in Percent)

Dry-bulb thermometer, °F	Difference between dry- and wet-bulb thermometers, °F										
	1°	2°	3°	4°	5°	6°	7°	8°	9°	10°	12°
20°	85	70	56	42	28	14					
25°	87	75	63	50	38	27	15	4			
30°	89	78	68	57	47	37	27	17	8		
35°	91	82	73	64	55	46	37	29	20	12	
40°	92	84	76	68	61	53	46	38	31	23	9
45°	93	86	79	71	65	58	52	45	39	33	20
50°	93	87	81	74	68	62	56	50	44	39	28
55°	94	88	82	76	71	65	60	55	49	44	34
60°	94	89	84	78	73	68	63	58	53	49	40
65° ⟶	95	90	85	80	75	70	66	62	57	53	44
70°	95	90	86	81	77	72	68	64	60	57	48
75°	96	91	87	82	78	74	70	66	63	59	51
80°	96	91	87	83	79	76	72	68	64	61	54

Using the table to obtain relative humidity. We first obtain the dry-bulb reading, which, for example, is 65°F on Fig. 39-1 on preceding page. We then obtain the wet-bulb reading, which is 55°F. The difference between the two readings is 10°F. In the column at the left of the table, we locate the dry-thermometer reading of 65°F. Then we follow this row over to the 10° difference column. There we find that the relative humidity is 53 percent.

7. THE TEMPERATURE-HUMIDITY INDEX (T.H.I.)

Since the rate of evaporation is controlled by the temperature and humidity of the air, the United States Weather Bureau sometimes uses the *temperature-humidity index* (T.H.I.) to predict discomfort, as shown in Table 39-2.

Table 39-2. Temperature-Humidity Index

T.H.I.	Discomfort prediction
70	About 10% of the population feels discomfort.
above 75	About 50% of the population feels discomfort.
above 80	Almost everyone feels discomfort.

The formula used to calculate the T.H.I. is as follows:

$$T.H.I. = 0.4 \ (Td + Tw) + 15$$
$$Td = \text{dry-bulb temperature}$$
$$Tw = \text{wet-bulb temperature}$$

For example, if $Td = 80$ and $Tw = 70$,

$$\begin{aligned} T.H.I. &= 0.4 \ (80 + 70) + 15 \\ &= 0.4 \ (150) + 15 \\ &= 60 + 15 \\ &= 75 \end{aligned}$$

8. HOW FOG FORMS

Sometimes the temperature of moist air close to the surface of the earth is cooled below the dew point. Water vapor then condenses on particles of dust to form droplets of water or crystals of ice. The particles are held up by the air close to the earth, forming *fog*.

9. CLOUDS

A *cloud* is similar to a fog, except that a cloud has a definite shape and is formed higher above the earth's surface. A cloud is formed when air above the earth's surface is cooled below the dew point. The cooling of the air is brought about by the expansion of rising moist air.

A cloud will consist of fine droplets of water if condensation occurs above the freezing point. However, if condensation takes place below the freezing point, a cloud will be made up of snow or ice crystals.

The shape and appearance of clouds are other atmospheric conditions that weatherpeople take into consideration when forecasting weather. Although there are many different kinds of clouds, three main types are recognizable. These are *cirrus*, *cumulus*, and *stratus* (Fig. 39-2 on next page). Sometimes, the prefix *cirro-* is added to the name of the cloud to indicate the altitude of the cloud. Above 7 or 8 kilometers, cumulus and stratus clouds are described as *cirrocumulus* and *cirro-stratus*.

Fig. 39-2. Types of clouds

a. Cirrus Clouds. These are thin, white, feathery clouds found at great heights above the earth. Because of their height, cirrus clouds always contain fine crystals of ice. Cirrus clouds indicate the possibility of rain or snow within a few days.

b. Cumulus Clouds. These are massive, billowy clouds resembling white smoke rising from a smokestack. Cumulus clouds develop from rising currents of air. The base of the cloud indicates the height at which moisture in the rising air began to condense. Cumulus clouds are usually seen in the sky on summer afternoons and generally indicate fair weather. However, when a cumulus cloud increases greatly in size and begins to darken, it is becoming a *thunderhead*. A thunderhead gives warning of a storm, characterized by thunder, lightning, and heavy rain. (Read "What Is Lightning?" on next page.)

c. Stratus Clouds. These are low-hanging layers of gray clouds. Dark-colored stratus clouds indicate that rain will fall within a short time.

10. DEW AND FROST

As the earth cools during the night, the air in contact with the cool earth also loses its heat. When the air is cooled below its dew point, the water vapor of the air will condense. We commonly see this condensation as dew or frost on the ground, grass, cars, etc.

If the temperature of the surface on which condensation occurs is above the freezing point, a fine mist, or *dew*, is formed. If the temperature at which condensation occurs is below the freezing point, crystals of ice called *frost* are formed.

Winds do not allow air to remain in contact with the cool earth long enough for condensation to take place. Dew and frost are more likely to form on calm, clear nights than on cloudy, windy nights.

WHAT IS LIGHTNING?

Lightning is a natural, high-current electrical discharge in the atmosphere. It does not last very long. While most commonly seen in thunderstorms, lightning can also occur in sandstorms, snowstorms, and in clouds above an erupting volcano.

Before lightning can be formed, there must be a separation of positive and negative charges in the air. Scientists disagree on what could cause such a separation. Some feel that during a storm, large particles—like raindrops and hailstones that fall from clouds—develop a charge different from that of the small droplets of water and ice that remain in the cloud. Others believe that the strong updrafts and downdrafts in the thundercloud create enough friction to cause the droplets in the cloud to develop opposite charges.

The most destructive lightning is the cloud-to-ground flash. Such bolts originate near the bottoms of clouds. An invisible discharge of electricity, called a *stepped leader*, makes its way down to the Earth's surface in jagged segments about 50 meters (165 feet) long. When the stepped leader gets to within 100 meters (330 feet) of the ground, a second leader begins to approach it from the ground. High objects like buildings and trees make it easier for the second leader to be formed.

When the two leaders make contact, a visible lightning bolt forms. It may seem that a bolt starts in the sky and ends on the ground, but it actually appears first near the ground and flashes up to the cloud.

Lightning stops when the separation of positive and negative charges in the atmosphere is eliminated. Until then, the brilliant flashes and shattering vibrations continue, until the storm eventually passes and the sky clears.

11. PRECIPITATION

Certain types of condensation that form in the air are too heavy to be supported by the air, and so they fall to the earth. When the water vapor in a cloud is cooled below the dew point, condensation occurs. *Precipitation* is the term given to those forms of condensation that fall to the earth, namely, rain, snow, sleet, and hail.

a. Rain. If the temperature at which condensation occurs is above the freezing point, droplets of water come together and fall to the earth as rain.

b. Snow. If the air temperature is below the freezing point, snowflakes may be formed directly from the condensing water vapor in a cloud.

c. Sleet. When falling drops of rain pass through a layer of air the temperature of which is below 32° Fahrenheit, the drops may freeze. The frozen raindrops fall to the earth as sleet.

d. Hail. When raindrops form in cumulus clouds, especially during a storm, the drops are under the influence of strong convection currents. These currents of air may carry the raindrops up and down many times. As the raindrops are swept upward, they sometimes freeze into particles of ice. As the particles are carried downward, additional water condenses on the particles. Repetition of this alternate up-and-down motion produces particles of ice, called *hail*, which are heavy enough to fall to the earth. Some hailstones have been known to be as large as grapefruits and can weigh up to several pounds.

12. ARTIFICIAL RAINMAKING

When rain is needed during a dry spell, and certain clouds happen to be present, scientists "seed" the clouds with pellets of dry ice (solid carbon dioxide). The dry ice lowers the temperature of the clouds to the dew point, which sometimes results in the formation of rain. In another method of artificial rainmaking, chemicals, such as silver iodide smoke, are sprayed into clouds. These smoke particles provide the surfaces on which the water vapor can condense to form rain.

13. WEATHER

Meteorologists are people who study weather—the condition of the atmosphere—and how it changes. These changes are produced by the movement of large bodies of air called *air masses*. An air mass usually picks up the characteristics of the region from which it originates. For example, an air mass from the north, originating over land, is generally cold and dry. An air mass from the south, originating over water, may be warm and moist.

The rotation of the earth causes air masses to move. The boundaries between different air masses are called *fronts* and are designated as cold, warm, or stationary. Air masses that contain cold, dry air have high pressure and are described as *highs* or H. Similarly, air masses that contain warm, moist air have low pressure and are described as *lows* or L.

As air masses are driven by winds, they mix and produce the weather in a given region. For example, a cold air mass—when meeting a warm air mass—pushes the warm air upward, forming clouds and then rain. When the temperature difference between two air masses is great, storms and heavy rains result.

14. WINDS

When air moves horizontally, almost parallel to the earth's surface, the movement is called *wind*. Winds are caused by differences in air pressure. Differences in air pressure result from the unequal heating of the earth's surface. Regions of high temperature are areas of low pressure; regions of low temperature are areas of high pressure. Winds always move from regions of high pressure to regions of low pressure. The difference in air pressure between two regions determines the velocity of the wind.

The direction of a wind is determined by a *weather vane*. The velocity of a wind is measured by an *anemometer* (Fig. 39-3 on next page).

15. ESTIMATING WIND VELOCITIES

Wind velocity can be estimated from the information in Table 39-3.

Table 39-3. Wind Velocities

If you observe that	The wind velocity is about
Flags hang limp without waving	1 mile per hour
Flags blow	9 to 12 miles per hour
Branches rustle	13 to 20 miles per hour
Whitecaps have formed on bodies of water	21 to 25 miles per hour
Branches are breaking off trees	40 to 100 miles per hour

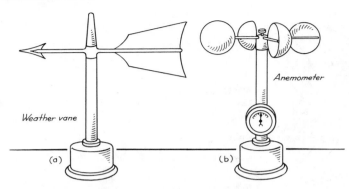

Fig. 39-3. Wind direction and velocity. (*a*) The weather vane changes its direction with the wind and shows the direction from which the wind comes. We name the wind by the direction from which it blows.

(*b*) The anemometer consists of hollow hemispheres mounted on arms and facing in four directions. The cups catch the wind and turn a shaft attached to an air-speed instrument, which indicates wind velocity in miles per hour.

16. EFFECT OF THE EARTH'S ROTATION ON WINDS   *LESSON 7th # ANSWER*

As we have already seen, temperature differences cause pressure differences. In turn, pressure differences create winds and air currents. Currents are like winds, except that the movement of air is vertical instead of horizontal. We have also noted that the air over the equator is warmer than the air over the poles. This causes the air over the equator to rise and move toward the poles, while the polar air flows toward the equator. The turning motion of the earth as it rotates on its axis, called the *Coriolis effect*, results in the characteristic wind patterns around the earth (Fig. 39-4 on next page). The Coriolis effect also causes the spiral-like, whirlpool pattern of local wind paths around "highs" and "lows."

Massive storms, called *cyclones*, may result from winds blowing toward areas of low pressure. Other cyclonic storms, such as *hurricanes*, form over water near the equator, as warm air rises and is twisted by the earth's rotation. The most destructive cyclonic disturbance is the *tornado*, which is caused by the rush of cold air into a low-pressure area. The movement of air is very sudden and very swift, reaching at times speeds that can exceed 500 miles per hour. Fortunately, tornadoes last for only brief periods but still do considerable damage.

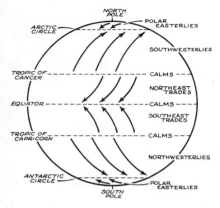

Fig. 39-4. The prevailing winds of the earth. The winds over the earth follow definite paths. The paths are curved, due to the rotation of the earth.

17. FORECASTING THE WEATHER

The United States Weather Bureau maintains weather stations throughout continental United States, as well as in the polar regions and distant islands. Information concerning temperature, pressure, humidity, and winds is sent to the Weather Bureau in Washington. This information is assembled and a weather map constructed (Fig. 39-5).

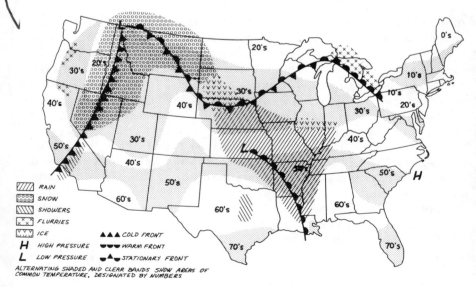

Fig. 39-5. A weather map

The map reveals not only the weather for that particular day, but also helps to predict the weather for several days ahead. Sudden changes in wind direction occasionally spoil a local prediction. But over the years, the Weather Bureau predictions have steadily grown more accurate, due to improved methods for gathering information. One example is the use of airplanes to fly into a hurricane and report its characteristics to the Weather Bureau. Other examples are the use of radar and weather satellites to track the course of clouds and atmospheric disturbances.

Multiple-Choice Questions

Write the number preceding the correct answer.

1. One of the following that is *not* a weather condition is (1) wind velocity (2) humidity (3) time of day (4) air pressure.
2. On an average day, it is coldest (1) at noon (2) in the early evening (3) just before sunrise (4) just before sunset.
3. Air pressure depends on humidity and the (1) dew point (2) temperature of the air (3) smoke and dust in the air (4) color of the clouds.
4. The barometer is rising steadily. The type of weather *most* likely to follow is (1) warm and rainy (2) calm and cloudy (3) cool and fair (4) windy and clear.
5. A region on a weather map that is marked L represents a low (1) relative humidity (2) air temperature (3) wind velocity (4) air pressure.
6. Weather can be forecast *most* accurately for a period of (1) several days (2) three weeks (3) one month (4) six months.
7. The percentage of water vapor in the air is called (1) barometric pressure (2) relative humidity (3) saturation (4) water level.
8. Warm air usually contains (1) more moisture than cold air (2) less moisture than cold air (3) no moisture (4) all the moisture it can hold.
9. We often feel uncomfortable on "muggy" days in summer. This is due to (1) the failure of perspiration to evaporate from the body freely (2) too rapid evaporation of perspiration (3) less oxygen in the air than usual (4) too little moisture in the air.
10. Relative humidity can be determined with a (1) thermometer (2) barometer (3) hygrometer (4) ruler.
11. Clouds are made up of (1) tiny droplets of water (2) water vapor (3) dust particles only (4) partially evaporated water.
12. When condensation occurs above the freezing point, clouds are made up of (1) tiny droplets of water (2) ice crystals (3) hailstones (4) water vapor.
13. Rain clouds are made up of (1) ice particles (2) smoke (3) steam (4) tiny droplets of water.

14. A thick, massive, dark-colored cloud associated with severe storms is the (1) cirrus (2) thunderhead (3) stratus (4) cumulus.
15. Dew is water that (1) falls from the upper levels of the air (2) condenses from cool air next to the earth (3) forms when warm air meets cold air (4) forms only when the sun shines.
16. Dew forms most readily on nights that are (1) calm and clear (2) cloudy (3) stormy (4) windy.
17. When the temperature of water vapor in a cloud is lowered to the dew point and the air temperature is above freezing, condensation may occur in the form of (1) hail (2) fog (3) snow (4) rain.
18. Rain falling through a layer of air colder than 32°F may result in (1) frost (2) dew (3) sleet (4) snow.
19. Hailstones are most likely to form in (1) cirrus clouds (2) stratus clouds (3) cumulus clouds (4) fog.
20. Scientists have been able to produce rain occasionally by (1) discharging blasts of hot air in clouds (2) dropping dry ice into clouds (3) exploding bombs at high altitudes (4) flying rapidly back and forth through clouds.
21. Winds are caused by (1) ocean currents (2) the motions of the earth (3) the waving of the branches of trees (4) the unequal heating of the earth's surface.
22. The movement of a wind is always from (1) north to south (2) east to west (3) a region of low pressure to a region of high pressure (4) a region of high pressure to a region of low pressure.
23. The instrument used to determine the velocity of a wind is the (1) weather vane (2) anemometer (3) hygrometer (4) barometer.
24. Weather experts now use radar to (1) measure ocean depths (2) measure precipitation (3) track atmospheric disturbances (4) obtain barometric readings.

Modified True-False Questions

If a statement is true, write the word true. *If a statement is false, write the word or expression that must be substituted for the italicized expression to make the statement true.*

1. Changing conditions of weather occur in the *stratosphere*.
2. The earth's atmosphere is heated chiefly by *convection*.
3. Clouds *increase* the temperature of the earth.
4. The air temperature of places near the poles is lower than that near the equator because the polar areas receive the *direct* rays of the sun.
5. With an increase in altitude, there is a (an) *increase* of 3°F in the air temperature for every 1,000 feet.
6. The barometer reading is high when the air is *moist*.
7. A falling barometer usually means we will have *fair* weather.

8. When the air contains all the water vapor it can hold at a particular temperature, the air is *saturated*.
9. The relative humidity considered most comfortable at 68°F is *70 percent*.
10. To predict discomfort, the Weather Bureau now uses the *hygrometer*.
11. In order for a cloud to form, the temperature of the air must fall below the *evaporation* point.
12. The base of a cloud indicates the elevation at which rising moist air *condensed*.
13. Frost forms when the temperature at which the moisture of the air condenses is *above* the freezing point.
14. The name given to all the forms of condensed water vapor that fall to the earth is *precipitation*.
15. The instrument used to indicate wind direction is the *anemometer*.
16. The temperature at which air is saturated with water vapor is called the *dew point*.
17. A T.H.I. reading above 80 indicates *great* discomfort.
18. The movement of *fronts* is used to predict weather.
19. Cyclonic storms are influenced by the *rotation* of the earth.
20. A sudden movement of cold air into a low pressure region may cause a *tornado*.

Chapter 40. How Sound Is Produced and Transmitted

1. USING SOUND

The exchange of ideas depends largely on *sound*. Speech and the ability to hear enable us to communicate with one another. In addition, music, radio, television, and movies provide us with enjoyment. Some sounds, such as a siren or smoke alarm, may warn us of danger.

The inability to hear is a serious handicap to people afflicted with deafness. However, much progress has been made in helping the deaf. Special schools, hearing aids, and lip reading are some of the important measures that have been developed to overcome the inability to communicate freely through the medium of sound.

2. WHAT IS SOUND?   *LESSON 9# ANSWER #   #7*

Sound is a form of energy produced by the vibration of matter (Fig. 40-1 on next page). When matter is vibrating, it is moving back and forth. For example, when you strike a tuning fork, you cause the tines of the fork to vibrate. In turn, these vibrations cause air molecules to vibrate. Also, when you speak, your vocal cords cause the surrounding air molecules to vibrate.

3. WHAT IS A SOUND WAVE?

A body that vibrates transfers the vibrations to surrounding matter. The vibrations spread out in all directions and travel through space as *sound waves*. A sound wave behaves like a stretched coiled spring when the tension is released on the spring.

4. TRANSMITTING SOUND

In order for sounds to be heard, the sound waves must be transmitted from the source of the vibrations to one's ears. Any phase of matter—solid, liquid, or gas—is a suitable medium for transmitting sound waves. Air, however, is the most common medium.

Sound waves travel through air at a speed of about 1,090 feet (about 330 meters) per second at a temperature of 0°C. As the air temperature rises, sound travels faster. An increase in temperature causes the air molecules to move faster.

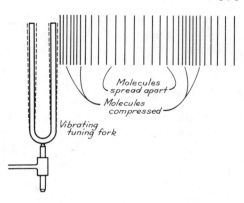

Fig. 40-1. Principle of a sound wave. In a sound wave, the molecules are first crowded together and then spread apart. Because the molecules are first compressed and then released, a sound wave is called a compression, or *longitudinal*, wave.

Scientists use the term *Mach number* to compare the speed of sound with the speed of a moving body. Thus, an airplane whose speed is Mach 1 is traveling at the speed of sound. The speed of *supersonic* jets can be as high as Mach 5. Such speeds call for special aircraft design.

Sound cannot travel in a vacuum because there are no air molecules to vibrate. (See Fig. 40.2.)

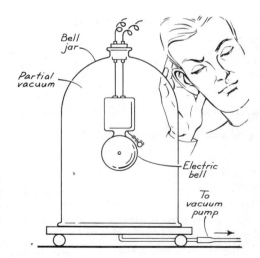

Fig. 40-2. Absence of sound in a vacuum. As air is removed from the bell jar, the ringing of the bell is not heard because sound waves cannot be transmitted through the partial vacuum.

You will recall from a previous chapter that the molecules in a liquid are packed more closely together than are the molecules in a gas, while in a solid the molecules are even more closely packed. As a result, liquids and solids transmit sound faster than does air.

5. HOW WE HEAR

The outer part of the ear (Fig. 40-3) catches the sound waves and leads them through a canal to the *eardrum*. This is a membrane (thin tissue) separating the

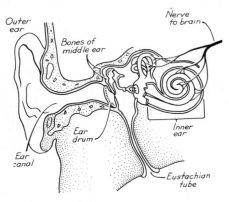

Fig. 40-3. Parts of the ear

outer ear from the middle ear. The vibrations strike the eardrum and cause it to vibrate. The vibrations are then carried to three small bones in the middle ear, called the *hammer*, *anvil*, and *stirrup*, which can also vibrate. The vibrating bones then transmit the sound vibrations to the inner ear. There, very sensitive nerves transmit the vibrations to nerve centers in the brain. The brain then interprets the sound for us.

The human ear cannot hear all sounds, despite the fact that air molecules are vibrating. The ear is sensitive to sounds only between approximately 16 and 20,000 vibrations per second. Some animals, such as the bat, are sensitive to sounds of higher vibration, called *ultrasound*.

6. CHARACTERISTICS OF SOUNDS

Sounds have three characteristics by which they may be recognized: *pitch*, *loudness*, and *tone*.

a. Pitch describes how high or low a sound is. Pitch depends on the number of vibrations per second, also called *cycles* per second. The number of vibrations produced by a vibrating body in a second is called the *frequency* of the sound. The more rapidly a body vibrates, the greater is the frequency and thus the higher is the pitch.

The frequency of commonly heard sounds may vary from about 100 to 4,000 cycles per second. Certain sound machines can generate much higher frequencies, called *ultrasonic* frequencies, or ultrasound, that range above 20,000 cycles per second. Sounds of these frequencies can be reflected very efficiently.

Ultrasonic frequencies are finding use in many industries and in medical research. For example, echoes produced by reflection of ultrasound waves are used in devices called *sonar* to determine the depth of an underwater body. A ship, equipped with sonar, sends out a sound pulse that strikes the underwater body and is reflected back to the source in a measured amount of time. Thus, from the speed of sound in the water, the depth of the body can be easily determined.

Ultrasound echoes may be used to detect the presence of gallstones in humans. In some instances, ultrasound waves may even be used to crush kidney stones so that they may be passed out with the urine, eliminating the need for surgery.

b. Loudness (also called *amplitude*) of a sound depends on the energy of the sound wave. The greater the energy, the louder the sound. For example, a violin string plucked vigorously produces a loud sound; the same string plucked gently produces a soft sound.

c. Tone or quality is the property which distinguishes one sound from another sound having the same pitch and loudness. Quality depends on the manner in which the object is vibrating and the shape of the sound waves that are produced. Different musical instruments produce their own characteristic tones.

7. MUSICAL INSTRUMENTS

There are three basic types of musical instruments: *wind*, *string*, and *percussion*.

a. Wind instruments are organ pipes, the saxophone, bugle, trombone, and clarinet. In these instruments, an air column is set into vibration. The length of the vibrating air column determines the pitch (or musical note) of the sound. Short air columns produce sounds with a higher pitch than do longer air columns.

b. String instruments are the violin, banjo, and guitar. The pitch of a string depends upon its length, thickness, and tightness. Short, thin, tight strings produce sounds with a higher pitch than do long, thick, loose strings.

The human vocal cords are sometimes likened to string instruments. Vocal cords are made to vibrate by air coming from the lungs. Muscles regulate the tightness of the vocal cords and thus determine the pitch of our voice.

c. Percussion instruments are the tambourine and drum. A sharp blow causes a stretched membrane to vibrate. The tightness of the membrane is controlled by the turning of knobs.

MAGNETIC RECORDING DEVICES

Magnetic recording is the most popular of all recording technologies. The reason for this is that magnetic signals can be recorded, edited, copied, and erased easily. And magnetic recording uses one of the most common substances on earth—rust!

Recording tape is essentially a long strip of plastic that has been coated with a magnetic material (most commonly gamma-iron oxide, a form of finely powdered rust). The particles are needle-shaped and usually 5 millionths of an inch thick and 25 millionths of an inch long. Plastic resins bind the particles to the tape. While still semiliquid, the tape is passed under a strong magnet. This orients the needles lengthwise on the tape.

Each needle of iron oxide on the tape can be thought of as a bar magnet. On an unrecorded tape, about half the particles have their north poles facing forward while the other half have their north poles facing backward.

In a tape recorder, the tape moves past a record/play head at a constant speed. The record/play head is simply a small electromagnet connected in some way to the sound source being recorded. During recording, the varying electric current in the head generates a changing magnetic field. Depending on the strength of the magnetic field at a given point, some, none, or all of the iron oxide particles may reverse their direction on the tape. The particles keep this new direction until exposed to another magnetic field.

During playback, the magnetic fields on the tape pass by the head and generate small electric currents. Other electronic devices then transform and amplify those currents into the sound heard from the speaker.

8. REPRODUCING SOUND

The telephone, phonograph, tape recorder, radio, and television represent the different ways in which sound may be reproduced. In these instruments, devices change sound energy into electrical energy. Other devices then change the electrical energy back to sound energy.

9. THE TELEPHONE

Commercial telephones (Fig. 40-4) contain a *transmitter* and a *receiver*. Both of these instruments are connected by wires, and the wires are attached to a source of electric current. A steel diaphragm and a box of carbon particles are contained in the transmitter, while an electromagnet is contained in the receiver. Attached to the poles of the electromagnet is a metal disc.

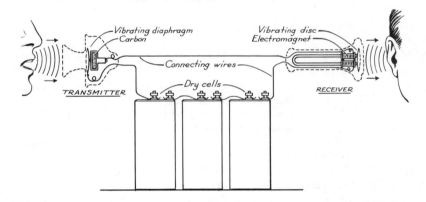

Fig. 40-4. How a telephone operates. The transmitter changes sound into an electric current of varying strength. The receiver changes the electric current back to sound.

According to the characteristics of the sound spoken into the transmitter, the steel diaphragm presses on the carbon particles in the box. The carbon particles are then pushed more closely together or farther apart. The movement of these carbon particles changes the resistance in the circuit, permitting varying amounts of electricity to flow. As a result, the electromagnet in the receiver becomes weaker or stronger. The change in strength of the electromagnet causes the metal disc to vibrate with the same frequency as the sound that entered the transmitter. Thus, the original sounds are accurately reproduced.

10. THE TAPE RECORDER

The simplest tape recorder consists of a microphone that contains an electromagnet, connected to a source of current. Different sounds, as they enter the microphone, produce electrical signals of different strength, somewhat like the telephone.

The varying electrical signals are fed into a roll of plastic tape that is coated with billions of very tiny particles of magnetic material, usually iron oxide. The electrical signals, in turn, produce special magnetic patterns on the tape that correspond to the sounds that are carried.

The tape is then passed through the playback device, which reverses the process and reproduces the original sounds.

Multiple-Choice Questions

Write the number preceding the correct answer.

1. Matter that is vibrating produces (1) sound (2) heat (3) magnetism (4) chemical changes.
2. When an object is producing sound, the vibrations travel through space as (1) matter (2) molecules (3) sound waves (4) radio waves.
3. The sound waves that leave a vibrating body travel (1) downward only (2) upward only (3) only in straight lines (4) in all directions.
4. You may not be able to see your friends on the other side of a high fence, but can hear them moving around. You may therefore conclude that (1) sound travels faster than light (2) light travels faster than sound (3) sound travels only in straight lines (4) sound waves can travel around corners.
5. The speed of sound in air at 0°C is about (1) 25,000 miles per second (2) 186,000 miles per second (3) 1,090 feet per second (4) 1,000 feet per minute.
6. With an increase in air temperature, the speed of sound through air (1) decreases (2) increases (3) remains the same (4) first increases then decreases.
7. At the same temperature, sound travels fastest through (1) air (2) steel (3) water (4) wood.
8. Of the following, the one that does *not* transmit sound is (1) a vacuum (2) iron (3) a gas (4) ice.
9. When hearing a sound, a person's eardrum is caused to vibrate by (1) three small bones in the middle ear (2) vibrating air particles (3) impulses from the auditory nerve (4) molecules in the vibrating object.
10. The number of vibrations per second of a sound is known as its (1) pitch (2) frequency (3) loudness (4) tone.

11. The pitch of a violin string can be changed by (1) tightening or loosening the string (2) putting more resin on the bow (3) moving the bow more rapidly over the string (4) pressing the bow harder or more lightly on the string.
12. A guitar string can be made to give off a louder sound by being (1) loosened (2) tightened (3) plucked faster (4) plucked harder.
13. As Mach number increases, the speed of an airplane (1) increases (2) decreases (3) remains the same (4) first increases then decreases.
14. When a person speaks, the vocal cords are made to vibrate by (1) muscles in the throat (2) nerves from the brain (3) air moving from the lungs (4) muscles in the chest.
15. A jet plane is sometimes called supersonic because it is able to travel at a speed greater than that of (1) a conventional propeller airplane (2) light (3) radio waves (4) sound.

Completion Questions

Write the word or expression that correctly completes the statement.

1. A person who does not possess the sense of hearing, due to some injury of the ear, is said to have a condition known as _____.
2. When matter is moving back and forth rapidly, it is said to be _____.
3. Sound travels _____ (*faster*, *slower*) in air than it does in solids.
4. Sounds will not travel in a (an) _____.
5. The membrane in the ear that is caused to vibrate by sound waves is the _____.
6. The characteristic of a sound that depends on its frequency is called _____.
7. The characteristic of a sound that depends on the energy of the vibrating body is _____.
8. A short string produces a sound with a _____ (*higher*, *lower*) pitch than does a long string of the same kind.
9. In the telephone, sound waves _____ (*do*, *do not*) travel over wires from the transmitter to the receiver.
10. Magnetic tape is coated with _____.

Thought Questions

For each of the following statements, describe an experiment that will prove each is true.

1. Sound waves require a medium for transmission.
2. The pitch of a sound is determined by its frequency.

3. Different musical instruments have different tonal qualities.
4. The pitch of a sound produced by a wind instrument depends upon the length of the vibrating air column.
5. In the telephone, sound energy is changed into electrical energy.

REVIEW OF UNIT VIII

1. *a.* List five places or things from which water evaporates into the atmosphere.
   b. Describe three ways by which the rate of evaporation of water can be increased.
2. Explain each of the following.
   a. A person feels more uncomfortable on a warm, muggy day than on a hot, dry day.
   b. Pilots who fly planes at great elevations are equipped with special masks.
   c. The amount of nitrogen on the earth remains fairly constant.
3. Describe the water cycle and explain its importance.
4. Explain each of the following observations.
   a. Moisture appears on the inside of a windowpane when the air cools quickly outdoors.
   b. Clothes hung on a line will dry faster on a cool, windy day than on a cool, calm day.
   c. A wet sheet of cloth hanging on a line feels colder than its surroundings.
5. The following terms are frequently used in science. Give the meaning or use of each of the terms.
   a. dew point   *c.* condensation
   b. evaporation   *d.* atmosphere
6. *a.* How could you show that evaporation is a cooling process?
   b. Name one important use that is made of this fact.
7. Explain:
   a. The mass of an empty basketball is determined. After the basketball has been inflated, the mass is again determined. The ball now has a slightly larger mass.
   b. A student fills a drinking glass to the brim with water and places a piece of cardboard over it. Holding the cardboard in place with the palm of the hand, the student inverts the glass. Next, the student withdraws the hand that was holding the cardboard. What happens? Why?
   c. Two holes should be punched in a tomato juice can before pouring out the juice.
8. Explain with labeled diagrams how the following operate.
   a. A medicine dropper
   b. a bicycle pump

9. Sketch in the missing part of the mercury barometer below, and name the missing part.

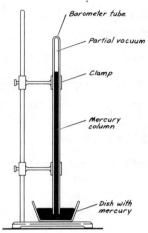

Barometer tube

Partial vacuum

Clamp

Mercury column

Dish with mercury

10. Explain how cumulus clouds form.
11. Why is the temperature reading of the wet-bulb thermometer on a hygrometer usually lower than the reading of the dry-bulb thermometer?
12. How does the unequal heating of the earth's atmosphere cause winds?
13. Explain how a fog is formed.
14. *a.* What is wind?
    b. What is one way we can tell the direction in which the wind is blowing?
    c. What is one way in which we can make use of the wind?
    d. Why should pilots know the speed and direction of the wind?
15. The United States Weather Bureau warns the people along the eastern coast about an approaching hurricane, thus preventing great loss of life.
    a. Name three classes of people who make use of weather forecasts and tell how the forecasts benefit each class.
    b. Name three instruments used in collecting weather data.
    c. State two ways in which weather information is made available to the public.

Unit IX.
The Earth and the Universe

Chapter 41. The Crust of the Earth

1. STRUCTURE OF THE EARTH

The earth consists of four major zones. From the center, the zones are the *inner core*, *outer core*, *mantle*, and *crust* (Fig. 41-1).

The center, or *inner core*, of the earth consists of solid iron and nickel. The solid core is covered by the *outer core*, which is a thick layer of hot, melted iron and

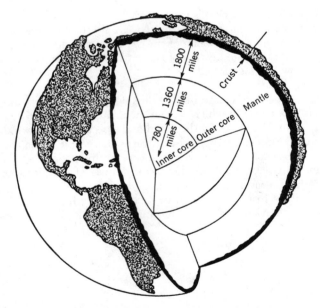

Fig. 41-1. The major zones composing the earth. The thickness of the crust is exaggerated.

nickel. This molten material is covered by the *mantle*, a layer of cooler, but still hot, dense, solid rock material. Above this layer is the outer layer of less dense solid rock material.

The outer layer of the earth, called the *crust*, is a thin layer that varies in thickness from about 3 to 40 miles. By studying the crust, *geologists* (scientists who study rocks) have been able to obtain ideas concerning the nature and origin of the earth, and the changes the earth has undergone.

As geologists penetrate the earth's crust, they find many valuable minerals and rocks. In addition, they find evidence of plant and animal life that inhabited the earth many ages ago.

The surface of the earth consists approximately of one-fourth land and three-fourths water. The land is made up of rock and a loose covering of rock fragments. A study of these rocks and fragments presents additional evidence as to how the earth has changed in the past and is still changing.

2. MINERALS

A *mineral* is a substance that is found in the earth and is usually in the form of crystals. The chemical composition of a particular mineral never changes. A rock is made up of one or more different kinds of minerals, each chemically different from the others.

About 2,000 minerals have been found in the rocks of the earth. Some of the more common minerals are feldspar, quartz, mica, and calcite. Since these are present in many different kinds of rock, they are known as the *rock-forming minerals*. Some minerals contain metals, such as copper and uranium, while others, such as diamond and sulfur, are nonmetallic.

3. IDENTIFYING A MINERAL

Minerals can be identified by their physical properties, some of which are color, luster (shine), hardness, crystal form, and how the mineral splits or breaks (cleaves).

Some minerals are readily identified by their chemical properties. For example, the mineral calcite, which contains calcium carbonate, is identified by a chemical test. When a drop of cold, dilute hydrochloric acid is placed on calcite, a bubbling reaction occurs in which the gas carbon dioxide is released.

4. PROPERTIES AND USES OF MINERALS

Table 41-1 lists some of the properties and uses of a few common minerals.

Table 41-1. Some Common Minerals

Mineral	Properties	Uses
Feldspar, the most abundant.	Hard mineral ranging in color from white to pink.	Source of *kaolin*, a clay used in making porcelain and chinaware, and in coating paper.
Quartz. (Grains of sand are actually crystals of quartz.)	Hardest common mineral. Pure quartz is transparent.	In optical instruments, watches, and in radio and television transmitters.
Mica.	Transparent and peels into thin, flat sheets.	Electrical insulators in toasters and irons.
Calcite, the chief mineral in limestone and marble.	Soft and colorless.	Limestone is used as a building material and to make glass and cement; marble is used in building construction.

5. NATURAL ROCKS

A *rock* is a stony material found in the earth that consists of one or more minerals. Limestone is an example of rock made up of a single mineral, calcite. The chemical makeup of a rock may change after exposure to air, water, or heat.

Rock is classified according to the manner in which the rock was formed. There are three main groups of natural rocks: *igneous*, *sedimentary*, and *metamorphic*. Some rocks have been made artificially.

a. Igneous Rocks. *Igneous rocks* were formed when hot, molten rock material within the earth cooled and hardened. Upon cooling and hardening, some of the minerals formed crystals. At present in some parts of the earth, molten lava flows out of volcanoes and cools and hardens into igneous rock.

Some igneous rocks, with their properties and uses, are listed in Table 41-2.

Table 41-2. Some Igneous Rocks

Rock	Properties	Uses
Granite, very abundant, contains crystals of quartz and feldspar plus at least one other mineral.	Hard, crystalline, and durable.	Buildings and monuments.
Obsidian, also known as volcanic glass, since it results from the rapid cooling of lava.	Noncrystalline.	Making ornaments.
Pumice, a volcanic rock that floats.	Very light and contains many air spaces.	Fine polishing of metal and wood.

b. Sedimentary Rocks. *Sedimentary rocks* were formed from sediments that were deposited in water. Sediments consist of small fragments of rock that were broken up by various agents into particles, such as pebbles, sand, gravel, and clay. These fragments were picked up by running water and deposited in a quiet body of water. In bygone ages, the fragments built up layers, called *strata*, with the bottom layers containing the coarser particles. (See Fig. 19-3, page 183.) After millions of years, the weight of the accumulating sediments exerted enough pressure on the bottom material to cause it to become compressed into sedimentary rock.

Sedimentary rocks were also formed when sediments were cemented together in water. Sedimentary rocks become surface rocks when they are pushed up above the water or when the water disappears.

Some sedimentary rocks, with their properties and uses, are listed in Table 41-3.

Table 41-3. Some Sedimentary Rocks

Rock	Composition	Properties	Uses
Shale, the most abundant.	Mud and clay, compressed and solidified under pressure.	Very soft and easily broken.	Making bricks, cement, and tiles. Some shale may be important commercially for its oil content.
Sandstone, the second most common.	Grains of sand held together by a cement that was present in water.	Porous and can be penetrated by water.	Making glass, as a building stone, and making sandpaper.
Conglomerate.	Grains of sand and pebbles held together by a cement that was present in water.	Resembles concrete.	Building stone.
Limestone, formed in water from shells of sea animals.	Chiefly calcite. (See *Note 1* below.)	Identified by chemical test for calcite, described on page 405, section 3.	Making cement, and in agriculture for "sweetening" the soil.
Soft coal (also called bituminous), found between layers of shale and sandstone.	Decayed plant remains, chiefly carbon. (See *Note 2* below.)	Soft and dull. Gives off light and heat when burned.	Fuel.

Note 1. Calcite is dissolved out of rock and soil of the land by water and carried to the oceans. Sea animals make their shells from the dissolved calcite. When the animals die, their shells become either cemented together or compressed, thus forming limestone.

Note 2. Soft coal is formed when the remains of trees, ferns, or mosses undergo slow decomposition and compression.

Fossils, the preserved remains of living things that existed on the earth millions of years ago have been found chiefly in sedimentary rocks. The study of fossils of all kinds offers a great deal of information about prehistoric plants and animals that have long vanished from the earth. (For more about fossils, see pages 181–182.)

c. Metamorphic Rocks. When igneous or sedimentary rocks were subjected to tremendous heat and pressure, they changed into the much harder *metamorphic rocks*. Frequently, a metamorphic rock has undergone such changes that it no longer resembles the rock from which it was formed.

The composition, origin, properties, and uses of some metamorphic rocks are listed in Table 41-4.

Table 41-4. Some Metamorphic Rocks

Rock	Origin and Composition	Properties	Uses
Gneiss	Formed from granite. Contains the same minerals as granite; namely, quartz and feldspar.	Very hard. Minerals arranged in bands.	Buildings and monuments.
Marble	Formed from limestone. Consists chiefly of calcite.	Hard and crystalline.	Buildings and statues.
Slate	Formed from shale. Consists of mud and clay.	Hard and splits into thin sheets.	Blackboards, pavements, and shingles on roofs.
Hard coal (also called anthracite)	Formed from soft coal. Consists chiefly of carbon. (Anthracite contains more carbon than does bituminous.)	Hard and shiny. Gives off light and heat when burned.	Fuel.

6. ARTIFICIAL ROCKS

Some rocks are made artificially as needed for use in building construction and in paving material. Two important artificial rocks, cement and concrete, are described in Table 41-5.

Table 41-5. Some Artificial Rocks

Rock	How made	Use
Cement	Heating a mixture of crushed limestone and shale to a high temperature and forming a powder. Becomes a solid mass when mixed with water and allowed to set.	Construction work.
Concrete	Mixing crushed stone, cement, and sand in proper proportions with water and allowing it to set.	Construction work, pavement.

Multiple-Choice Questions

Write the number preceding the correct answer.

1. The amount of the earth's surface consisting of land is (1) one-eighth (2) one-fourth (3) one-half (4) three-fourths.
2. The way a mineral shines is a physical property known as (1) luster (2) hardness (3) color (4) chemical composition.
3. Cold, dilute hydrochloric acid is used to test for the mineral (1) mica (2) feldspar (3) quartz (4) calcite.
4. The clay needed for making chinaware is obtained from the mineral (1) sand (2) copper (3) quartz (4) feldspar.
5. Grains of sand are crystals of (1) mica (2) uranium (3) quartz (4) calcite.
6. Sand is important in the manufacture of (1) iron (2) bricks (3) glass (4) glue.
7. A rock formed by the cooling of molten material is (1) granite (2) limestone (3) sandstone (4) shale.
8. A volcanic rock that floats on water is (1) obsidian (2) granite (3) pumice (4) quartz.
9. When sediments are deposited by water, the smallest particles are found (1) on the bottom (2) on the top (3) in the middle layers (4) throughout the layers.

10. Of the following, the kind of rock least suitable for use as a building stone is (1) granite (2) limestone (3) sandstone (4) shale.
11. Sandstone is a sedimentary rock because it is (1) formed by heat (2) formed under water (3) made in desert areas (4) made of sand.
12. A natural rock that is made up of pebbles cemented together is (1) flint (2) granite (3) conglomerate (4) lava.
13. The kind of rock formed from the shells of sea animals is (1) limestone (2) sandstone (3) shale (4) slate.
14. Coal was made from (1) clay (2) plants (3) sand (4) shells.
15. The center of the earth is thought to be composed of (1) melted iron and nickel (2) solid iron and nickel (3) gold and iron (4) nickel and marble.
16. Fossils are found chiefly in (1) igneous rock (2) lava (3) metamorphic rock (4) sedimentary rock.
17. A mineral that occurs in transparent, thin sheets is (1) quartz (2) mica (3) obsidian (4) marble.
18. A rock commonly used in sheets in our schoolrooms is (1) limestone (2) sandstone (3) shale (4) slate.
19. Marble is a metamorphic rock formed from (1) granite (2) limestone (3) shale (4) sandstone.
20. An example of an artificial rock is (1) concrete (2) flint (3) marble (4) granite.

Completion Questions

Write the word or expression that correctly completes the statement.

1. The outer portion of the earth is called the _____.
2. Bubbles of _____ are released when cold, dilute hydrochloric acid reacts with calcite.
3. Kaolin is obtained from the mineral _____.
4. _____ is the hardest of the common rock-forming minerals.
5. The type of rock formed from the cooling of molten material is called _____.
6. The chief rock used in the manufacture of Portland cement is _____.
7. Coal consists chiefly of the element _____.
8. Heat and pressure may change certain rocks into _____ rocks.
9. Shale can be changed into the rock called _____.
10. A mixture of crushed stone, cement, and sand is called _____.

Modified True-False Questions

If a statement is true, write the word true. *If a statement is false, write the word or expression that must be substituted for the italicized expression to make the statement true.*

1. The crust of the earth is between *one to ten* miles thick.
2. A naturally occurring substance made up of crystals of a particular chemical composition is called a (an) *mineral.*
3. The mineral calcite is chiefly *quartz.*
4. Limestone is closely related to *quartz.*
5. The cooling of molten lava produced *igneous* rock.
6. Granite is an example of a (an) *igneous* rock.
7. A light, porous rock is *pumice.*
8. The most abundant sedimentary rock is *sandstone.*
9. Heat and pressure are required to form *sedimentary* rock.
10. Crushed limestone and shale are used in the manufacture of *cement.*

Thought Questions

1. Explain the difference between a mineral and a rock.
2. Although sedimentary rocks are formed under water, in some regions they are found above sea level. Explain.

Chapter 42. The Changing Crust of the Earth

1. THE EARTH'S CRUST IS CONSTANTLY CHANGING

The face of the earth is a rocky surface consisting of mountains, valleys, volcanoes, and plateaus. The rocks are constantly being broken down into smaller fragments and transported elsewhere. At the same time, new surface features are being built up by other forces. Thus, the earth's crust is constantly undergoing change.

2. WEATHERING

Weathering is the process by which rocks are broken down into smaller fragments by the atmosphere and other factors in the environment. There are two types of weathering, *mechanical* and *chemical.*

a. Mechanical weathering is a breakdown of rock into smaller pieces with no change in chemical composition. The major factors in mechanical weathering are:

(1) *Temperature Changes.* Rocks become heated by the sun during the day and cool off at night. During the day, the outside of the rocks expands more than does the inside. At night, the outside contracts more than does the inside. This unequal expansion and contraction causes the rocks to split and break apart.

(2) *Frost Action.* Sometimes water seeps into the pores or cracks of rocks and later freezes. When water freezes, it expands and produces a force great enough to split the rocks into smaller pieces. Since sandstone is very porous, it readily absorbs water. As a result, it is the type of rock chiefly affected by frost action.

(3) *Plant Roots.* The roots of plants may find their way into small cracks in rocks. As the roots grow, they expand and split the rocks.

(4) *Animal Burrows.* Tunnels in soil, such as those made by ants, allow water to reach bedrock under the soil. There, frost action can split the rocks.

(5) *Flaking.* In this process, the outer layers of a rock peel off where they have been loosened by changes that occurred just under the surface of the rock.

b. Chemical weathering is a breakdown of rock in which a *chemical change* occurs, caused by at least one of the following reactions:

(1) *Oxygen.* In the presence of moisture, oxygen from the air combines with the iron found in many rocks. This chemical reaction, called *oxidation*, produces rust. Since rust crumbles easily, the rocks fall apart.

(2) *Acids.* (*a*) Certain protists, such as lichens that grow on rocks, and bacteria that decay dead matter, produce acids that slowly dissolve some minerals in rocks. (*b*) Carbon dioxide of the atmosphere dissolved in water produces a weak acid. When water containing this acid flows over limestone, the limestone is dissolved and carried away by the water. In this manner, limestone caves, such as the Mammoth Cave of Kentucky, are formed.

3. EROSION

Erosion is the process by which rocks are broken down and the fragments transported elsewhere. Some agents of erosion are *wind*, *glaciers*, and *running water*.

a. Erosion by Wind. Wind is the chief agent of erosion in dry regions. Wind-driven particles of sand and dust cut into rock, as sandpaper might, and wear it away. This constant action of the wind decomposes the weaker parts of rock, causing the rest of the rock to crumble to sand. Dust storms and sand storms result as the wind constantly carries the sand from one place to another.

b. Erosion by Glaciers. Glaciers are huge sheets of ice, sometimes hundreds of feet thick. Glaciers move very slowly, picking up and carrying rocks and soil with them. These particles wear away the rocks and land over which the glaciers move. When glaciers pass through river valleys, they deepen and widen the valleys (Fig. 42-1). They wear down and round off mountains. They dig large holes in the earth's surface, which later may be filled with water to form lakes.

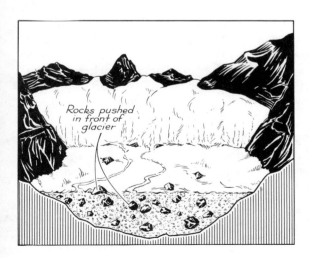

Fig. 42-1. Glaciers change the earth's surface. The shape of a river valley is changed by a glacier passing through it. The river valley takes on a U-shape.

c. Erosion by Running Water. Running water is the chief agent of erosion affecting the earth's surface. Running water of streams and of runoff rainfall picks up and carries a great deal of material, such as sand and pebbles. Running water also drags larger and heavier particles, such as gravel, along a river bottom. These particles wear away the rocks and land over which the water flows. Running water can in time cut through a mountain, producing a valley. The Grand Canyon was formed by the eroding action of the Colorado River.

4. FORCES INSIDE THE EARTH AFFECT ITS SURFACE

a. Internal Heat. When holes are drilled into the earth, the temperature increases 1F° for every 60 feet down. When you consider that the center of the earth is about 4,000 miles below the surface, you can understand why scientists believe that the interior of the earth is very hot. Supporting such a belief is the hot molten rock, or lava, that flows out of volcanoes. Such facts show that the mantle, outer core, and inner core consist of very hot matter.

b. Theory of Movements of the Earth's Crust (Plate Tectonics). The continents and sea floor are the visible parts of the earth's crust. The continents and sea floor are parts of six major crustal sections called *plates*. The plates slide

Fig. 42-2. The world today. Note the distances between the continents and the extent of the Atlantic Ocean. Compare them with Fig. 42-3 on next page.

along very slowly on the upper layer of the mantle, which is hot and plastic. This movement, which has been going on for many millions of years, is between 0.5 and 1.5 inches per year.

A map of the world today shows the locations of our continents and oceans (Fig. 42-2 on previous page). Evidence points to the idea that about 250 million years ago there was only one large supercontinent, called *Pangaea*, surrounded by water. At different times, Pangaea broke up into large sections that separated and formed the smaller continents and the oceans. A map of the world as it might have looked over 150 million years ago is shown in Fig. 42-3.

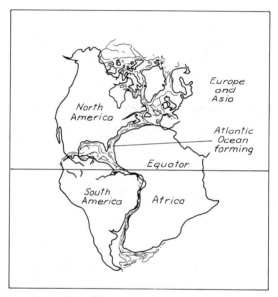

Fig. 42-3. The world 150 million years ago. Pangaea has broken up and the continents have begun moving away from one another.

It is thought that the movement of the plates is caused by hot convection currents (page 267, section 10) that circulate in the mantle under the crust. In some places on the sea floor, where the currents rise close to the crust, the crust cracks. There the hot mantle matter pushes up hot lava and causes the sea floor to spread apart on either side of the crack. As this occurs, the plates move apart, but very slowly.

Some features of the earth's surface are the result of plate movements. Where plates collided in the distant past, as they do now in the western regions of the Pacific Ocean, mountains such as the Himalayas, were pushed upward. Where plates scraped alongside one another, as they do now in the eastern section of the Pacific Ocean, they formed *faults*. An example of a fault of this type is the San Andreas fault located in California and off its western coast.

Volcanic eruptions and earthquakes are common along regions of plate collisions and faults. In the past, earthquake movements have caused sea bottoms to rise and land to sink beneath oceans. At times, ocean waters have been trapped inland where they formed land-locked seas. Salt deposits remain where the water of trapped seas evaporated.

Many changes in the earth's crust also resulted from the shrinking that took place as the earth slowly cooled since the time of its origin. This shrinking bent and twisted the crust in some areas.

5. DEPOSITS OF ERODED MATERIALS

When the agents of erosion drop the materials they have been carrying, the deposits form new physical features on the earth's surface. Thus, as some parts of the earth's crust are being worn away, other parts are being built up.

Agents responsible for wearing away the earth's crust in some places and building up elsewhere are *wind*, *glaciers*, *ground water*, and *running water*.

a. Deposits by Wind. Wind carries dust and sand. When the wind loses speed or strikes an obstacle in its path, the wind deposits the material it has been transporting. Eventually, a mound of sand, called a *sand dune*, is built up. Sand dunes are common along the sea coasts and the shores of large lakes, as well as inland. Sand dunes cause great damage when they bury buildings and even entire forests. In the Middle West of the United States is a region that has been called the "dust bowl." It was characterized by severe dust storms. In the past, millions of acres of valuable farmland and tens of thousands of homes were destroyed by deposits of dust and sand several feet deep.

Very fine dust, called *silt*, has been carried by the wind and then deposited as thick layers of soil, called *loess*. Topsoil composed of loess is usually very fertile.

b. Deposits by Glaciers. Glaciers carry rocks, sand, and clay. Glaciers travel very long distances and carry with them a vast amount of loose rocky materials. When a glacier reaches a region of higher temperature, the glacier melts and deposits its load over a wide area. Glaciers cause damage in some regions by depositing rocks and boulders over fertile soil. In other regions, glacial deposits form flat stretches of fertile lands, called *glacial plains*.

Many thousands of years ago, a glacier moved from Canada into the United States, as far as the southern part of New York State. When the glacier melted, it left behind much fertile soil. It also formed the sandy southern shore of Long Island in New York State.

c. Deposits by Ground Water. Water absorbed by the soil is called *ground water*. In some areas where ground water containing dissolved carbon dioxide flows over limestone, the limestone dissolves and is carried away by the water. In this way, the action of ground water forms caves (Fig. 42-4a).

Water containing dissolved limestone may drip from the ceiling of caves and form icicle-like projections of solid limestone, called *stalactites*. Similar projections, called *stalagmites*, form on the floor of caves (Fig. 42-4b).

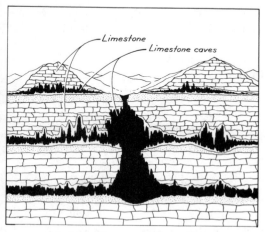

(a) Limestone cave formation   **(b) Stalactites and stalagmites**

Fig. 42-4. Action of ground water on limestone. (*a*) Limestone under the earth's surface is dissolved and carried away by water containing acid. This action produces underground tunnels, called caves.

    (*b*) Dripping water containing dissolved limestone produces stalactites and stalagmites.

d. Deposits by Running Water. Running water carries clay, sand, pebbles, and rocks. Whenever the speed of running water is slowed, the water deposits its sediment. The largest particles settle to the bottom first, and the finest particles last, thus producing layers of sediment (Fig. 42-5 on next page).

Some features formed by river deposits are *deltas, alluvial fans, flood plains,* and *levees.*

(1) Deltas. Where a river empties into a quiet body of water, the river deposits its sediment, forming a *delta*. A delta may continue to build up into a large tract of land that extends outward into the body of water. Since deltas are composed of very fertile material, the mouth of some important rivers, such as the Nile and the Mississippi, provide good soil for agriculture.

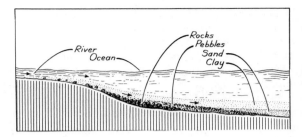

Fig. 42-5. Running water assorts its deposits. As running water slows down, it deposits its materials in a definite order: first rocks, then pebbles and sand, and finally the fine particles of clay.

(2) *Alluvial Fans.* Where a river flows from a hilly region onto a level region, the river slows down and deposits its sediment in the shape of a fan, called an *alluvial fan.*

(3) *Flood Plains.* Heavy rains or the melting of snow and ice result in an increased amount of water carried by a river. This may cause the river to flood, or overflow its banks. Here the speed of the river is reduced, and fine, fertile material is deposited over large areas on both sides of the river. These flat, level stretches of land are called *flood plains.* Because of their fertility, flood plains, such as along the Nile and the Mississippi, are rich agricultural regions.

(4) *Levees.* When sediment drops along river banks without reaching the flood plains, the sediment raises the banks, forming *levees.*

Multiple-Choice Questions

Write the number preceding the correct answer.

1. The breaking down of the rocks of the earth's surface is known as (1) stratification (2) weathering (3) evaporation (4) decay.

2. The breaking of a rock in which there is a change in the composition of the rock is called (1) mechanical weathering (2) erosion (3) chemical weathering (4) condensation.

3. Limestone caves have been produced by (1) cave men (2) earthquakes (3) solution by underground water containing carbon dioxide (4) volcanoes.

4. The process by which rocks are broken and the fragments removed is called (1) erosion (2) deposition (3) mechanical weathering (4) stratification.

5. The main cause of erosion in desert regions is (1) heat (2) plants (3) water (4) wind.

6. The Great Lakes, the Finger Lakes, and the rounded hills of New England are the result of (1) the elevation of the earth's surface (2) erosion by running water (3) glacial action (4) volcanic action.

7. U-shaped river valleys result from the action of (1) plants (2) temperature changes (3) glacial erosion (4) ground water.

8. The most important single agent that wears away rock and changes the earth's surface is (1) glacial action (2) wind (3) running water (4) frost action.

9. The most common agent of erosion is (1) earthquakes (2) glaciers (3) tornadoes (4) running water.

10. Movements of the earth's crust may produce (1) rain (2) earthquakes (3) winds (4) weathering.

11. The presence of great salt deposits far inland indicates (1) weathering has taken place (2) the evaporation of the water of a trapped sea (3) thunderstorms occurred (4) the presence of plants and animals.

12. In a field, we find rocks that differ greatly from the rocks common to the area. These different rocks were probably carried there by (1) animals (2) floods (3) glaciers (4) the earth's rotation.

13. Deposits of limestone hanging from the ceiling of a cave are called (1) stalactites (2) stalagmites (3) icicles (4) dunes.

14. Running water will deposit sediment when (1) it flows downhill (2) there is a rainstorm (3) it loses velocity (4) it contains carbon dioxide.

15. A deposit of land in the ocean at the mouth of a river is (1) a delta (2) a dune (3) an island (4) a sand bar.

Modified True-False Questions

If a statement is true, write the word true. *If a statement is false, write the word or expression that must be substituted for the italicized expression to make the statement true.*

1. By the action of the agents of the atmosphere, the surface of the earth *remains the same.*

2. *Chemical* weathering is the breaking of rocks without changing their composition.

3. The splitting of rocks by freezing water is an example of weathering known as *frost action.*

4. Sandstone is most readily weathered by the freezing action of water because it is a very *rough* rock.

5. The rock affected chiefly by water containing dissolved carbon dioxide is *shale.*

6. *Rivers* are the agents of erosion capable of smoothing down or wearing away mountains.

7. As you dig deeper into the earth's crust, the temperature *increases.*

8. When its velocity *increases*, the wind deposits the materials it is carrying.

9. Mounds built up by winds are called *deltas*.
10. The southern shore of Long Island resulted from deposits built up by *winds*.
11. The water that seeps into the earth is called *running water*.
12. *Stalagmites* are projections built up on the floor of a cave by dripping ground water containing dissolved limestone.
13. Deposits formed by running water consist of layers with the *finest* particles on bottom.
14. The fertile deposit of land at the mouth of the Nile River is an example of a *sand dune*.
15. A river in flood stage may build level stretches of land, called *flood plains*.

Completion Questions

Write the word or expression that correctly completes the statement.

1. Rocks that are regularly heated and then cooled tend to _____ .
2. In the presence of moisture and _____ , rocks containing iron will rust and crumble.
3. Lichens that grow on rocks produce _____ which dissolve some minerals present in the rocks.
4. The action of the Colorado River over a long period of time is responsible for the surface feature known as the _____ .
5. A large, movable section of the earth's crust is called a(n) _____ .
6. About 250 million years ago, the number of continents on the earth was _____ .
7. Where crustal plates scrape alongside one another, they form features called _____ .
8. Scientists believe that the cause of the slow movements of the continents is the presence of _____ that circulate in the earth's mantle.
9. Very fine dust carried by the wind and deposited as soil is called _____ .
10. Where a(n) _____ flows from a hilly region onto a plain, sediments are deposited on the plain in the shape of a fan.

Chapter 43. The Solar System

The space around us and all the matter in it—the heavenly bodies, such as stars and our solar system—make up the *universe*.

1. THE SOLAR SYSTEM

Our *solar system* consists of the sun and its family of heavenly objects that continuously travel around the sun. These objects, the sun's family, include the planets, satellites, planetoids, comets, and meteors.

2. THE CENTER OF THE SOLAR SYSTEM

LESSON 3# ANSWER

The *sun* is the center of our solar system. The sun is really a star. A *star* is a ball of hot gases undergoing nuclear reactions that cause the star to give off its own light. In addition to light, the sun gives off a tremendous quantity of heat. The temperature of the interior of the sun is estimated at about 25 million°F, while the temperature on the sun's surface is about 10,000°F. The light and heat are thought to result from nuclear fusion reactions (page 273, section 3) on the sun. The earth is about 93 million miles away from the sun.

3. THE SIZE AND BRIGHTNESS OF THE SUN

The sun, with a diameter of 864,000 miles, is more than 100 times the diameter of the earth. Although there are stars smaller than the sun, the sun is a small star compared to some other stars. For example, Sirius is about twice the diameter of the sun, while Antares is about 400 times the diameter of the sun. Although many stars are brighter than the sun, the sun is the one most conspicuous to us because it is the nearest star to our planet.

4. IMPORTANCE OF THE SUN

The heat and light produced by the sun are forms of energy that make possible the existence of life on our planet. The sun's energy is used by plants to manufacture food. Animals obtain this solar energy when they eat plants. We also obtain stored-up energy from the sun when we burn coal and oil. These fuels were formed from the remains of organisms that inhabited the earth millions of years ago.

5. SUNSPOTS

From time to time, dark spots appear on the surface of the sun. These spots, called *sunspots*, are not actually dark, but appear so by comparison with the brighter surface of the rest of the sun. A sunspot is believed to be an electrical storm that reaches from the surface of the sun to the interior. Sunspots appear in greatest numbers in cycles of approximately every eleven years. When present in large numbers, interference (static) is noticed in radio and other electrical communications.

6. PLANETS

Planets are solid objects shaped like spheres. Nine planets including the earth are known. Planets do not give off their own light. They shine only because they reflect the light they receive from the sun. The planets revolve around the sun in a path shaped like a circle. This path is called the *orbit* of the planet (Fig. 43-1).

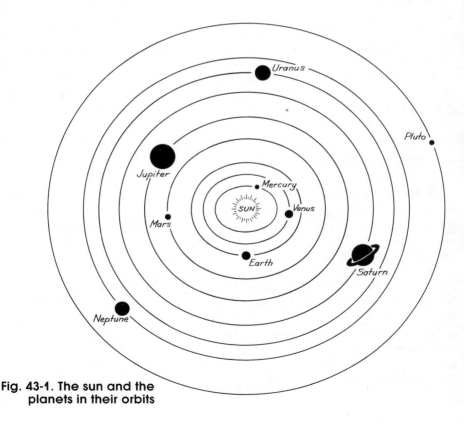

Fig. 43-1. The sun and the planets in their orbits

Planetary orbits never cross one another. The farther a planet is from the sun, the larger is its orbit and the longer it takes the planet to travel around the sun. Planets also spin on their axes.

7. THE EARTH

The *earth* is the planet on which we live. It is just one of the nine planets traveling around the sun. The orbit of the earth lies between the orbits of Venus and Mars. The diameter of the earth is about 7,900 miles. The circumference of the earth is approximately 25,000 miles. The diameter from the North Pole to the South Pole is called the *axis*.

8. MOTIONS OF THE EARTH

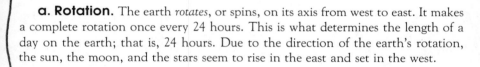

a. Rotation. The earth *rotates*, or spins, on its axis from west to east. It makes a complete rotation once every 24 hours. This is what determines the length of a day on the earth; that is, 24 hours. Due to the direction of the earth's rotation, the sun, the moon, and the stars seem to rise in the east and set in the west.

b. Revolution. At the same time that it rotates on its axis, the earth *revolves*, or travels around the sun in its orbit once every 365¼ days. This is what determines the length of a year on the earth; that is, 365¼ days. The earth revolves in the same direction that it rotates: from west to east.

9. OTHER PLANETS

a. Mercury. Mercury, the smallest planet, is the planet nearest to the sun. The part of Mercury exposed to the sun is extremely hot. Mercury makes one rotation in 59 days and makes one revolution in 88 days. There is probably no life on this planet because it is so hot.

b. Venus. Venus is called the "twin" planet of the earth because its size is almost the same as that of the earth. Venus is the planet closest to the earth. Because it is the brightest of all planets, Venus is often seen shining brightly in the sky as a morning or evening "star."

Information received from unmanned space vehicles that landed on Venus indicates that its atmosphere consists almost entirely of carbon dioxide and that its surface temperature is around 800°F. Accordingly, scientists do not believe that life as we know it exists there.

c. Mars. Observations through telescopes have revealed many things about Mars. It is about half the size of the earth. Its color is usually red, but the color changes when strong windstorms blow dust from one region to another. Polar ice caps are present as are light and dark markings that change with the seasons.

Photographs and other information radioed back to earth from unmanned space vehicles reveal other details. The surface of Mars has craters similar to those on the moon. The atmosphere on Mars consists of about 96% carbon dioxide, 2.5% nitrogen, and only traces of oxygen and other gases. The amount of water vapor in the Martian atmosphere varies with the season. So far, there is no evidence of life on Mars.

d. Jupiter. Before 1973, our knowledge of Jupiter was based mainly on telescopic observations. Since then, explorations by unmanned spaceships that passed close to Jupiter have revealed much more about it. Thus, we now know that Jupiter's atmosphere is made up mainly of hydrogen, with some methane and ammonia also present. Photographs show a red spot—about the size of our Pacific Ocean—present in the atmosphere at all times. There is no sign of life on Jupiter.

e. Saturn. Spaceships that went to Jupiter also passed Saturn, the second largest planet. Information relayed back to earth indicates that Saturn has as many as 17 moons and four main rings. The rings are believed to be millions of small particles revolving rapidly around Saturn.

f. Uranus, Neptune, Pluto. These are the other three planets of our solar system. Pluto, the outermost planet, is the most recently discovered (1930).

Planets in Order of Increasing Distance From the Sun

Planet	Approximate size (diameter) in miles	Approximate distance from sun in millions of miles	Revolves around the sun in	Number of satellites (moons)
Mercury	3,100	36	88 days	0
Venus	7,700	67	225 days	0
Earth	7,900	93	365¼ days	1
Mars	4,200	142	687 days	2
Jupiter	88,700	483	12 years	16 (?) moons 1 ring
Saturn	75,000	886	29½ years	21 (?) moons 4 rings
Uranus	32,000	1,783	84 years	5 moons 9 rings
Neptune	28,000	2,794	165 years	8 moons 4 rings
Pluto	1,420 (?)	3,670	248 years	1 (?)

THE SOLAR SYSTEM MADE EASY

Would you like an easy way of remembering the planets in their order from the sun? Just memorize the following sentence. The initial letter of each word stands for a planet.

The sentence: Mary's Violet eyes Make Jack Sit Up Nights Pining.

---

10. THE MOON

The earth's nearest neighbor, the *moon*, is the only natural satellite of the earth. A *satellite* is a heavenly body that revolves around a planet while the planet revolves around the sun. As the table (previous page) shows, some planets have more than one satellite.

The moon is about 2,100 miles in diameter, or a little over one-fourth that of the earth, and is about 240,000 miles from the earth. The rough surface of the moon is due to craters, mountains, and volcanoes. There is no atmosphere or water on the moon. A complete rotation of the moon takes the same time as a complete revolution: $27\frac{1}{3}$ days. As a result, the same side of the moon always faces us. The opposite side has been photographed from a spacecraft that traveled around the moon. The photographs show that this side of the moon has features similar to those we usually see.

Astronauts have walked on the moon, studied its surface, brought back samples of its soil and rocks, and have left instruments on it. As a result of this work, scientists believe that, although the surface of the moon is cold, the interior may be warm. Furthermore, the instruments on the moon reveal that moonquakes (similar to earthquakes) occur. There is no evidence of life on the moon.

11. PHASES OF THE MOON

The moon is visible to us only because the moon, like all the planets and all other satellites, reflects the light it receives from the sun. The sun lights up the half of the moon that faces it. As the moon revolves around the earth, different amounts of the lighted half of the moon are seen from the earth. The changes in appearance of the lighted area are called the *phases of the moon* (Fig. 43-2 on next page).

a. New Moon. At this phase, the moon and the earth are on the same side of the sun. Since the dark side of the moon faces the earth, we cannot see the moon at new moon. At this phase, the moon rises in the east in the daytime.

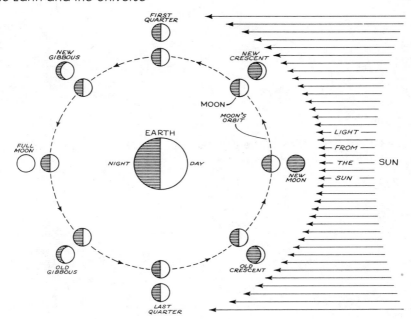

Fig. 43-2. The moon appears to change shape. For two weeks, from new-moon to full-moon phase, the amount of the lighted half of the moon seen from the earth increases. The amount visible goes from complete darkness to complete illumination. In the next two weeks, from full-moon to new-moon phase, the amount of lighted area seen decreases to complete darkness.

b. Full Moon. Two weeks after new moon, the moon and the sun are on opposite sides of the earth. At this time, the fully lighted half of the moon faces the earth and we see the moon as a large circular disc. At this phase, the moon rises in the east during the evening.

12. ECLIPSES

An *eclipse* is the blotting out of the light of one heavenly body by the presence of another heavenly body. As the moon revolves around the earth, the moon may cause an eclipse of the sun by preventing the light of the sun from reaching the earth. This is called a *solar eclipse* (Fig. 43-3 on next page). At other times, light from the sun is blocked by the earth. Then, the moon may be eclipsed when it passes into the earth's shadow. This is a *lunar eclipse* (Fig. 43-4 on next page). A solar eclipse can occur only during the new-moon phase, while the lunar eclipse can take place only during the full-moon phase.

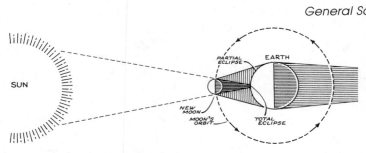

Fig. 43-3. How a solar eclipse occurs. An eclipse of the sun takes place when the sun is hidden by the moon. The new moon then casts its shadow on the earth.

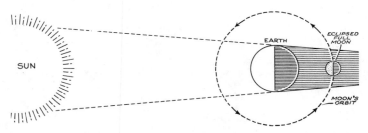

Fig. 43-4. How a lunar eclipse occurs. An eclipse of the moon takes place when the full moon passes into the earth's shadow.

13. TIDES

The daily regular rise and fall of the water in the ocean is called the *tide*. The rising or incoming tide is called a *high tide*, or *flood tide*. The falling or outgoing tide is called a *low tide*, or *ebb tide*. There are two high tides and two low tides every day. Tides are caused mainly by the pull of gravity exerted upon the earth by both the moon and the sun.

14. HIGH AND LOW TIDES

As the moon exerts its pull on the earth, the water on the side of the earth facing the moon rises. That is, the water is pulled toward the moon. This results in a high tide in the ocean water in that region. Another high tide occurs at the same time on the opposite side of the earth, and low tides occur between these two regions. With each approximate quarter rotation of the earth, the high tides change to low tides and the low tides become high tides. Consequently, approximately every 6 hours the tide changes from high to low and then from low to high.

15. SPRING AND NEAP TIDES

The sun also exerts a pull on the earth's water, but to a much lesser degree than the moon does. This is because the sun is so much farther from the earth than the moon is.

a. Spring Tides. When the sun, moon, and earth are in a straight line, the combined pull of the moon and the sun increases the range of the tides. These unusually high and low tides are called *spring tides* (Fig. 43-5). They occur twice each month, at the new-moon and full-moon phases.

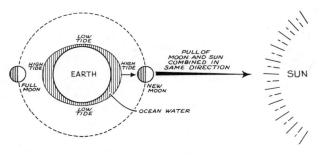

Fig. 43-5. Spring tides

b. Neap Tides. Twice each month, at the first-quarter and last-quarter phases of the moon, the moon and the sun are at right angles to the earth. In these phases, the sun's pull on the earth weakens the moon's pull and decreases the tidal range. The less pronounced low and high tides are known as *neap tides* (Fig. 43-6).

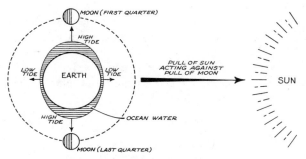

Fig. 43-6. Neap tides

PLANETOIDS, COMETS, AND METEORS

16. PLANETOIDS

Located between the orbits of Mars and Jupiter are more than a thousand small heavenly bodies each called _planetoids_ or _asteroids_. The planetoids range in size from less than 1 mile in diameter to about 500 miles in diameter. Like planets, planetoids revolve around the sun in their own orbits and reflect sunlight.

Some scientists believe that the planetoids are the pieces of a large planet that once revolved between Mars and Jupiter. As the planet came close to Jupiter, the planet was probably pulled apart by Jupiter's gravitational attraction.

17. COMETS

Comets are members of the solar system. They have very large, flat elliptical orbits. A comet looks like a streak of light. A comet consists of a head and a tail, each hundreds of thousands of miles long. The head of a comet is made up of solid matter composed of frozen water, methane, and other substances. The tail is composed of streams of glowing gases. The comet is visible because of the light reflected and given off by these gases. Each comet travels around the sun in its own orbit. The tail of the comet is formed as the comet nears the sun. The tail always points away from the sun. The most famous comet is _Halley's comet_, which reappears regularly about every 76 years. It was last observed in 1986.

In 1973, Dr. Lubos Kohoutek, a Czechoslovakian astronomer, discovered a new comet which has been named after him. This comet is expected to return in about 80,000 years.

18. METEORS

Meteors, because of their appearance, are frequently called "shooting stars." Actually, meteors are small bits of iron, nickel, or stone traveling through space at high speeds. When they come close enough to the earth, the earth's gravity pulls them toward the earth. As they enter the earth's atmosphere, friction between the air and the rapidly moving meteor causes the meteor to burst into flame. Although many small meteors are burned up in the upper atmosphere, some do reach the earth. Meteors that reach the earth are called _meteorites_.

Multiple-Choice Questions

Write the number preceding the correct answer.

1. All bodies that make up our solar system revolve around the (1) earth (2) moon (3) North Star (4) sun.
2. The sun is a (1) star (2) planet (3) satellite (4) galaxy.
3. The distance in miles from the earth to the sun is about (1) 7,900 (2) 25,000 (3) 240,000 (4) 93,000,000.
4. Dark areas on the sun caused by electrical storms are called (1) satellites (2) meteors (3) sunspots (4) planetoids.
5. The path of the earth around the sun is (1) a flat ellipse (2) almost circular (3) square (4) triangular.
6. The planet whose orbit lies between the orbits of Venus and Mars is (1) the moon (2) the earth (3) Mercury (4) Jupiter.
7. As the earth rotates, a place located on the equator travels about 25,000 miles in one (1) hour (2) day (3) month (4) year.
8. The earth is a heavenly body that (1) is stationary at the center of the solar system (2) moves around all other planets (3) moves around the moon (4) moves around the sun.
9. The time it takes the earth to make a complete revolution around the sun is (1) a day (2) a week (3) a month (4) a year.
10. The planet closest to the sun is (1) Pluto (2) Saturn (3) Mercury (4) Jupiter.
11. A planet often visible in our early evening sky is (1) the moon (2) Orion (3) Polaris (4) Venus.
12. The largest planet is (1) Pluto (2) Mercury (3) Neptune (4) Jupiter.
13. The planet characterized by rings is (1) Uranus (2) the earth (3) Pluto (4) Saturn.
14. The distance in miles from the earth to the moon is about (1) 2,000 (2) 240,000 (3) 2,000,000 (4) 93,000,000.
15. The moon revolves around the earth about once each (1) month (2) day (3) week (4) year.
16. Moonlight is caused by (1) burning gases on the moon (2) nuclear energy produced on the moon (3) reflected sunlight (4) the moon's hot surface.
17. The moon rises in the (1) west (2) east (3) north (4) south.
18. We cannot see the new moon because (1) it occurs at night (2) it occurs below the horizon (3) the earth's shadow hides it (4) the lighted side of the moon is away from the earth.
19. When the moon is full, the side that we see is (1) eclipsed by the sun (2) entirely lighted by the sun (3) in the earth's shadow (4) partially lighted by the sun.
20. The full moon rises at (1) noon (2) evening (3) midnight (4) early morning.
21. During the first quarter of the moon, the side of the moon that we see is (1) unlighted by the sun (2) entirely lighted by the sun (3) partially lighted by the sun (4) eclipsed by the sun.

22. The time between one full moon and the next full moon is about (1) 10 days (2) 14 days (3) 17 days (4) 27 days.
23. The heavenly body that causes an eclipse of the sun is a (1) meteor (2) moon (3) planet (4) star.
24. An eclipse of the moon will occur during the phase called the (1) first quarter (2) last quarter (3) full moon (4) new moon.
25. A spring tide occurs at the phase of the moon called (1) first quarter (2) last quarter (3) new moon (4) new crescent.

Completion Questions

Write the word or expression that correctly completes the statement.

1. Compared to the size of other stars, our sun is a _____ (*small, large*) star.
2. The path in which a planet travels around the sun is called its _____.
3. The direction the earth revolves around the sun is from _____ to _____.
4. The planet most distant from the sun is _____.
5. The many heavenly bodies located between the orbits of Mars and Jupiter are called _____.
6. The only members of the solar system that have a head and a tail are the _____.
7. A recently discovered member of the solar system with a head and a tail is _____.
8. _____ are heavenly bodies commonly called "shooting stars."

Matching Questions

Match the items in column A with those in column B.

Column A	Column B
1. source of energy for all living things	*a.* earth
2. electrical storms	*b.* sunspots
3. most recently discovered planet	*c.* Mars
4. about half the earth's size	*d.* Jupiter
5. smallest planet	*e.* new moon
6. most satellites	*f.* Pluto
7. solar eclipse	*g.* Venus
8. planet closest to earth	*h.* full moon
9. 25,000 miles in circumference	*i.* sun
10. lunar eclipse	*j.* Mercury

Chapter 44. Movements of the Earth Affect Us

1. MOTIONS OF THE EARTH

In Chapter 43, we noted that the earth undergoes two separate motions at the same time. First, the earth rotates on its axis from west to east, taking 24 hours to make a complete rotation. Second, the earth revolves around the sun in its orbit, taking 365¼ days to make one complete revolution. Rotation of the earth causes day and night, and revolution is one of the causes of seasons.

2. ROTATION CAUSES DAY AND NIGHT

As the earth rotates on its axis, only one-half of the earth faces the sun at any given time. That part of the earth facing the sun has *day*, while the opposite side of the earth has *night* (Fig. 44-1). During one rotation of the earth, most places on the earth have a period of day and a period of night. However, not all places on the earth have equal lengths of day and night every day of the year.

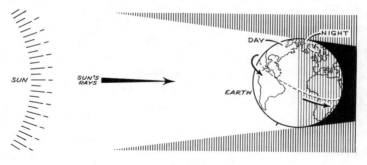

Fig. 44-1. Day and night on the earth

3. INCLINATION OF THE EARTH'S AXIS CAUSES UNEQUAL DAY AND NIGHT

If the earth were to rotate on an axis that was straight upright, or vertical, every place on the earth would receive 12 hours of daylight and 12 hours of darkness every day of the year. However, since the axis of the earth is *inclined* (tilted) at an angle of 23½°, the Northern and Southern hemispheres have unequal lengths of day and night (Fig. 44-2 on next page).

433

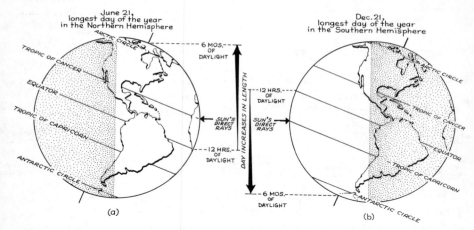

Fig. 44-2. Days and nights differ in length. (*a*) The Northern Hemisphere
is tilted toward the sun. As a result, the days are longer than the nights in the
Northern Hemisphere.

    (*b*) The Southern Hemisphere is tilted toward the sun. As a result, the days are
longer than the nights in the Southern Hemisphere.

On the average, on March 21 and September 23, neither hemisphere is tilted
toward the sun. Both hemispheres face the sun for 12 hours and turn away from
the sun for the other 12 hours. As a result, day and night are equal in length in
all places on the earth on these dates. The dates, when day and night are equal,
are called the *equinoxes*. The March date is known as the *spring equinox*, while the
September date is the *autumnal equinox*.

4. WHAT ARE SEASONS?

Seasons are periods of the year marked by differences in temperature and lengths
of day and night. Seasonal changes from summer to autumn and then to winter
in a given area are due to the changes in the amount of heat received from the
sun. The more daylight the area receives, the warmer it becomes. As the summer
season progresses toward the winter, and day length decreases, the rays of the sun
change from direct rays to slanting rays. And, as the winter progresses toward the
summer, and day length increases, the sun's rays become more direct (Table 44-1).

Distance from the sun is *not* a factor in causing seasons. Many people *mistakenly*
believe that the earth is nearest the sun in the summer and farthest away from the
sun in the winter. Actually, the earth is three million miles closer to the sun on
January 1 than it is on July 1.

Table 44-1. Seasonal Changes

Northern Hemisphere	Southern Hemisphere
On June 21:	
Tilted toward the sun. Direct rays are at Tropic of Cancer. Summer season: longer days, higher temperature.	Tilted away from the sun. Receiving slanting rays at Tropic of Capricorn. Winter season: shorter days, lower temperature.
On September 23 (Autumnal Equinox):	
Direct rays are at the equator.	
Autumn begins.	Spring begins.
Equal day and night.	
On December 21:	
Tilted away from the sun. Receiving slanting rays at Tropic of Cancer. Winter season: shorter days, lower temperature.	Tilted toward the sun. Direct rays are at Tropic of Capricorn. Summer season: longer days, higher temperature.
On March 21 (Spring Equinox):	
Direct rays are at the equator.	
Spring begins.	Autumn begins.
Equal day and night.	

5. REVOLUTION AND INCLINATION CAUSE SEASONS

Seasonal changes result from (*a*) the revolution of the earth, and (*b*) the tilt (inclination) of the earth's axis at an angle of 23½° (Figs. 44-3 and 4 on next page). As the earth revolves, the direct rays of the sun move from the Northern Hemisphere to the Southern Hemisphere.

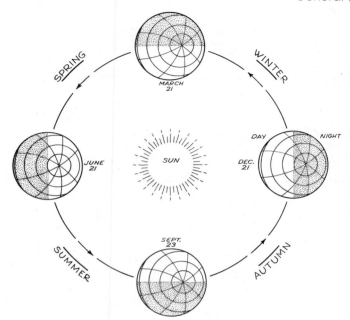

Fig. 44-3. Revolution is one cause of seasons. Note the locations of day and night in the Arctic region as seasons change.

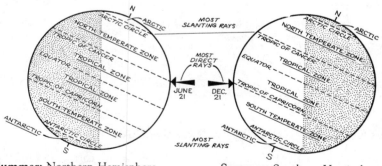

Summer: Northern Hemisphere
Winter: Southern Hemisphere

Summer: Southern Hemisphere
Winter: Northern Hemisphere

Fig. 44-4. Seasons on the earth. The shifting of the direct rays of the sun from one hemisphere to the other causes seasons. On June 21, the direct rays are at the Tropic of Cancer and summer begins in the Northern Hemisphere. Then the slanting rays are at the Tropic of Capricorn and winter begins in the Southern Hemisphere. On December 21, the direct rays are at the Tropic of Capricorn and summer begins in the Southern Hemisphere, while winter begins in the Northern.

6. SHADOWS

Light travels in a straight line. When an object that does not permit light to pass through it is placed in the path of the sun's rays, a *shadow* is cast. The length of a shadow depends on the direction of the sun's rays: the more the rays slant, the longer the shadow. The extent to which the sun's rays are slanting depends on: (*a*) the time of the year, and (*b*) the time of the day.

7. NOON SHADOWS

In the northern region of the United States, the length of the shadow at noon on December 21 is greater than the length of the shadow at noon June 21.

Since the rays of the sun in all seasons are most direct at noon, early morning and late afternoon shadows are longer than noon shadows. Also, since the sun is more nearly directly overhead at noon, the shorter noon shadows point to the north.

Table 44-2. Seasonal Shadow Length

From December 21 to June 21:	From June 21 to December 21:
In the Northern Hemisphere, the sun rises in the southeast and sets a little farther to the northwest each day until the sun reaches its northernmost point, and is highest in the sky on June 21.	In the Northern Hemisphere, the sun rises in the northeast and sets a little farther to the southwest each day until the sun reaches its southernmost point, and is lowest in the sky on December 21.
As the sun's path becomes higher in the sky, the sun's rays become less slanting and the shadows cast become shorter (Fig. 44-5, left).	As the sun's path becomes lower in the sky, the sun's rays become more slanting and the shadows cast become longer (Fig. 44-5, right).

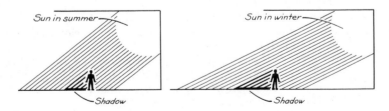

Fig. 44-5. Shadows change in length. When the sun is higher in the sky in the summer, the shadow is shorter. In the winter, when the sun is lower in the sky, the shadow is longer.

Multiple-Choice Questions

Write the number preceding the correct answer.

1. Day and night occur on earth because the (1) earth revolves around the sun (2) earth rotates on its axis (3) sun gives off light only part of the time (4) sun revolves around the earth.
2. The equinoxes occur on (1) June 21 and March 21 (2) September 23 and December 21 (3) June 21 and September 23 (4) March 21 and September 23.
3. Summer days are longer than winter days in the Northern Hemisphere because (1) the axis of the earth is inclined toward the sun in summer (2) the earth turns more slowly in summer (3) the sun is closer in summer (4) the sun is hotter in summer.
4. The inclination of the earth's axis is one of the causes of (1) night and day (2) seasonal changes (3) tides (4) hurricanes.
5. In the Northern Hemisphere, summers are warmer than winters because (1) in the summer, the Northern Hemisphere receives more direct rays of the sun (2) the air is a better insulator in summer (3) the earth spins on its axis (4) the sun is closer to the earth in summer.
6. On June 21, the sun's direct rays heat the earth most at the (1) equator (2) International Date Line (3) Tropic of Cancer (4) Tropic of Capricorn.
7. At the time the United States is having spring, Brazil in the Southern Hemisphere is having (1) spring (2) summer (3) fall (4) winter.
8. During June in the United States, the sun rises in the (1) south (2) southeast (3) east (4) northeast.
9. In the Northern Hemisphere, the sun can be seen for the longest time during any one day about (1) March 21 (2) June 21 (3) September 23 (4) December 21.
10. On September 23, the sun at noon is almost directly over the (1) equator (2) Tropic of Cancer (3) Arctic Circle (4) Tropic of Capricorn.
11. One reason for the formation of shadows is that (1) certain objects interfere with the passage of light rays (2) some objects reflect light (3) light travels very fast (4) some bodies are transparent.
12. In March, a boy in the United States sees the sun rise in the eastern sky. From the same location in December he will see the sun rise in the eastern sky farther to the (1) north (2) south (3) east (4) west.
13. On the shortest day of the year, the noonday shadow of a tree is (1) at its greatest length (2) at its shortest length (3) halfway between its greatest and shortest lengths (4) the same length as at any other noon.
14. At noon in the U.S., all shadows point (1) east (2) north (3) south (4) west.
15. Shadows are shortest at (1) 9 A.M. (2) noon (3) 3 P.M. (4) 6 P.M.
16. On June 21 at 12:00 noon, a boy observes that a flagpole outside his home casts no shadow. His home must be near the latitude line known as the (1) Arctic Circle (2) equator (3) Tropic of Cancer (4) Tropic of Capricorn.

Completion Questions

Write the word or expression that correctly completes the statement.

1. In addition to rotating on its axis, the earth is also _____ .
2. The time required for a complete rotation of the earth is _____ .
3. The earth's axis is tilted at an angle of _____ degrees.
4. During the winter, the _____ Hemisphere is tilted toward the sun.
5. A place on the earth is having its summer season when it is receiving the _____ rays of the sun.
6. One cause of seasonal changes is the inclination of the earth on its axis. Another cause is _____ .
7. On December 21, the direct rays of the sun are at the _____ .
8. In the Northern Hemisphere, as the earth moves from its December position to its June position, the height of the sun above the southern horizon _____ .
9. Shadows are longer when the sun's rays are more _____ .
10. Shadows are _____ (*shorter, longer*) in the late afternoon than at noon.

Modified True-False Questions

If a statement is true, write the word true. *If a statement is false, write the word or expression that must be substituted for the italicized expression to make the statement true.*

1. It takes the earth 365¼ days to make one complete *rotation* around the sun.
2. *Revolution* of the earth is one of the causes of seasons.
3. The *longest* day of the year in the Southern Hemisphere is December 21.
4. Day and night are equal in length in all places on the earth on dates called *equinoxes.*
5. In the summer, the earth is *closest* to the sun.
6. *Opaque* objects cast shadows.
7. When the sun is lower in the sky, shadows are *shorter.*

Thought Questions

1. Why are temperatures in a given area higher in summer than they are in winter?
2. On June 21, why does the Arctic region have daylight for 24 hours?

Chapter 45. Locating Places and Measuring Time

1. LOCATING PLACES ON THE EARTH

To locate places on the earth, we use *latitude* and *longitude*.

2. LATITUDE

Latitude refers to the distance north or south of the *equator*. The equator is an imaginary line, a *circle*, drawn around the center of the earth halfway between the North and South poles. As you know, any circle consists of 360 equal parts, called *degrees*. Thus, a degree is 1/360 of a circle. Each degree is further divided into 60 equal, smaller parts, called *minutes*.

Latitude is expressed in degrees and minutes. One degree of latitude is equal to about 70 miles. Since the equator is used as the reference line, its latitude is zero degrees (0°). Places located north of the equator have north latitude; places south of the equator have south latitude (Fig. 45-1).

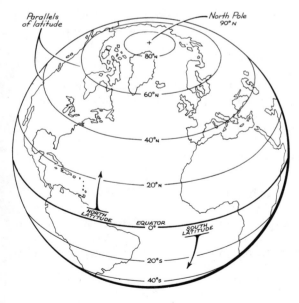

Fig. 45-1. Parallels of latitude. Distance north and south of the equator is measured on imaginary lines, the parallels, that encircle the earth from east to west.

Latitude is measured on imaginary circles, called *parallels of latitude*. They are drawn around the earth parallel to the equator. The greatest latitude a place can have is 90°. The latitude of the North Pole is 90° north, while the latitude of the South Pole is 90° south.

To find the latitude of a given place, an instrument, the *sextant*, is used. The sextant consists of a telescope, mirrors, and a scale marked in degrees. When using the sextant on a starlit night in the Northern Hemisphere, an observer first sights the North Star through the telescope. Then, with the aid of the mirrors, the observer aligns the image with the horizon and reads the scale. The result gives the latitude in degrees.

When using the sextant during the day, the observer uses the same procedure as at night but sights the sun at noon, when it is highest in the sky.

3. LOCATION OF THE PRIME MERIDIAN

Merely knowing the latitude of a place does not accurately fix its location on the earth. Latitude tells us only how many degrees the place is north or south of the equator. The other distance that must be known is how many degrees the place is east or west of another reference line. That line is the *prime meridian*, an imaginary line, a circle, running from the North Pole to the South Pole through Greenwich, England. The prime meridian, the reference line, has a longitude of 0°.

Fig. 45-2. Meridians of longitude. Distance east and west of the prime meridian is measured on imaginary circles called meridians.

4. LONGITUDE

The distance in degrees and minutes east or west of the prime meridian is called *longitude*. All places east of the prime meridian have east longitude; all places west of the prime meridian have west longitude. Longitude is measured on imaginary circles, called *meridians of longitude*. They are drawn from the North Pole to the South Pole. The maximum longitude a place may have is 180° east or west (Fig. 45-2 on previous page).

An observer finds the longitude of a place by first reading the time on a very accurate clock called a *chronometer*. The chronometer is permanently set at *Greenwich time*, the time at Greenwich, the city through which the prime meridian (0° longitude) passes. (Note: Greenwich time is also called *Universal time*.) Then, the observer determines the time, called *local time*, at the place in question. Local time is found from the position of the sun at that moment.

Recall that one hour of time equals 15° of longitude. With this in mind, by finding the number of hours that local time differs from Greenwich time, the number of degrees of longitude the place is away from Greenwich is readily found.

The position of a place is stated as its latitude and longitude (Fig. 45-3).

Fig. 45-3. Locating a place on the earth. The intersection of the given parallel of latitude and meridian of longitude locates the given position. To find the location of the place marked by an X on the map, we find that its latitude is 40°N and its longitude is 75°W, or simply 40° N 75°W.

5. DETERMINING TIME

A *year*, 365¼ days, is the length of time it takes the earth to revolve around the sun. A *day*, 24 hours, is the length of time it takes the earth to make a complete rotation on its axis.

In making one complete rotation, the earth passes through 360° of longitude in 24 hours, or through 15° of longitude every hour. Since the earth turns from west to east, places in the east see the sun before places in the west. For example, New York City is 15° east of Chicago. The sun, therefore, rises one hour earlier in New York City than it does in Chicago. New York City, at longitude 75° west, sees the sun rise five hours later than does London, England, at 0° longitude. When it is noon in London, it is 7:00 a.m. in New York City (Fig. 45-4).

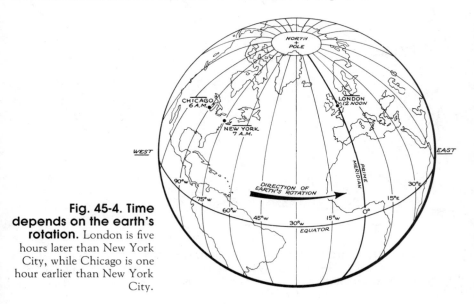

Fig. 45-4. Time depends on the earth's rotation. London is five hours later than New York City, while Chicago is one hour earlier than New York City.

6. STANDARD TIME

The earth is divided into 24 *standard time belts*, or *zones*, each 15° of longitude wide. The *time meridian* (meridian of longitude) for a belt is at about the center of the belt. There is one hour difference between each time belt. The standard time in the belt just east of us is one hour later than ours. The standard time in the belt just west of us is one hour earlier than ours.

Although all places east and west of each other within a particular time belt have slightly varying time according to the sun, they have exactly the same standard time. This uniformity of time permits the people in each belt to carry out train schedules, appointments, school hours, etc., with no confusion.

7. STANDARD TIME BELTS IN THE UNITED STATES

The United States (excluding Alaska and Hawaii) is divided into four standard time belts (Fig. 45-5). Alaska and Hawaii are in time belts that lie beyond the westernmost edge of the Pacific Time belt.

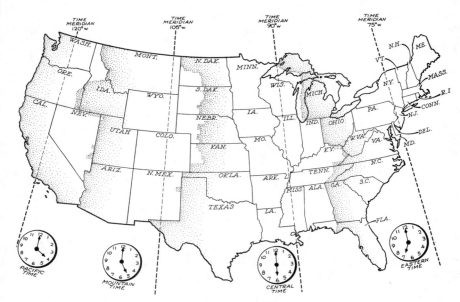

Fig. 45-5. Standard time belts of the United States. The time in each of the four time belts is determined by the meridian in approximately the center of the belt. Note that the boundaries of these belts, indicated by shaded areas, are not regular. A regular boundary might divide a city, causing that city to have two different standard times.

8. DAYLIGHT SAVING TIME

To provide an extra hour of daylight each day during the spring and summer months, many places in the United States move their clocks to *daylight saving time*, which is one hour ahead of standard time. Under daylight saving time, we gain one hour of daylight as we start our day one hour earlier. In the fall, clocks are turned back to standard time.

9. INTERNATIONAL DATE LINE

One hour is gained for every 15° longitude traveled westward; that is, the time is one hour earlier. On the other hand, one hour is lost for every 15° longitude traveled eastward; that is, the time is one hour later. Thus, in a complete trip around the earth, 24 hours would be either lost or gained, according to the direction traveled. This would cause the calendar date to be one day ahead or one day behind the date of the starting point. In order to maintain uniformity of calendar dates, a correction is made at the *international date line*, an imaginary line that generally follows the 180° meridian (Fig. 45-6).

Fig. 45-6. Calendar days change at the international date line.
Crossing the international date line westward adds one day; for example, Tuesday becomes Wednesday. Crossing this line eastward loses one day; for example, Wednesday becomes Tuesday.

Multiple-Choice Questions

Write the number preceding the correct answer.

1. The distance of a place north or south of the equator is called its (1) position (2) longitude (3) latitude (4) meridian.
2. A degree of latitude equals approximately (1) 50 miles (2) 70 miles (3) 90 miles (4) 120 miles.
3. An observer may determine his latitude during the day by finding the elevation of (1) the North Star (2) a meridian (3) a parallel of latitude (4) the noon sun.
4. Longitude is measured from the (1) North Pole (2) South Pole (3) prime meridian (4) equator.
5. 0° longitude is the (1) center of the earth (2) equator (3) international date line (4) prime meridian.
6. An instrument used by an observer to determine longitude is the (1) calendar (2) chronometer (3) galvanometer (4) meter stick.
7. As the sun rises in New York City, it (1) has not yet risen in Chicago (2) has risen in Chicago (3) is rising in Chicago (4) is setting in Chicago.
8. When the sun is rising in Hollywood, California, it (1) has not yet risen in Albany, New York (2) has already risen in Albany (3) has set in Albany (4) is also rising in Albany.
9. At noon in London, it is (1) morning in New York (2) noon in New York (3) afternoon in New York (4) midnight in New York.
10. The number of standard time belts on the earth is (1) 4 (2) 12 (3) 24 (4) 48.
11. An airplane pilot flying from California to New York will (1) have a day the same length as one going in the opposite direction (2) have a longer day than a pilot going in the opposite direction (3) have a shorter day than one going in the opposite direction (4) see the sun rise twice in the same day.
12. To provide an extra hour of daylight during the summer months, some communities go on (1) Eastern Standard Time (2) Daylight Saving Time (3) solar time (4) international time.
13. The change from Eastern Standard Time to Daylight Saving Time is made at 2 A.M. on Sunday. This hour is chosen for the changeover because (1) the sun crosses the Greenwich meridian at this time (2) the sun crosses the international date line at this time (3) the stars are in the proper position at this time (4) this time causes the least inconvenience to most people.
14. For every 15° of longitude traveled westward (1) 1 hour is gained (2) 1 hour is lost (3) 2 hours are gained (4) 2 hours are lost.
15. The imaginary line where a correction in days is made to avoid confusion in calendar dates is the (1) equator (2) prime meridian (3) parallel of latitude (4) international date line.

Completion Questions

Write the word or expression that correctly completes the statement.

1. The equator is used as the reference line in determining _____.
2. Distances north or south of the equator are measured on imaginary circles called _____.
3. The latitude of the North Pole is _____.
4. An instrument used in determining latitude is a (an) _____.
5. Distance east or west of the prime meridian is known as _____.
6. East and west distances are measured on imaginary circles called _____.
7. The length of a (an) _____ is determined by the time it takes the earth to make a complete rotation.
8. The earth turns through _____ degrees every hour.
9. There is a difference of _____ hour(s) between each standard time belt.
10. When it is noon in London, the time in New York City is _____.

Matching Questions

Match the items in Column A with those in Column B.

Column A	Column B
1. fixed east-west line	*a.* noon in London
2. parallels	*b.* latitude
3. 4:00 A.M. in California	*c.* 8:00 A.M. in New York City
4. 6:00 A.M. in Arizona	*d.* international date line
5. meridians	*e.* one hour
6. 15° longitude	*f.* longitude
7. follows approximately 180° meridian	*g.* Utah
8. 90° south latitude	*h.* equator
9. central time	*i.* Kansas
10. mountain time	*j.* South Pole

Thought Questions

1. At night, in the Northern Hemisphere, how are the North Star and a sextant used to determine a ship's latitude?
2. A certain town is located at 20° S, 60° W.
   a. What do these numbers and letters mean?
   b. In which continent is the town located?

Chapter 46. Beyond The Solar System

1. STARS ARE OUTSIDE THE SOLAR SYSTEM

A *star* is a ball of gas that produces its own light and heat, probably by nuclear reactions. As we have learned, our sun is a star, and some stars are larger than ours. With the exception of the sun, the stars we see are not members of the solar system. Rather, they are members of star systems that are very distant from us.

Stars are present in all parts of the sky during the day, but we cannot see them because of the brightness of the sun. On a clear night, even without a telescope, we may see 2,000 stars. With the aid of a large telescope, however, we may observe millions of stars. *Astronomers* (scientists who study heavenly bodies) have photographed millions of very faint stars that can be seen only through very powerful telescopes.

Because stars are a great distance from the earth, they appear to be stationary. Actually, however, the stars are moving at high speeds through space.

2. THE CHANGING NIGHT SKY

As the earth rotates on its axis and revolves around the sun, the appearance of the night sky constantly changes. As the earth rotates from west to east, stars appear to be changing their positions in the sky. Stars seen overhead at midnight appear several hours later to set in the west. Other stars, not seen at midnight, appear to rise in the east. Although the night sky is constantly changing in appearance, the stars keep similar positions with relation to one another.

As the earth revolves eastward, the stars seem to move a little farther westward. Since different parts of the sky face the earth at different seasons, different groups of stars are seen, as the star maps show. (See Figs. 46-1 and 46-2 on pages 450, 451.)

> ### STAR MAPS
>
> To use a star map for locating stars, face any compass direction—North, East, West, or South. Then, hold the map in front of you above your head. Point the compass direction on the map to the direction you are facing.

3. SIZES OF STARS

Because of its closeness to the earth, the sun appears to be very large. Although the sun has a diameter of 864,000 miles, it is only an average star. For example, the star Antares has a diameter 400 times that of the sun, while the giant star Epsilon Aurigae is believed to have a diameter about 3,000 times that of the sun.

4. COLORS OF STARS

Except for the color of the sun, which is yellow, most other stars seen with the unaided eye seem to have the same color. However, when studied with telescopes and other instruments, stars are seen to be red, yellow, white, or blue. We can estimate the surface heat of a star by its color. A red star, such as Antares, indicates a low temperature, about 5,000°F. A yellow star, such as our sun, has a medium temperature of about 10,000°F. A white or blue-white star, such as Rigel, has a high temperature, 55,000°F.

5. DISTANCE OF STARS FROM THE EARTH

Because astronomers must deal with very great distances, they use the *light-year* to express distance. A light-year is the distance a ray of light travels in one year. Since light travels about 186,000 miles per second, in one year a ray of light will travel about 6 trillion (6,000,000,000,000) miles. On the basis of a light-year, our sun is a very small distance away from the earth, only 93 million miles—only about eight light-minutes away. In contrast, consider Proxima Centauri, the star outside the solar system which is nearest the earth. It is about 25 trillion miles, or 4.3 light-years, away from the earth. The brightest star in the sky, Sirius, is about 8 light-years away from the earth. Some stars are so far from the earth that the light they give off travels millions of years before reaching the earth.

Fig. 46-1. A summer sky

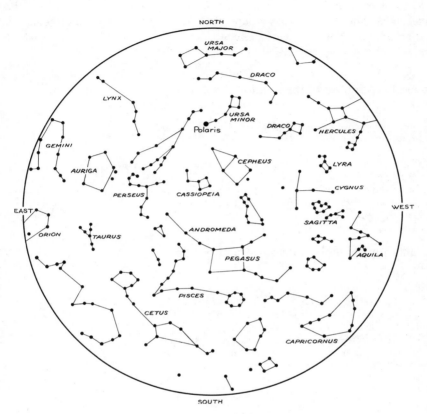

Fig. 46-2. A winter sky

6. STAR GROUPS AND CONSTELLATIONS

Most of the stars we see at night are arranged in patterns, or groups, called *constellations*. There are 88 such groups. Ancient peoples gave names to constellations according to their imagined resemblances to persons, gods, animals, or objects, as the following drawings show.

The Big Dipper (Part of Ursa Major, the Great Bear)

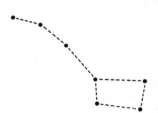

1. Composed of seven bright stars arranged in the shape of a dipper with a handle. The handle of the dipper is the tail of the Great Bear.
2. In early spring, the dipper is seen in the northeast sky standing on its handle; in early summer, in an inverted position above the pole of the sky; in the fall, in the western sky, with the bowl forward; in early winter, below the pole of the sky, with the bowl right side up.

The Little Dipper (Part of Ursa Minor, the Little Bear)

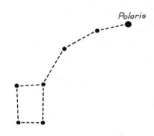

1. Composed of seven stars arranged in the shape of a small dipper. Six stars are faint; the seventh star, Polaris, is bright. Polaris is the last star in the handle of the Little Dipper.
2. Polaris seems to remain in the same location at all times. The other stars in the Little Dipper circle around Polaris.

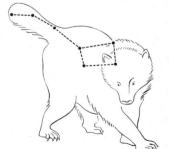

Ursa Major, the Great Bear

The constellation in which the Big Dipper is found.

Ursa Minor, the Little Bear

Contains the Little Dipper, in which is found the important star, Polaris.

Orion, the Hunter

1. Orion is seen in the eastern sky in the early evening when winter begins. It is the brightest of the constellations.
2. The constellation has an oblong shape with four bright stars situated in the corners of the figure. Three bright stars in almost a diagonal line in the center are the belt of the Hunter.

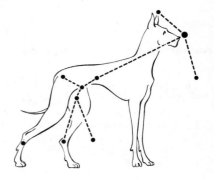

Canis Major, the Great Dog

1. Found in Canis Major is Sirius, the brightest star in the sky. Sirius is located in the nose of the Great Dog.
2. To locate Sirius, follow the three stars in Orion's belt southward.

Cassiopeia, the Lady in the Chair

1. The figure is made up of a group of stars forming an outline of a chair. Five stars form the letter *W*, or the letter M, depending on the season.
2. Cassiopeia is almost directly opposite the Big Dipper on the other side of Polaris.

Andromeda, the Chained Lady

1. Seen in the autumn sky, south of Cassiopeia.
2. Identified by a line of three bright stars: one in the head, one near the left upper thigh, and one in a foot of the lady.
3. Near the faint stars in the belt is a barely visible cloud of millions of stars, called the *Great Nebula of Andromeda*. This is a galaxy far beyond our galaxy.

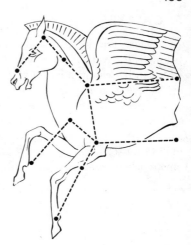

Pegasus, the Winged Horse

1. Pegasus is seen in the eastern sky in the early part of the evening when autumn begins.
2. Four bright stars make up the "square of Pegasus." One of these bright stars belongs to both Pegasus and Andromeda.
3. To locate Pegasus, first locate Andromeda and then follow the bright stars of Andromeda's head and thigh to Pegasus.

7. THE NORTH STAR

To navigators in the Northern Hemisphere, the most important star in the sky is the *North Star*, or *Polaris*. The North Star is also known as the *polestar*. Because the star is almost directly in line with the North Pole of the earth, the North Star seems to remain almost stationary in the sky. For centuries, navigators have used Polaris as a guide star for determining latitude and direction on the earth (Fig. 46-3). The North Star is situated in a group of stars, the *Little Dipper*, found in the constellation Ursa Minor.

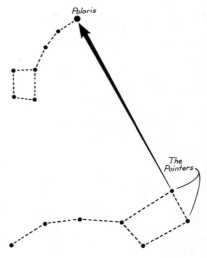

46-3. Locating the North Star. Polaris is located by following a line through the two stars, the "pointers," that make up the outer part of the bowl of the Big Dipper.

8. GALAXIES

A *galaxy* is a cluster of millions of stars. The galaxy to which our sun and planets belong is the *Milky Way*. Away from city lights, on a clear night, part of the Milky Way can be seen as a faint band of light across the sky—the appearance that gives our galaxy its name. Careful observations have revealed that the Milky Way consists of about 100 billion stars.

Some stars seen in constellations are not single bodies. For example, what seems to be a star in the constellation Andromeda is really a galaxy itself consisting of millions of stars. This galaxy is over two million light-years away from us. Astronomers believe that there are millions of other galaxies in outer space.

HOW VAST THE UNIVERSE?

Shortly after the invention of the telescope in 1608, Galileo, an Italian scientist, improved it and turned it skyward. He not only saw the mountains and craters on the moon, but also the revolution of satellites around Jupiter.

Since then, as larger, more powerful telescopes were made, we learned more and more about the universe. Is there more to learn? Are there other galaxies more distant than that in Andromeda, which is over two million light-years away? Is there an end to space and the universe? Answers to these questions and others must await the outcome of research aided by more powerful instruments that are to be put into use. Among such instruments are the *Keck telescope*, the *Very Large Telescope*, and the *Hubble Space Telescope*.

The *Keck Telescope* is expected to measure 33 feet in diameter. It will be located on the summit of Mauna Kea, a volcanic mountain in Hawaii. Mauna Kea rises to about 14,000 feet above sea level. There, observations will not be hampered by the glare of city lights.

The *Very Large Telescope*, a European project, will be 52.5 feet in diameter. It will be emplaced in a mountainous region of Chile where city lights will not be a problem.

The *Hubble Space Telescope*, scheduled to be placed in orbit by a space shuttle, will also be free of light interference. Although this space telescope will be only about 8 feet in diameter—smaller than some land-based telescopes—it will be able to detect heavenly objects as far away as 14 billion light-years.

Multiple-Choice Questions

Write the number preceding the correct answer.

1. Stars are seen because they (1) are larger than the earth (2) are many light-years away (3) give off their own light and heat (4) reflect sunlight.
2. Stars are not visible during the day because (1) the earth is turned away from them (2) they do not give off light during the day (3) they are farther from the earth during the day (4) of the brightness of the sun.
3. It is believed by most scientists that (1) all of the stars have been discovered (2) most of the stars have been discovered (3) all of the stars will have been discovered within the year (4) countless numbers of stars are yet to be discovered.
4. The stars appear to move westward across the sky during the night. The reason is that the (1) earth rotates from east to west (2) earth rotates from west to east (3) earth revolves around the sun (4) sun revolves around the earth.
5. The star nearest the earth is (1) the sun (2) the moon (3) the North Star (4) Venus.
6. The color of high-temperature stars is (1) yellow (2) colorless (3) red (4) blue-white.
7. A light-year is a unit of (1) speed (2) time (3) distance (4) volume.
8. A group of stars forming a fixed pattern in the sky is called a (1) galaxy (2) constellation (3) meteor (4) comet.
9. The brightest constellation is (1) Orion (2) the Milky Way (3) Cassiopeia (4) Andromeda.
10. An example of a constellation is (1) Cassiopeia (2) the Milky Way (3) the North Star (4) the Pointers.
11. During the night, the Little Dipper seems to (1) change its shape (2) stand still (3) circle around the North Star (4) move closer to the North Star.
12. If extended beyond and above the North Pole, the axis of the earth would point toward the (1) equator (2) moon (3) North Star (4) South Pole.
13. The North Star is in the group of stars called (1) the Big Dipper (2) the Little Dipper (3) Orion (4) Cassiopeia.
14. The "pointer" stars helpful in finding the North Star are part of the constellation named (1) Canis Major (2) Pegasus (3) the Big Dipper (4) the Little Dipper.
15. The Milky Way is believed to be (1) a form of northern lights (2) a very large number of stars in a group (3) light from some giant sun (4) reflected light from our moon.

Completion Questions

Write the word or expression that correctly completes the statement.

1. _____ are scientists who study heavenly objects.
2. Stars appear to move westward across the sky during the night because the earth _____ from west to east.
3. Proxima Centauri is the star outside the solar system _____ (*closest to, farthest from*) the earth.
4. The constellation in which five bright stars form the letter *W* is _____.
5. The star Sirius is found in the constellation _____.
6. The star that appears always to be directly over the North Pole of the earth is the _____.
7. Another name for the star referred to in question 6 is _____.
8. The star mentioned in question 6 is found in the constellation _____.
9. Our solar system is part of the galaxy called the _____.
10. It is thought that there are _____ (*no other, many*) galaxies in outer space.

REVIEW OF UNIT IX

1. Tell where each of the following can be found near your school.
   a. a place where fossils can be found
   b. a place where a useful mineral can be found
   c. a place where sedimentary rocks can be found
   d. a place where igneous rocks are used commercially
   e. a place where metamorphic rocks are used commercially
   f. an artificial rock
2. A pupil puts a few drops of hydrochloric acid on a sample of marble. What happens?
3. Write a complete sentence explaining the meaning of each of the following terms and give an example of each.
   a. igneous rock   d. stalactite
   b. fossil   e. stalagmite
   c. sediment   f. delta
4. Explain each of the following.
   a. The inscriptions on old tombstones are often difficult to read.
   b. Sandstone is not used as a building stone in a region where there is plentiful rain and freezing temperatures.
   c. Large round boulders are often found in fields in New York State.
   d. Forces from within the earth cause changes in the earth's surface.
   e. Stones and pebbles with jagged or sharp corners are rarely found on a beach.

5. Two important processes that cause changes in the earth's surface are weathering and erosion.
   a. Describe each process.
   b. Give two examples of each process.
6. Both oxygen and carbon dioxide are important agents of chemical weathering. Explain how each carries on chemical weathering.
7. Tell how each of the following changes the earth's surface.
   a. plants   d. glaciers
   b. wind   e. running water
   c. freezing water   f. ground water
8. The water from a steep hillside runs into a small lake.
   a. Does the water wear away the land faster where it runs rapidly or where it runs slowly?
   b. At what season of the year will most soil be carried away?
   c. How would planting trees on the hillside help to slow down erosion?
   d. Why does a stream on the hillside flow in a deep gully?
9. Tell where each can be found near your school.
   a. a pond being filled by sand from a stream
   b. a slope being gullied after each rain
   c. a place where soil conservation is being practiced
10. At one time it was believed that the earth was the center of the solar system and that the sun, moon, and stars revolved around it. What is the present belief?
11. Name three planets other than the earth.
12. Explain why a higher tide occurs at the new-moon phase than at the first-quarter phase.
13. Why do "shooting stars" falling through the atmosphere seldom reach the earth?
14. Draw diagrams showing the position of the earth, sun, and moon during:
    a. an eclipse of the sun
    b. an eclipse of the moon
15. In which case (A or B) can an eclipse occur? Why?

16. The following words or expressions are frequently used in science. Give the meaning or use of each of these words or terms.
    a. solar system   c. orbit   e. revolution
    b. planet   d. rotation

17. Give a reason for each of the following.
    a. Although the sky may be clear, the moon is not visible every night.
    b. An eclipse of the sun can occur only at new moon.
    c. Days are warmer in summer than they are in winter.
    d. The shadow of a flagpole is longer in the morning than at noon.
18. Indicate the direction of the shadow from the post by writing the word *north*, *east*, *south*, or *west*.

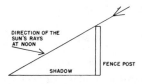

19. Draw a diagram to show the position of the axis of the earth in relation to the sun in December and in June.
20. a. At noon, in the Northern Hemisphere, in which direction does your shadow point?
    b. In mid-afternoon, what is the approximate direction in which your shadow points?
21. Explain the following statements.
    a. The sun does not actually rise and set; it merely appears to do so.
    b. The Big Dipper is in a different position at midnight from its position at 9:00 P.M.
22. Sketch in the missing part of the diagram of the Little Dipper and name the missing part.

23. Give an example of a constellation of the Northern Hemisphere.
24. Define the following terms.
    a. longitude
    b. latitude
    c. chronometer

Final Review Questions

1. If a glowing splint is thrust into a bottle filled with oxygen, the splint will (1) burst into flame (2) glow more dimly (3) be extinguished (4) show no change.
2. When iodine is added to some cornstarch and water, the mixture will turn (1) blue-black (2) brick-red (3) bright orange (4) yellow.
3. A heavenly body that appears to twinkle at night is (1) a meteor (2) a planet (3) a star (4) the moon.
4. Sexual reproduction involves (1) one parent (2) two parents (3) fission (4) sporing.
5. A lifting magnet may be made by winding an iron bolt with (1) aluminum foil (2) bare copper wire (3) bare iron wire (4) insulated copper wire.
6. Which organism has no eyes, no lungs, no bones, and no gills? (1) cricket (2) earthworm (3) goldfish (4) mole.
7. In pasteurized milk (1) most harmful bacteria have been destroyed (2) fat has been decreased (3) protein has been increased (4) cream has been increased.
8. Which electrical device has no magnet? (1) bell (2) fuse (3) telegraph sounder (4) telephone receiver.
9. When swimming under water, we notice the pressure is greater (1) as we go deeper (2) as we near the surface (3) when the water is clear (4) when the water is smooth.
10. Which substance can be removed from water by filtration? (1) alcohol (2) ink (3) sand (4) sugar.
11. A hand lens is most often used to (1) examine small insects (2) identify bacteria (3) study cell structure (4) study the moon's surface.
12. The milkweed spreads its seeds mainly with the help of (1) animals (2) insects (3) water (4) wind.
13. One reason for placing straw on newly graded steep banks along a road is to (1) make the bank look better (2) prevent erosion (3) provide food for wildlife (4) provide minerals for growing grass.
14. 1000 milliliters equals (1) 1 cubic centimeter (2) 1000 cubic centimeters (3) 1 liter (4) 0.001 liter.
15. Pollen is produced in the (1) corolla (2) ovary (3) receptacle (4) stamen.
16. A small, green insect that sucks plant juices is the (1) aphid (2) beetle (3) grasshopper (4) wasp.
17. A great abundance of rich topsoil is likely to be found (1) at the seashore (2) in an old river valley (3) on a hillside (4) on top of a mountain.
18. A solid that melts at 0°C freezes at (1) 0°C (2) −10°C (3) −273°C (4) 0°K.
19. Which lists the stages of the life cycle of the butterfly in correct order? (1) egg, nymph, pupa, adult (2) egg, pupa, larva, adult (3) egg, larva, pupa, adult (4) larva, egg, pupa, adult.

20. A spectrum is often formed when sunlight shines through (1) an aquarium (2) plastic shades (3) translucent window glass (4) Venetian blinds.

21. In summer the temperature of the air is usually highest about (1) 10 A.M. (2) 11 A.M. (3) noon (4) 2 P.M.

22. Which can settle most quickly in water? (1) clay (2) grains of sand (3) leaves (4) pebbles.

23. The hummingbird feeds on (1) insects (2) miscroscopic life (3) nectar (4) seeds.

24. The formula of a compound is (1) H_2 (2) O_2 (3) $H_2 + O_2$ (4) H_2O.

25. Limewater turns milky in the presence of (1) carbon dioxide (2) hydrogen (3) oxygen (4) water vapor.

26. If two cells are placed base to base in a flashlight, it is most probable that the (1) flashlight cannot be assembled (2) lamp will not light (3) bulb will not stay in place (4) switch cannot be moved.

27. Footprints of dinosaurs have been discovered in (1) rocks formed from mud (2) petrified wood (3) amber (4) ice.

28. To test for the presence of limestone in a rock, one may add (1) ammonia (2) distilled water (3) iodine (4) lemon juice.

29. Which animal hibernates in the winter? (1) frog (2) gray squirrel (3) rabbit (4) fox.

30. Which fruit contains only one seed? (1) apple (2) cherry (3) pear (4) tomato.

31. Houseflies are most likely to be found in large numbers near (1) a pond (2) a small stream (3) newly cultivated soil (4) uncovered garbage.

32. Which dimension is closest to two centimeters? (1) the circumference of a nickel (2) the diameter of a penny (3) the thickness of a dime (4) the width of a dollar bill.

33. Which of the following has the lowest kindling temperature? (1) coal (2) paper (3) sulfur (4) wood splints.

34. Olives in cylindrical bottles appear (1) larger (2) smaller (3) flatter (4) lighter in color.

35. Of the following drugs, the one that is most addicting is (1) aspirin (2) alcohol (3) marijuana (4) heroin.

36. The time from new moon until the next full moon is approximately (1) 1 week (2) 2 weeks (3) 3 weeks (4) 4 weeks.

37. All solutions are (1) colorless (2) colored (3) homogeneous (4) non-homogeneous.

38. Concrete can be made by mixing water with sand, gravel, and (1) cement (2) clay (3) shale (4) plaster of Paris.

39. Burrs are useful to the burdock plant because they (1) keep insects away (2) produce the flower (3) resist plant disease (4) scatter the seed.

40. Which plant is usually started from a slip or cutting? (1) geranium (2) tulip (3) lettuce (4) pumpkin.

41. The age of the earth has been estimated from the radioactive decay of a form of (1) carbon (2) uranium (3) oxygen (4) amber.

42. When there is an electric current in a wire, which statement is always true? (1) The insulation is burned off. (2) A lamp is lighted. (3) The wire becomes brittle. (4) A magnetic field exists around the wire.

43. Which simple machine is similar in action to that part of a meat grinder which forces the meat toward the cutting blades? (1) lever (2) pulley (3) screw (4) wedge.

44. The needles of a fir tree are its (1) leaves (2) twigs (3) flowers (4) seeds.

45. Of the following atomic numbers, the atom that has the most electron shells is (1) 1 (2) 3 (3) 11 (4) 19.

46. Bits of paper on a rug are forced into the bag of a vacuum cleaner by (1) the motor (2) the brush (3) atmospheric pressure (4) electricity.

47. The leaves of a house plant turn toward (1) light (2) water (3) heat (4) darkness.

48. Which of the following is a good electrical insulator? (1) copper (2) glass (3) iron (4) silver.

49. Placing a cellophane bag over the stem and leaves of a plant will show that plants (1) give off water vapor (2) need sunlight (3) need minerals (4) use carbon dioxide.

50. The center electrode of a dry cell is made of (1) copper (2) zinc (3) aluminum (4) carbon.

51. A plant whose leaves are arranged in a rosette or whorl is the (1) dandelion (2) goldenrod (3) cucumber (4) rose.

52. A balanced aquarium should contain water, animals, and (1) pebbles (2) shells (3) colored rocks (4) green plants.

53. A pulley is used to (1) raise a flag to the top of a flagpole (2) open a tin can (3) sharpen a pencil (4) switch on the lights.

54. If a cup of soil is shaken up in a jar of water, which part of the soil settles last? (1) large pebbles (2) small pebbles (3) clay (4) sand.

55. All food chains begin with (1) food webs (2) green organisms (3) bacteria (4) fungi.

56. Oppositely charged particles form (1) ions (2) molecules (3) atoms (4) bonds.

57. Which tree keeps its leaves all winter? (1) apple (2) elm (3) maple (4) spruce.

58. Common colds are most likely to be spread by (1) coughs and sneezes (2) houseflies (3) mosquitoes (4) unpasteurized milk.

59. Which of the following is most likely to be magnetic? (1) a dime (2) a gold ring (3) a lead pencil (4) a paper clip.

60. Ball bearings are most commonly found in a (1) model airplane (2) pair of pliers (3) pair of roller skates (4) pencil sharpener.

61. In a house, water pressure is greatest in the (1) attic (2) basement (3) first-floor kitchen (4) upstairs bathroom.

62. The large blood vessels that are visible on the back of the hand are (1) arteries (2) capillaries (3) corpuscles (4) veins.

63. Which substances are listed in correct order, proceeding from a low to a high kindling temperature? (1) phosphorus, wood, sulfur, (2) phosphorus, sulfur, wood (3) sulfur, phosphorus, wood (4) sulfur, wood, phosphorus.

64. Sound travels fastest through (1) air (2) steel (3) a vacuum (4) water.

65. Which animal cuts down trees? (1) beaver (2) muskrat (3) squirrel (4) woodchuck.

66. Which of the following devices contains the most levers? (1) an eggbeater (2) an electric drill (3) a piano (4) a portable radio.

67. A proton has an atomic mass unit (amu) of (1) 0 (2) 1 (3) 16 (4) 32.

68. If a person slides across the seat of a car on a cold winter day and receives a shock as he or she touches the door handle, the shock is caused by (1) heat (2) a short circuit (3) static electricity (4) current electricity.

69. The purpose of a camera lens is to (1) cut out the bright rays of sunlight (2) produce an image on the film (3) keep dust away from the film (4) regulate the amount of light entering the camera.

70. In the formula $CaCO_3$, the sum of the subscripts is (1) 3 (2) 5 (3) 6 (4) 10.

71. A common insulation used on wires carrying electric current is (1) glass (2) lead (3) porcelain (4) rubber.

72. A vibrating rubber band produces the highest pitch if it is (1) loose and long (2) loose and short (3) tight and long (4) tight and short.

73. Sand is made up of colorless crystals of (1) iron (2) mica (3) quartz (4) shale.

74. Air at normal atmospheric pressure is used to operate (1) an airbrake (2) a doorcheck (3) a saxophone (4) a siphon.

75. To start a fire with the aid of the sun, one should use a (1) concave lens (2) flat mirror (3) magnifying lens (4) rectangular aquarium.

76. It is thought that the first living things arose in (1) sediments (2) ice (3) water (4) petrified wood.

77. Which device will prevent overloading an electric circuit? (1) battery (2) fuse (3) motor (4) plug.

78. Limestone is dissolved by water containing (1) carbon dioxide (2) iodine (3) nitrogen (4) oxygen.

79. Which plant grows in swamps? (1) cattail (2) corn (3) lilac (4) oats.

80. A full moon rises at approximately (1) 7 A.M. (2) noon (3) 7 P.M. (4) midnight.

81. Monuments are often made of (1) granite (2) lodestone (3) quartz (4) shale.

82. A fish is adapted to absorb oxygen from water through its (1) fins (2) gills (3) lungs (4) scales.

83. Birds are the only animals that (1) can fly (2) eat insects (3) have feathers (4) make nests.

84. A magnet will not pick up a (1) needle (2) paper clip (3) penny (4) pocketknife.

85. Iron rusts fastest when covered with (1) oil (2) paint (3) paper (4) water.

86. To measure air pressure, a pupil needs (1) an anemometer (2) a barometer (3) a hygrometer (4) a thermometer.

87. Which bird feeds on small mammals? (1) canary (2) owl (3) robin (4) woodpecker.

88. In the equation $2H_2O_2 \rightarrow 2H_2O + O_2$, the total number of atoms is (1) 4 (2) 5 (3) 8 (4) 16.

89. When water is taken apart by electricity, what two substances are formed? (1) carbon and oxygen (2) hydrogen and oxygen (3) hydrogen and carbon (4) hydrogen and nitrogen.

90. For seed dispersal, the maple tree depends chiefly on (1) animals (2) other plants (3) wind (4) water.

91. If bubbles are formed when hydrochloric acid is dropped on a stone, the stone is probably (1) limestone (2) mica (3) sandstone (4) quartz.

92. A science student weighs a deflated basketball. She then inflates the ball and finds it is heavier. She has proven that air (1) can inflate all hollow objects (2) is a gas (3) is compressible (4) is matter.

93. Nerve endings that first receive stimuli from touch, heat, and cold are located in the (1) brain (2) bones (3) muscles (4) skin.

94. The distance from the earth to the moon and back is about (1) 240,000 miles (2) 480,000 miles (3) 93,000,000 miles (4) 186,000,000 miles.

95. Of the following, which is *not* an example of a chemical change? (1) electrolysis (2) burning (3) making sawdust from wood (4) changing hydrogen into water.

96. Earthworms eat dead leaves. The earthworms are eaten by bullfrogs or robins. Boas eat the bullfrogs, and foxes or cats eat the robins. The food relationship among these animals is an example of (1) parasites (2) a food chain (3) hosts (4) a food web.

97. A cell part that duplicates itself when a cell divides is a (1) nuclear membrane (2) cell membrane (3) chromosome (4) vacuole.

98. Which develops into a frog? (1) caterpillar (2) earthworm (3) moth (4) tadpole.

99. Green plants lose most of their excess water through their (1) flowers (2) leaves (3) roots (4) stems.

100. If the same amount of soap were added to a quart of water from each of the following sources, which would make the best suds? (1) lake water (2) ocean water (3) rainwater (4) river water.

101. Which of the following organisms has no leaves? (1) cabbage (2) clover (3) mushroom (4) potato.

102. Which common insect is a parasite? (1) housefly (2) bumblebee (3) flea (4) walking stick.

103. Which part of the eye regulates the size of the pupil? (1) iris (2) lens (3) lid (4) retina.

104. Which of the following animals gives the most care to its young? (1) frog (2) spider (3) robin (4) salmon.

105. Which of the following is the softest? (1) chalk (2) diamond (3) glass (4) slate.

106. Smog is most closely related to (1) smoke (2) fog (3) smoke and fog (4) dew.

107. Which animal lives and works in a colony? (1) garter snake (2) ant (3) kingfisher (4) woodchuck.

108. Which metal is a liquid at room temperature? (1) tin (2) iron (3) mercury (4) aluminum.

109. Which kind of tree is rapidly dying off because of a fungus disease? (1) maple (2) elm (3) poplar (4) apple.
110. The dandelion has (1) alternate leaves (2) a single leaf (3) opposite leaves (4) rosette leaves.
111. Which device uses an electromagnet? (1) light bulb (2) battery (3) telephone receiver (4) fuse.
112. Which simple device uses gears? (1) door handle (2) electric lamp (3) paper-towel rack (4) eggbeater.
113. When baking soda and vinegar are mixed together, which gas is released? (1) nitrogen (2) carbon dioxide (3) oxygen (4) hydrogen.
114. The age of a tree that has recently been cut down may be determined by examining its (1) annual rings (2) bark (3) buds (4) flowers.
115. Table salt is a compound made up of sodium and (1) carbon (2) calcium (3) chlorine (4) iodine.
116. Erosion takes place fastest on a hillside when the area is (1) a mass of weeds (2) bare ground (3) covered with sod (4) forested.
117. An acorn is the fruit of which tree? (1) sycamore (2) poplar (3) chestnut (4) oak.
118. Which animal sometimes destroys chickens? (1) weasel (2) woodchuck (3) deer (4) red squirrel.
119. The vitamin that can prevent the oxidation of certain oils is vitamin (1) A (2) C (3) D (4) E.
120. Which one of these animals gives most care to its young? (1) cat (2) frog (3) trout (4) turtle.
121. When water is cooled from 1°C to 0°C, the water (1) expands (2) contracts (3) first expands and then contracts (4) first contracts and then expands.
122. Air pressure makes it difficult to (1) hoe in dry clay soil (2) remove a rusty nail from a board (3) ride a bicycle on a hard sand beach (4) close a car door when all windows are closed.
123. The industry that does most in destroying valuable topsoil is (1) air transportation (2) agriculture (3) cattle-raising (4) offshore oil-drilling.
124. Houseflies usually lay their eggs in (1) stagnant water (2) fragrant flowers (3) garbage (4) dry soil.
125. A person should observe a solar eclipse (1) with the naked eye (2) through a clear glass (3) through a darkened negative film (4) through a frosted glass.
126. Which bird would be most likely to build its nest in a birdhouse? (1) bluebird (2) crow (3) kingfisher (4) meadow lark.
127. When air is heated, it will (1) contract (2) burn (3) condense (4) expand.
128. The seeds of milkweed are usually scattered by (1) birds (2) wind (3) insects (4) water.
129. The center of our solar system is (1) the earth (2) the North Star (3) the sun (4) Venus.

130. Oxygen is carried in the blood mainly by (1) food (2) plasma (3) red corpuscles (4) white blood cells.
131. An electron-dot formula shows the number of electrons in (1) the first electron shell (2) the next to the outermost electron shell (3) the outermost electron shell (4) all the electron shells.
132. An enemy of the field mouse is the (1) owl (2) pigeon (3) rabbit (4) squirrel.
133. Most food nutrients are absorbed into the blood from the (1) large intestine (2) mouth (3) small intestine (4) stomach.
134. Electrons flow most easily through (1) copper (2) glass (3) rubber (4) string.
135. In molecules where atoms share electrons, the bonding is called (1) ionic (2) atomic (3) molecular (4) covalent.
136. Photosynthesis takes place only in (1) soil (2) bacteria (3) fungi (4) organisms containing chlorophyll.
137. Oxidation in which heat and light are given off is called (1) combustion (2) decay (3) rusting (4) tarnishing.
138. Potato beetles are most destructive in that stage of their life history known as the (1) adult (2) egg (3) larva (4) pupa.
139. A parasitic relationship exists between a (1) flea and a dog (2) robin and an earthworm (3) rose and a bee (4) squirrel and an acorn.
140. The order in which vertebrates evolved on earth is usually shown as (1) fishes, green plants, humans, reptiles (2) mammals, birds, reptiles, protists (3) birds, green plants, mammals, fishes (4) fishes, amphibians, reptiles, mammals.
141. A seed tester should be used in a place that is (1) cool and dry (2) cool and moist (3) warm and dry (4) warm and moist.
142. Which tree is an example of an evergreen? (1) apple (2) elm (3) hemlock (4) willow.
143. To determine whether a rock has been worn away by a glacier, look for (1) cracks in the rock (2) river valleys nearby (3) scratches in the rock (4) sediments on the rock.
144. The chief value of the seed coat to the lima bean is to (1) absorb carbon dioxide (2) furnish oxygen (3) protect the embryo (4) provide stored food.
145. During food-making in plants, the gas removed from the air is (1) carbon dioxide (2) nitrogen (3) oxygen (4) water vapor.
146. An element *not* present in stainless steel is (1) iron (2) copper (3) chromium (4) nickel.
147. Granite is a rock that resulted from the (1) cementing of sand (2) cooling of molten minerals (3) eruption of a volcano (4) pressure on clay.
148. The chlorophyll in green leaves may be removed by (1) alcohol (2) hot water (3) oxygen (4) salt solution.
149. Underground caves were formed by ground water dissolving (1) clay (2) granite (3) limestone (4) shale.
150. A stethoscope is used to (1) listen to the heart action (2) test for sugar (3) test the eyes (4) determine the temperature of the body.

151. A mouse is classified as (1) an amphibian (2) a mammal (3) a crustacean (4) a reptile.
152. Heat passes through liquids chiefly by (1) absorption (2) conduction (3) convection (4) radiation.
153. Jet planes are propelled by (1) the thrust of hot gases (2) propeller blades (3) ailerons (4) steam turbines.
154. In order to burn well, a fire must have fuel and a good supply of (1) oxygen (2) carbon dioxide (3) nitrogen (4) water vapor.
155. Which part of the camera focuses the light rays? (1) lens (2) film (3) diaphragm (4) shutter.
156. The temperature of a room is often controlled by a (1) thermometer (2) thermostat (3) hygrometer (4) humidifier.
157. If the normal number of chromosomes in the cells of a pea plant is 14, the number of chromosomes we would expect to find in an egg cell of the plant is (1) 2 (2) 14 (3) 28 (4) 7.
158. Limestone caves were formed because the ground water contained dissolved (1) oxygen (2) chlorine (3) carbon dioxide (4) iron oxide.
159. An element *not* usually present in organic compounds is (1) carbon (2) argon (3) chlorine (4) hydrogen.
160. Which of these plants has flowers that are usually pollinated by bees? (1) clover (2) corn (3) fern (4) rye.
161. Mobile X-ray units offer free X rays in order to detect the presence of (1) cancer (2) heart disease (3) pneumonia (4) tuberculosis.
162. The heavenly body on which humans have walked is (1) a large meteor (2) a comet (3) the moon (4) Mars.
163. A praying mantis feeds on (1) leaves (2) seeds (3) insects (4) juices of plants.
164. A compass is actually a (1) piece of metal with a static charge (2) piece of unmagnetized steel (3) small magnet on a pivot (4) stationary magnet.
165. When hydrogen burns in air, the substance formed is (1) heat (2) light (3) water (4) carbon dioxide.
166. White light from the sun is best separated into the spectrum colors by the use of a (1) glass prism (2) reading glass (3) microscope (4) telescope.
167. One method of slowing the rate of erosion on a steep hill is to (1) plant trees on the hillside (2) plow up and down the hill (3) remove rocks from the hillside (4) dig a drainage ditch at the bottom of the hill.
168. The average distance in miles from the earth to the sun is (1) 8,000 (2) 186,000 (3) 240,000 (4) 93,000,000.
169. Acidity in the soil can be tested with (1) limewater (2) Fehling's (Benedict's) solution (3) filter paper (4) litmus paper.
170. Imprints of plants that lived long ago are found in (1) volcanic rocks (2) sedimentary rocks (3) concrete (4) sand dunes.
171. The particle theory of light was developed by (1) Einstein (2) Huygens (3) Michelson (4) Newton.

172. One of the functions of the roots of a maple tree is to (1) anchor the tree (2) make food (3) produce seeds (4) protect the tree in cold weather.

173. Mosquitoes usually breed in (1) garbage (2) manure piles (3) running water (4) stagnant water.

174. Which instrument is used to measure air pressure? (1) aneroid barometer (2) calorimeter (3) hygrometer (4) mercury thermometer.

175. When water freezes, it (1) exerts great pressure (2) increases in weight (3) takes up less space (4) undergoes a chemical change.

176. Which food is rich in simple sugar? (1) crackers (2) eggs (3) peanuts (4) candy.

177. Which plant is classed as a fungus? (1) club moss (2) fern (3) mushroom (4) poison ivy.

178. The earth's attraction for objects on or near it is called (1) density (2) force (3) gravity (4) pressure.

179. When an airplane is in flight, the air pressure on the top surface of the wing is (1) less than on the bottom surface (2) the same as on the bottom surface (3) slightly more than on the bottom surface (4) much more than on the bottom surface.

180. Which is an example of a parasitic animal? (1) tapeworm (2) grasshopper (3) horse (4) salamander.

181. Which substance is needed for the proper functioning of the thyroid gland? (1) chlorine (2) iodine (3) iron (4) phosphorus.

182. Lenses that are worn directly on the cornea are called (1) reflecting lenses (2) refracting lenses (3) prismatic lenses (4) contact lenses.

183. A sudden slipping of rock along a fault in the crust of the earth may cause (1) an earthquake (2) a hurricane (3) a tornado (4) a volcanic eruption.

184. Which bird is nearly extinct in the United States? (1) bluebird (2) egret (3) goldfinch (4) whooping crane.

185. A common substance containing an acid is (1) baking soda (2) flour (3) soapflakes (4) vinegar.

186. A predatory bird feeds on (1) animals (2) leaves (3) nuts (4) seeds.

187. Alcohol and carbon dioxide are formed from carbohydrates by the action of (1) algae (2) mosses (3) molds (4) yeasts.

188. Hard water may be softened by adding (1) chlorine (2) fluorine (3) table salt (4) washing soda.

189. A light-year is used to measure (1) brightness of light (2) distance (3) time (4) velocity.

190. Casts of animal tracks can be made by using water and (1) gravel (2) humus (3) plaster of Paris (4) sand.

191. Which bird eats seeds? (1) sparrow (2) hawk (3) hummingbird (4) woodpecker.

192. Liquids that heat slowly have (1) high specific heat (2) low specific heat (3) high specific gravity (4) low specific gravity.

193. In human beings, digestion begins in the (1) liver (2) mouth (3) small intestine (4) stomach.

194. Which of the following satellites can best help a ship's captain find his position? (1) the moon (2) a satellite that carries a radio transmitter (3) a satellite that carries a telescope (4) a satellite that sends out weather information.
195. Fruits are most valuable in the diet for their (1) fat content (2) high water content (3) mineral and vitamin content (4) protein content.
196. Which part of the flower produces the pollen? (1) ovary (2) pistil (3) stamen (4) style.
197. Which planet appears red in the sky? (1) Mars (2) Pluto (3) Saturn (4) Venus.
198. Sound waves will travel through (1) solids and liquids but not through gases (2) solids and gases but not through liquids (3) solids, gases, and vacuum (4) solids, liquids, and gases.
199. Our government has passed laws requiring automobile manufacturers to add certain devices to auto engines in order to (1) increase braking power (2) make cars less expensive (3) reduce the price of gasoline (4) decrease air pollution.
200. A drug that speeds up heart action is called (1) an antiseptic (2) a disinfectant (3) a narcotic (4) a stimulant.
201. Which substance is sometimes used as an electrical insulator? (1) aluminum (2) copper (3) mica (4) steel.
202. The energy value of foods is measured in (1) calories (2) degrees (3) inches (4) percent.
203. When all the colors of the spectrum are mixed, the light becomes (1) black (2) blue (3) red (4) white.
204. Matter and energy (1) are unrelated (2) can be destroyed (3) are interconvertible (4) are the same.
205. The remains of green plants have formed (1) asbestos (2) coal (3) mica (4) uranium.
206. A plant whose flowers are usually pollinated by the wind is the (1) bean (2) clover (3) corn (4) pumpkin.
207. The vocal cords are located in the (1) larynx (2) lungs (3) mouth (4) nose.
208. Which star is closest to the earth? (1) Sirius (2) the North Star (3) the sun (4) Proxima Centauri.
209. Sandstone is a sedimentary rock because it is (1) formed by heat (2) formed under water (3) made in desert areas (4) made of sand.
210. Through which organ is digested food absorbed? (1) kidney (2) liver (3) pancreas (4) small intestine.
211. An example of a lever is the (1) knife blade (2) ramp (3) saw (4) seesaw.
212. In the fermentation of sugar, one of the products formed is (1) alcohol (2) oxygen (3) starch (4) water.
213. An area marked **H** on a weather map indicates high (1) air pressure (2) relative humidity (3) temperature (4) wind speed.
214. An important function of the heart is to (1) change oxygen into carbon dioxide (2) manufacture red blood corpuscles (3) pump air into the lungs (4) pump blood through the body.

215. Which begins to digest in the mouth? (1) starch (2) protein (3) fat (4) sugar.
216. Sprouting of a seed is called (1) transpiration (2) fertilization (3) pollination (4) germination.
217. The source of carbon dioxide for photosynthesis is (1) chlorophyll (2) water (3) sunlight (4) air.
218. Alcohol is considered a depressant because it (1) dulls the senses (2) aids in building tissues (3) increases digestion (4) softens the walls of the arteries.
219. In the human eye, the image is formed on the (1) pupil (2) lens (3) retina (4) iris.
220. Cheese is a good source of (1) water (2) sugar (3) starch (4) protein.
221. Which part of the flower catches and holds the pollen? (1) ovary (2) stigma (3) style (4) petals.
222. During a severe winter of heavy snowfall, which animal has the greatest difficulty in surviving? (1) black bear (2) deer (3) mouse (4) fox.
223. Which is an example of a natural rock? (1) cinder block (2) concrete (3) brick (4) marble.
224. Which material is often used to demonstrate lines of magnetic force around a magnet? (1) copper filings (2) lead filings (3) iron filings (4) aluminum filings.
225. Two chlorine isotopes differ in the number of (1) electrons (2) protons (3) neutrons (4) electron shells.
226. Of the following birds, the one that feeds principally on insect life is the (1) crow (2) downy woodpecker (3) owl (4) pigeon.
227. Two elements commonly found in most fuels are (1) carbon and nitrogen (2) carbon and hydrogen (3) nitrogen and oxygen (4) nitrogen and hydrogen.
228. The observation that a current-bearing wire develops a magnetic field around the wire was first made by (1) Oersted (2) Faraday (3) Volta (4) Newton.
229. Vibrating objects usually produce (1) sound waves (2) heat waves (3) light waves (4) electrical waves.
230. Which tree does not lose its leaves each fall? (1) spruce (2) willow (3) birch (4) chestnut.
231. Bile helps in the digestion of (1) carbohydrates (2) fats (3) minerals (4) proteins.
232. An example of an inclined plane is a (1) can opener (2) nutcracker (3) ramp (4) pulley.
233. Which gas makes up about one-fifth of the atmosphere? (1) carbon dioxide (2) water vapor (3) nitrogen (4) oxygen.
234. Substances that conduct electricity with little or no resistance are called (1) insulators (2) ions (3) domains (4) superconductors.
235. Parts of the ocean near large cities have no fish and no algae in them. A likely reason for this condition is (1) the passage of large ships (2) water pollution (3) a disease that kills both plants and animals (4) increased air travel.
236. Which causes the greatest number of injuries in the home? (1) falls (2) fires (3) firearms (4) poisons.
237. The most important function of the leaf is to (1) beautify the plant (2) manufacture food for the plant (3) protect the plant (4) take in moisture.

238. Which substance in milk helps most in the formation of good teeth? (1) calcium (2) milk sugar (3) butterfat (4) iron.
239. The turtle is an example of a (1) fish (2) mammal (3) rodent (4) reptile.
240. An example of a storage cell is a (1) fuel cell (2) nickel-cadmium cell (3) solar cell (4) dry cell.
241. An example of sedimentary rock is (1) mica (2) pumice (3) sandstone (4) quartz.
242. Distillation produces water that is (1) less pure than filtered water (2) less pure than aerated water (3) clear but has a high bacteria content (4) completely pure.
243. Chlorophyll is made in (1) mushrooms (2) green plants (3) animals (4) soil.
244. Days and nights are caused by (1) revolution of the earth (2) change in the temperature of the sun (3) inclination of the earth's axis (4) rotation of the earth.
245. Plant and animal remains preserved in rocks are called (1) fossils (2) stalactites (3) humus (4) phosphates.
246. Mushrooms are protists that (1) have flat leaves (2) grow from cones (3) grow from seeds (4) grow from spores.
247. The opening from the throat to the ear that allows the air pressure in the ear to become balanced on both sides of the eardrum is the (1) larynx (2) esophagus (3) eustachian tube (4) windpipe.
248. Fish, lean meat, and eggs are important in the diet because they are our chief source of (1) carbohydrates (2) minerals (3) proteins (4) fats.
249. In an airplane, an altimeter is used to measure (1) temperature of outside air (2) relative humidity in the cabin (3) air speed of the plane (4) height above sea level.
250. The energy of all living things can be traced to (1) animals (2) soil (3) the sun (4) water.
251. Nitrogen-fixing bacteria live on the roots of (1) clover (2) oats (3) corn (4) wheat.
252. Food that is being digested passes through the (1) gall bladder (2) liver (3) pancreas (4) small intestine.
253. The voltage of a single dry cell is 1.5 volts. The voltage of two dry cells connected in parallel is (1) 0.75 v (2) 1.5 v (3) 2 v (4) 3 v.
254. Moonlight is caused by (1) burning gases on the moon (2) nuclear energy produced on the moon (3) the moon's hot surface (4) reflected sunlight.
255. Which rock is formed by the cooling of molten rock? (1) granite (2) limestone (3) sandstone (4) shale.
256. The North Star is part of the constellation (1) Big Dipper (2) Cassiopeia (3) Little Dipper (4) Orion.
257. Birds that have sharp, curved bills are most likely to eat (1) fruit (2) insects (3) mice (4) seeds.
258. One should always cover his mouth when coughing because covering the mouth (1) helps cure a cold (2) is considered polite (3) stops the coughing spells (4) prevents the spread of germs.

259. During the winter months, it is desirable to increase the humidity in homes because low humidity (1) causes irritation of the skin and membranes of the nose and throat (2) causes paint and wallpaper to fade (3) makes it difficult to heat the home (4) makes the furniture sticky.

260. Which is not necessary to start a fire? (1) combustible material (2) heat (3) light (4) oxygen.

261. A policeman directing traffic at night often wears a white cape and gloves because white (1) absorbs more light (2) is cooler (3) is easier to see (4) reduces glare.

262. The current, in amperes, in a circuit where the voltage is 6 volts and the resistance is 2 ohms is (1) 1/3 (2) 2 (3) 3 (4) 12.

263. If an empty, unstoppered bottle is lowered mouth downward into a jar of water, (1) the bottle will be about half filled (2) some water will be forced into the bottle (3) the bottle will burst (4) the bottle will fill with water.

264. Tides on the earth will be lowest when the (1) moon and sun are pulling at right angles to the earth (2) moon is in new phase (3) moon is in the first quarter (4) moon is in the last quarter.

265. Rocks are frequently split apart by (1) meteorites (2) running water (3) sudden temperature changes (4) wind.

266. Soil in the forest is very fertile because it (1) contains a large amount of humus (2) is protected from the air (3) is undisturbed (4) receives little light.

267. Toads, frogs, fish, and chickens all (1) eat grain (2) have scales (3) live in water (4) use oxygen.

268. Flowers that have no petals are usually pollinated by (1) birds (2) human beings (3) insects (4) winds.

269. Soda pop fizzes because it contains (1) baking soda (2) carbon dioxide gas (3) color and flavoring (4) sugar.

270. An insect that passes through a nymph stage is the (1) cabbage butterfly (2) potato beetle (3) grasshopper (4) tomato worm.

271. A change from AC to DC is called (1) stepping-up (2) stepping-down (3) amplification (4) rectification.

272. Artificial rainmaking depends on (1) adding water vapor to the clouds (2) causing downward air currents in the clouds (3) causing the clouds to vibrate (4) release of particles on which water can condense.

273. It is dangerous to use gasoline indoors as a cleaning fluid because gasoline vapor (1) has a high kindling temperature (2) has a low kindling temperature (3) may stain the clothes (4) produces unpleasant odors.

274. When a dish is placed above a candle flame, a black spot may appear on the dish. This is due to (1) a change in the porcelain (2) carbon dioxide produced by the flame (3) carbon from the paraffin vapor (4) water vapor produced by the flame.

275. Ten books are placed on one end of a lever and two similar books on the other end. To make the two books balance the ten books, the fulcrum must be (1) at the center of the lever (2) between the center and the ten books (3) between the center and the two books (4) directly under the ten books.

276. Of the following, which is *not* present in a VCR? (1) silicon chips (2) semiconductors (3) transistors (4) vacuum tubes.

277. When a concrete road is laid, black asphalt strips are put between sections of the concrete in order to (1) aid in night driving (2) allow for expansion and contraction of the concrete (3) make it easy to count the sections (4) prevent skidding in wet weather.

278. When a glass tumbler is held over a burning candle, moisture appears inside the tumbler. This is due to the (1) changing of carbon dioxide to water vapor (2) evaporation of water from the candle (3) meeting of warm and cool air (4) production of water vapor by oxidation.

279. A woodchuck survives the winter because it (1) has stored food in its burrow (2) has stored food in its body (3) feeds on shrubs and berries all winter (4) feeds on mice.

280. When starch or protein is digested, it is changed into (1) a soluble form (2) a gaseous form (3) blood (4) living tissue.

281. Which one of the following items can be recovered from a lake by a magnet? (1) a baseball (2) a pair of gold-framed glasses (3) a pocketknife (4) a fifty-cent piece.

282. Which aircraft could fly in a vacuum? (1) glider (2) dirigible (3) helicopter (4) rocket ship.

283. Which plants were common to the coal age? (1) maples (2) ferns (3) grasses (4) oaks.

284. Foods contain carbon because a raw material used by plants in food making is (1) water (2) carbon dioxide (3) green coloring matter (4) minerals.

285. In humans, the gene for dark hair is dominant over the gene for light hair. How many recessive genes for hair color does a naturally light-haired person have? (1) 1 (2) 2 (3) 3 (4) 0.

286. That the evolution of living things is still occurring is shown by the results of (1) fission (2) fossil formation (3) cross-breeding (4) amber.

287. When shale weathers, it becomes (1) clay (2) mica (3) sand (4) slate.

288. Which organisms make their own food? (1) yeasts (2) puffballs (3) onions (4) bacteria.

289. Which animal feeds indirectly on green plants? (1) rabbit (2) deer (3) hummingbird (4) hawk.

290. Oily rags should not be left in closets where there is poor circulation of air because (1) fumes of the oil may be poisonous (2) oil in rags will stain the woodwork (3) slow oxidation of the oil may cause rags to burn (4) rags serve as a breeding place for mice.

291. A magnetic compass on a demonstration desk is not pointing correctly. The object disturbing it could be a piece of (1) glass (2) wood (3) chalk (4) metal.

292. As a balloon rises, the gas within it (1) freezes (2) condenses (3) settles (4) expands.

293. When two dry cells are connected in series, the voltage available is (1) 1½ volts (2) 6 volts (3) 3 volts (4) 4 volts.

294. Carbon dioxide is a good substance to use in certain types of fire extinguishers because it does not burn and (1) it pours easily (2) it is heavier than air (3) it has a pleasant odor (4) it will not cause rust.

295. The stars appear to move westward across the sky during the night. The reason is that the (1) earth rotates from east to west (2) earth rotates from west to east (3) earth revolves around the sun (4) sun revolves around the earth.

296. On a warm day, moisture often collects on cold objects. The reason is that (1) cold objects give off water (2) water vapor condenses when air is cooled enough (3) cold air is heavier than warm air (4) moist air rises.

297. An electric motor turns because the electricity passing through its coils produces (1) magnetism (2) heat (3) a chemical change in the coils (4) sound.

298. A boy living in the southern part of Argentina would never see (1) the moon (2) Venus (3) the Big Dipper (4) the northern horizon.

299. If you wish to make an electromagnet, which would not be necessary? (1) insulated wire (2) iron filings (3) a soft iron core (4) a source of electricity.

300. Erosion can be prevented by (1) burning brush on unused land (2) destroying weeds (3) planting trees (4) plowing the land.

301. An inclined plane multiplies (1) force (2) work (3) resistance (4) time.

302. Man is classified as a warm-blooded animal because he (1) can stand warm weather (2) has lungs (3) lives on land (4) maintains a constant body temperature.

303. The balance of nature is most often upset by (1) disease (2) erosion (3) humans (4) storms.

304. Which animal lays its eggs in water? (1) duck (2) frog (3) rattlesnake (4) turtle.

305. Which of the following can be carried on only when there is light? (1) transpiration (2) germination (3) photosynthesis (4) respiration.

306. Wheels reduce (1) effort (2) resistance (3) work (4) friction.

307. Which of the following absorbs most of the heat from the sun? (1) the atmosphere (2) clothing (3) houses (4) trees.

308. Winter in the Northern Hemisphere begins when the (1) earth's axis is tipped more than 23½° (2) earth is farthest from the sun (3) North Pole points 23½° away from the sun (4) sun's rays reach both poles.

309. Which of the following appears to move fastest through the sky? (1) meteorite (2) planet (3) star (4) moon.

310. A permanent change in a gene that is inherited is called a (1) cross-breed (2) mutation (3) dominant (4) recessive.

311. Which of the following foods produces the most heat energy per pound? (1) bread (2) butter (3) carrots (4) roast beef.

312. A boy's face is white and he appears to be fainting. He should (1) be made to sit or lie with his head lower than the rest of his body (2) be made to sit or lie with his head higher than the rest of his body (3) have cold water thrown in his face (4) be made to walk rapidly until he recovers.

313. A window made of two panes of glass with air between helps keep a house warm because (1) glass is a good conductor of heat (2) air is a good insulator (3) less wind can blow through the glass (4) more sunlight enters.

314. One part of an automobile that should never be lubricated is the (1) engine (2) wheel bearings (3) transmission (4) brake drums and linings.

315. Wind is mainly the result of (1) clouds (2) high humidity (3) storms (4) unequal heating of air.

316. Rubbing alcohol taken from a medicine cabinet is poured over the hands. The hands feel cold because (1) evaporation adds cold to the hands (2) evaporation removes heat from the hands (3) liquids cause the skin to feel cold (4) the alcohol is cold.

317. When a ray of sunshine passing through the edge of an aquarium is broken up into colors, the aquarium is acting as a (1) lens (2) mirror (3) prism (4) rainbow.

318. If carbon dioxide is produced when a fuel burns, the fuel contains (1) carbon (2) chlorine (3) helium (4) nitrogen.

319. A Celsius thermometer put into a person's mouth would read (1) about 98°C (2) much less than 98°C (3) much more than 98°C (4) exactly 100°C.

320. Weather is determined by the movement of (1) clouds (2) the sun (3) the moon (4) air masses.

321. The eye is most like a (1) camera (2) movie projector (3) photoelectric cell (4) telescope.

322. The most important reason for using roller bearings in a machine is to (1) balance the machine (2) change the direction of force (3) reduce friction (4) reduce speed.

323. One way to magnetize a needle is to stroke it with a (1) dry cell (2) hard rubber rod (3) permanent magnet (4) silk cloth.

324. Contour plowing and terracing are good practices because they (1) allow water to run off quickly (2) conserve soil (3) destroy weeds (4) enable plants to receive more sunlight.

325. The best proof that dinosaurs once lived on the earth is that (1) books have been written about them (2) fossils of dinosaurs have been found (3) they appear in pictures (4) they looked like elephants.

326. When a comb attracts your hair, the comb is (1) charged (2) uncharged (3) magnetized (4) demagnetized.

327. If a lamp is rated at 6 volts, how many dry cells in series are needed to light it properly? (1) 1 (2) 2 (3) 3 (4) 4.

328. In which of the following places is it most dangerous to light a match? (1) a car (2) an oxygen tent (3) a cellar (4) outdoors in a high wind.

329. In which of the following places would breathing be most difficult? (1) Miami, Florida (2) the North Pole (3) Death Valley (4) Pike's Peak.

330. A boy burns a piece of bread over a gas flame until there is nothing left but a gray ash. He can conclude that bread contains (1) fat (2) minerals (3) starch (4) vitamins.

331. The part of the atmosphere closest to the earth is called the (1) stratosphere (2) ionosphere (3) thermosphere (4) troposphere.

332. Which insect is helpful to farmers because it aids in pollination? (1) ladybird beetle (2) bee (3) grasshopper (4) mosquito.

333. A person looking into a flat mirror sees the image of himself or herself (1) smaller than usual (2) inverted (3) magnified (4) reversed.

334. When a seed starts to germinate, the gas released is (1) carbon dioxide (2) helium (3) nitrogen (4) oxygen.

335. Iron filings are placed in a damp test tube and the tube is filled with pure oxygen. The tube is then inverted in a vessel of water. Which would probably be the result on the following day? (1) There would be no change. (2) The water would rise about one-fifth the height of the tube. (3) The water would rise about four-fifths the height of the tube. (4) The water would rise to the top of the tube.

336. Which of the following needs no air pressure to support or lift it? (1) airplane (2) balloon (3) helicopter (4) rocket.

337. A compass would be least affected when brought near a (1) magnet (2) piece of glass (3) screwdriver (4) wire connected to batteries.

338. The life of an aviator who climbed to an altitude of 40,000 feet in an open cockpit plane would be in danger because of the (1) extreme heat (2) excessive moisture (3) lack of sufficient oxygen (4) excessive dryness.

339. An example of a device that works on decreased air pressure is the (1) aneroid barometer (2) lever (3) straw (4) air brake.

340. About one-half of the weight of a rock is oxygen. In a rock weighing one ton, the weight of the oxygen is about (1) 2,000 lb. (2) 1,000 lb. (3) 500 lb (4) 100 lb.

341. A pupil inhales and exhales air in a classroom heated to 71°F. The temperature of the air he exhales will be (1) below 71°F (2) 71°F (3) between 71°F and 98.6°F (4) above 98.6°F.

342. Oil sprayed on stagnant water destroys the mosquito's pupae in the water because the oil (1) shuts off the food supply (2) shuts off the supply of air (3) is heavy (4) attracts enemies of the mosquito.

343. In which state would a solar heating system work most effectively? (1) Florida (2) Maine (3) New York (4) North Dakota.

344. The chief reason for chlorinating water is to (1) check harmful bacteria (2) remove unpleasant tastes (3) add a nutritious substance (4) protect the teeth.

345. An example of an inorganic substance is (1) water (2) starch (3) sugar (4) wood.

346. Cooling below the dew point produces (1) condensation (2) evaporation (3) humidity (4) hail.

347. When the sun is rising in Hollywood, California, it (1) has not yet risen in Albany, New York (2) has already risen in Albany, New York (3) has set in Albany, New York (4) is also rising in Albany, New York.

348. Dropping a magnet will cause it to (1) become stronger (2) become weaker (3) last longer (4) produce an electric current.

349. Which is the surest means of preventing smallpox? (1) chlorination of water (2) fluoridation of water (3) vaccination of children (4) pasteurization of milk.

350. Which type of fire extinguisher should not be used on burning electrical appliances? (1) carbon dioxide (2) carbon tetrachloride (3) soda-acid (4) chemical powder.

351. House plants should be turned frequently to avoid a one-sided growth caused by (1) heat (2) light (3) soil (4) water.

352. Which animal helps to loosen and aerate the soil? (1) rabbit (2) earthworm (3) fish (4) robin.

353. A pan of water outdoors would lose water more rapidly on (1) a clear, sunshiny day (2) a foggy morning (3) a rainy night (4) an evening when dew is forming.

354. Brightly colored flowers are usually pollinated by (1) wind (2) water (3) insects (4) humans.

355. Heat reaches us from the sun by (1) radiation (2) conduction (3) expansion (4) convection.

356. Some planets appear brighter than stars because the planets (1) are hotter (2) are larger (3) are nearer to the earth (4) give off more light.

357. A mammal differs from other animals in that a mammal (1) possesses a backbone (2) has teeth (3) has two pairs of legs (4) produces milk for its young.

358. Which does a green leaf give off to the air? (1) water vapor (2) excess food (3) chlorophyll (4) nitrates.

359. The most difficult way to determine the differences in a variety of minerals is by their (1) chemical composition (2) color (3) shape (4) hardness.

360. When riding in traffic on a bicycle, you should not (1) face oncoming traffic (2) use hand signals when turning (3) stop at "stop" signs (4) keep to the right.

361. When tested with iodine for starch, which will not turn blue-black? (1) corn muffins (2) mashed potatoes (3) sliced mushrooms (4) wheat bread.

362. Salt that has been dissolved in water can be recovered by (1) evaporating the water (2) filtering the salt solution (3) pouring off the upper part of the solution (4) siphoning off the lower part of the solution.

363. Any place north of you must have (1) a colder summer and a colder winter (2) a colder summer and a warmer winter (3) a warmer summer and a colder winter (4) fewer hours of daylight during the winter.

364. Protozoans such as the ameba are classified as (1) protists (2) animals (3) plants (4) bacteria.

365. The bark is important to a tree because it (1) absorbs water when it rains (2) helps protect the tree against insects and diseases (3) carries on the food-making process (4) stores food for the tree.

366. In a balanced aquarium, the fish supply the plants with (1) carbon dioxide (2) water (3) oxygen (4) starch.

367. When the humidity is low, there is likely to be a (1) discharge of static electricity (2) heavy dew (3) sticking of doors and drawers (4) sweating of a pitcher of ice water.

368. Which animals aid most in reforestation? (1) bears (2) porcupines (3) rabbits (4) squirrels.

369. The ability of fish to live in water is known as (1) adaptation (2) balance of nature (3) conservation (4) germination.

370. Clogged pores of the skin may produce (1) fever (2) pimples (3) oil (4) sweat.

371. Since a plant stem holds the plant upright, the leaves can get (1) mineral salts and starch (2) minerals and nitrogen (3) moisture and food (4) sunlight and air.

372. If a radar beam travels at about 186,000 miles per second, the beam will reach the moon in about (1) 1½ seconds (2) 1½ minutes (3) 1½ hours (4) 1½ days.

373. A creek that runs muddy after every rainstorm indicates that (1) the area around the creek is heavily forested (2) the creek has poor drainage (3) the land is being cleaned of undesirable dirt and mud (4) soil is eroding.

374. In color photography, the film contains (1) a color spectrum (2) colored lenses (3) colored threads (4) particles of dyes of different colors.

375. What characteristic do all insects have? (1) chewing mouth-parts (2) colored wings (3) poison sacs (4) six legs.

376. We cannot see the new moon because (1) it occurs at night (2) it occurs below the horizon (3) the earth's shadow hides it (4) the lighted side of the moon is away from the earth.

377. In which life process is air pressure involved most? (1) breathing (2) circulation (3) excretion (4) sensation.

378. Rapid oxidation gives off (1) little heat and much light (2) little heat and no light (3) much heat and much light (4) no heat and no light.

379. Which is of greatest help in controlling insects? (1) birds (2) insecticides (3) rodents (4) screens.

380. Of the following, the safest location during a nearby thunderstorm would be (1) an open field (2) in a steel-frame building (3) in a swimming pool (4) under a tree.

381. A substance associated with heart disease is (1) LSD (2) heroin (3) codeine (4) nicotine.

382. A balloon is partially filled with air and then sealed. The balloon will contract when (1) carried to a higher elevation (2) left in a cooler place (3) left in a warmer place (4) placed in a partial vacuum.

Index